Calculus and Linear Algebra

Harcourt, Brace & World, Inc.
New York / Chicago / Burlingame

Calculus and Linear Algebra

Herbert S. Wilf
UNIVERSITY OF PENNSYLVANIA

to Morton

Preface

The gap between mathematics as practiced by mathematicians and mathematics as taught to freshmen has widened considerably in recent years. This has occurred because of the constancy of the latter in the face of sweeping changes in the former. Nor is mathematics alone in this respect. Physics, engineering, economics, and other quantitative disciplines all exhibit ever wider estrangement between the subject as viewed by a professional research worker and as seen by a beginning undergraduate.

The choice of calculus as the proper subject for first-year mathematics has been dictated in part by the needs of the other science courses which are normally taken and in part by its use in advanced mathematics courses. These considerations are still valid, but they have undergone subtle changes.

First, not too long ago mathematics was a rather unpopular major subject, and so a calculus instructor could safely assume that he was addressing a group of students whose primary interests lay elsewhere. Now, an astonishing number of incoming students are primarily interested in mathematics. This, it seems to me, imposes an obligation on the first-year course to display a branch of mathematics other than analysis, so that students who have not decided upon a major will get a better idea of the flavor of the subject and so that prospective mathematics majors will be better aware of and better equipped for the road that lies ahead of them.

Second, after intensive urging by the mathematical community, the high schools are moving rapidly to upgrade their mathematics offerings. It is now by no means uncommon to encounter students with a full year of calculus already behind them in high school. This poses a challenge and an opportunity to the universities: the challenge of revising their own curricula to match the changes in secondary school education which they themselves have instigated, and the opportunity to reach deep, substantive areas of mathematics much earlier in the undergraduate years.

Third, the needs of the sciences have also changed. A physicist of today is likely to use as much, or more, of algebra than analysis. The ideas of abstract algebraic structures, and of linear algebra in particular, pervade the quantum theory and the theory of elementary particles, as well as many of the other rapidly advancing branches of physics. In engineering, algebra rules the roost in information theory, theory of electrical circuits and networks, analysis of structures, logical design, and many other areas. To a lesser, but still important, extent, the quantitative areas of economics lean heavily on linear algebra. Altogether, then, while the calculus retains its primacy overall, it cannot be denied that algebraic concepts have come increasingly toward the forefront.

These considerations all point in the same direction, toward the earliest possible introduction of abstract algebra, and particularly linear algebra, coupled with a pruning out of the calculus course of those topics which can be readily handled at the secondary school level. This book was written in response to these needs.

The material covered in the first two-thirds of the book constitutes a course in the calculus of functions of one variable. Stress is laid on the conceptual aspects of the subject. Differentiation and integration are developed more or less simultaneously so that their interrelations can be more clearly seen. The first few sections contain motivational material which seems to be quite useful for orientation.

I have compromised with the thorny question of epsilons and deltas. I feel that they are too important to be neglected and at the same time too difficult to be carried through consistently. Therefore, I introduce the formalism quite early, just to get across the point of view. It is not, however, used meaningfully in proofs until later, during the work on infinite series, where it is indispensable. In this way, the idea has a chance to percolate for a while before stringent demands are made on it.

The work on linear algebra is concentrated on the objective of reaching a full understanding of the theory of simultaneous linear equations. This requires a good deal of sophisticated material, which is not omitted. Surprisingly enough, the students have found this part of the course much easier than the calculus. Considerable effort is expended in developing the idea of an abstract structure, and this is then applied to the theory of equations. The final chapter provides a brief introduction to the calculus of functions of several variables. It appears in this volume largely because the intertwining of algebraic and analytical concepts which occurs there offers the reader an opportunity to see vectors, determinants, and matrices at work on the problems of calculus.

It is my belief that in the years to come such a first-year course as this will become more commonplace. If so, then the means will be at hand for helping some of the other sciences to narrow the gaps in their curricula. For the "queen of the sciences" to lead her subjects would hardly be surprising.

HERBERT S. WILF

Philadelphia, Pennsylvania

Contents

1 Foundations of the Calculus   2

1.1.	Differential Calculus	3
1.2.	Integral Calculus	9
1.3.	The Concept of Function	16
1.4.	The Concept of Limit	21

2 Theory of Differentiation and Integration   32

2.1.	The Derivative	33
2.2.	Geometrical Aspects of Differentiation	39
2.3.	Continuity and Differentiability	43
2.4.	The Integral	46
2.5.	Properties of the Integral	51
2.6.	The Integral as a Function of its Upper Limit	56
2.7.	Rolle's Theorem and the Mean-Value Theorem	60

3 The Machinery of Differentiation and Integration 70

3.1.	Rules for Differentiation	71
3.2.	Elementary Integrals	81
3.3.	Logarithmic Functions	83
3.4.	The Exponential Function	88
3.5.	The Trigonometric Functions	94
3.6.	Inverse Functions	101
3.7.	Monotone Functions	104
3.8.	The Inverse Trigonometric Functions	106
3.9.	The Mechanics of Integration: Integration by Parts	109
3.10.	The Mechanics of Integration: Integration by Substitution	116
3.11.	The Mechanics of Integration: Rational Functions	122

4 Applications of the Calculus 128

4.1.	Repeated Differentiation; Maxima and Minima	129
4.2.	Extremum Problems	137
4.3.	Curve Sketching; L'Hospital's Rule	142
4.4.	Numerical Methods	150
4.5.	Arc Length	156
4.6.	The Volume of a Solid of Revolution	163
4.7.	Convexity	167
4.8.	Contact, Curvature, and Approximation	172
4.9.	Improper Integrals	179

5 Sequence and Series 184

5.1.	Sequences of Real Numbers	185
5.2.	The Cauchy Convergence Criterion	189
5.3.	Infinite Series of Real Numbers	193
5.4.	Tests for Convergence: The Comparison Test	197
5.5.	Tests for Convergence: The Integral Test	201
5.6.	Tests for Convergence: Order of Magnitude	206
5.7.	Alternating Series	208
5.8.	Absolute Convergence	211

5.9.	Sequences and Series of Functions	215
5.10.	The Radius of Convergence	217
5.11.	Taylor's Theorem	226

6 *Vector Spaces* 236

6.1.	Abstract Mathematical Structures; Groups	237
6.2.	Vector Spaces	245
6.3.	Mathematical Induction	250
6.4.	Linear Independence	254
6.5.	Subspaces	258
6.6.	Bases	264
6.7.	Homomorphisms	266

7 *Matrices, Determinants, and Linear Equations* 276

7.1.	The Algebra of Linear Mappings	277
7.2.	Matrices	284
7.3.	Matrix Algebra	290
7.4.	Determinants and Simultaneous Linear Equations	296
7.5.	More on Permutations	301
7.6.	Determinant Functions	306
7.7.	Properties of Determinants	311
7.8.	Solution of Linear Equations	317
7.9.	Computational Methods	329
7.10.	Applications	338

8 *An Introduction to the Differential Calculus of Several Variables* 346

8.1.	Introduction	347
8.2.	Distance, Limits, and Continuity	350
8.3.	Partial Derivatives	354
8.4.	The Chain Rule	361
8.5.	Contact	366
8.6.	Extrema	371

Appendix: Analytic Geometry   381

Answers to Selected Exercises   393

Index   405

Calculus and Linear Algebra

Differential Calculus
Integral Calculus
The Concept of Function
The Concept of Limit

1

Foundations of the Calculus

1.1. *Differential Calculus*

Calculus has been called "the study of change." Therefore, in this first section we will examine some particular examples of changing phenomena in order to see how we can use the calculus to gain a better understanding of these phenomena. Strictly speaking, these first few sections are unnecessary. They are intended only for the purpose of motivating certain concepts which might otherwise seem somewhat artificial. We first plan to give a typical problem in the differential calculus, then a typical problem in integral calculus. In each case we will find that the basic processes of the calculus, namely, differentiation and integration, are forced upon us if we try to answer the questions which are posed in a natural way.

In the differential calculus we are generally given a relationship which describes how one variable depends upon another. For instance, we may be told how the population of a certain country depends upon time, or how the speed of a projectile depends upon its distance above the ground. We are then asked to find out how the rate of change of the first variable depends upon the second. Thus, being given the position of a car at every instant of time, we may be asked to find the rate of change of its position, i.e., its speed, at every instant of time. Or, being given its speed, we may be asked for the rate of change of its speed, i.e., its acceleration, as it depends on time. After looking at such examples, we will then consider the opposite kind of problem, in which the rate of change is given and we wish to recover the original dependence. Thereby, we will be led to the integral calculus.

Proceeding now to a particular problem, let us imagine an automobile which starts from rest at a certain time which we will call $t = 0$. It then travels in a straight line in such a way that its distance from its starting point after 1 sec is 1 ft, after 2 sec is 4 ft, after 3 sec is 9 ft, etc. In general, if t is any real, nonnegative number, we suppose that after t sec the car has moved t^2 ft from its initial position. A graph of the distance the car has traveled after t sec, plotted against t, is shown in Fig. 1.1.

Figure 1.1

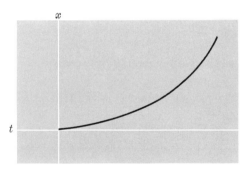

Since we now know exactly where the car is at every instant it seems that we should be able to answer any conceivable question about its motion. Certainly we can answer such questions about its position. How long does the car take to move 2 ft from its rest position? Evidently 1.414 ... sec.

Exercises

1. How long does the car take to move 3 ft from its rest position? L ft from its rest position? Two ft from its position at time $t = 2$? L ft from its position at time $t = 2$? Five ft from its position at time $t = t_0$? L ft from its position at time $t = t_0$?

2. How far does the car move in its first second of travel? Its third second? In the 2-sec period from $t = 1.5$ sec to $t = 3.5$ sec? In the h-sec period from $t = 4$ sec to $t = 4 + h$ sec? In the h-sec period from $t = t_0$ sec to $t = t_0 + h$ sec?
3. Do you think the car is going faster after 4 sec than after 3 sec? Why?
4. If the position of the car at the time t were t^3 ft, answer all parts of Exercise 2 above.
5. Two automobiles start from rest at the same time and place, traveling in the same direction. The first travels t^2 ft in t sec, the other goes only $\frac{1}{2}t^2 + t$ ft in t sec.

    (a) Plot, on the same graph, their positions at each time t.
    (b) At what time does the first car pass the second?
    (c) Plot the distance between the cars at each time t.
    (d) How much does the distance between them change in the time interval from 3 sec to $3 + h$ sec? From t_0 sec to $t_0 + h$ sec?
    (e) A beam of light leaves the second car at the instant $t = 4$ sec, and travels with constant speed c toward the first car. At what time does it reach the first car (the "cars" are, of course, points)?

It is also true that we can answer questions about the speed of the car as well as about its position, but to get these answers will require considerably more effort. Before trying to do this, note that we do not even know what is meant by the term "speed" in the present situation. We will see in the process of arriving at a sensible definition that we will, in fact, have solved the problem also.

First, let us ask if our car is moving at constant speed. If it is, we then have the well-known rule

$$\text{distance} = \text{speed} \times \text{time} \tag{1.1}$$

to get the answer for us. In the time period from 1 to 2 sec, the car traveled 3 ft. If its speed were constant, then it would be traveling 3 ft/sec during that time period. However, in the time from 1 to 1.5 sec the car traveled 1.25 ft, corresponding to a constant speed of 2.5 ft/sec. Since these answers are different, we reject the hypothesis of constant speed during the time interval from 1 to 2 sec. Clearly then, we are dealing with a considerably harder problem than the constant speed variety.

To handle such problems we introduce the concept of *average speed.* We say that the average speed of the automobile during a certain period of time is the total distance traveled during that time period, divided by the duration of the time period. In symbolic notation, suppose we are considering the period of time extending from $t = t_1$ to $t = t_2$ sec. Then the average speed is given by the formula

$$\text{average speed} = \frac{(\text{position at time } t = t_2) - (\text{position at time } t = t_1)}{t_2 - t_1}$$

Evidently, what we are doing is just using the formula (1.1), and interpreting the word "rate" as average speed, rather than the speed at any particular instant.

Exercises

1. Compute the average speed of the car in each of the following time intervals [the notation (a,b) means the interval of time starting at $t = a$ sec and ending at $t = b$ sec]:

    $$(1,2)\ (3,5)\ (2,T)\ (a,b)\ (1,1 + h)\ (1 - h,1)\ (T,T + h)\ (T,T - h)$$

2. Find a time interval in which the average speed is 4 ft/sec.
3. Find a time interval starting at $t = 1$ sec in which the average speed is 3 ft/sec.
4. Find a time interval including the point $t = \frac{1}{2}$ sec in which the average speed is 1 ft/sec.
5. Find a time interval during the first half of which the average speed is less than 5 ft/sec and during the second half of which the average speed is greater than 5 ft/sec.

Table I

h (sec)	Beginning of time interval (sec)	End of time interval (sec)	Average speed (ft/sec)
1	1	2	3
0.5	1	1.5	2.5
0.25	1	1.25	2.25
0.1	1	1.10	2.10
0.05	1	1.05	2.05
0.01	1	1.01	2.01
-0.01	0.99	1.00	1.99
-0.0001	0.9999	1.00	1.9999
$+0.00001$	1	1.00001	2.00001

We now turn to the central question of this section, namely, the definition and computation of the speed of the car at a particular instant of time. To be specific, suppose we wish the speed at the instant $t = 1$ sec. The answer to this question hinges upon computing the average speed in very small time intervals including the time $t = 1$. Therefore, we show in Table I the average speed of the car in the time period $(1, 1 + h)$ for various (positive and negative) small values of h.

We observe from Table I that the average speed in a small time interval, including the instant $t = 1$ sec, is very close to 2 ft/sec, and gets closer to 2 ft/sec as the duration of the time interval is decreased. To confirm this empirical observation we can derive a simple formula which includes all of the information in Table I. In fact, the distance traveled in the time interval $(t, t + h)$ is

$$(t + h)^2 - t^2 = 2th + h^2$$

and so the average speed of the car in that time interval is

$$\frac{2th + h^2}{h} = 2t + h$$

Substituting 1 for t, we see that the average speed in the time interval $(1, 1 + h)$ is $2 + h$ ft/sec. We can readily check that the Table I entries are in accord with this result. It is now obvious that when the time interval is very short (i.e., when h is small, either positive or negative) the average speed is very close to 2 ft/sec and that it gets closer to 2 ft/sec as the time interval gets smaller. We note, however, that there is no such time interval at all in which the average speed is *equal* to 2 ft/sec. The decisive step of the differential calculus consists in taking 2 ft/sec as the answer to our question because of the unique property of that number as the *limit* of average speeds about the instant of time in question. To summarize, we say that the *instantaneous speed* of the car at the time $t = 1$ sec is 2 ft/sec because the average speed of the car in a small time interval including the instant $t = 1$ is nearly 2 ft/sec, and that average speed can be made *as close as we wish* to 2 ft/sec by taking the time interval small enough.

As a further illustration we now find the speed of our hypothetical car at an arbitrary time t. At time t the position of the car is

$$x = t^2$$

and we have already seen that its average speed in the time interval
$(t,\ t + h)$ is $2t + h$. When h is very small, so that the time interval
is very short, this average speed is very close to $2t$ ft/sec, and can
be made as close as we wish to $2t$ ft/sec by keeping h small enough.
Consequently, following the philosophy already described above, we
identify the number $2t$ ft/sec as the instantaneous speed of the car
at the time t. Thus at 6 sec the speed of the car is 12 ft/sec, etc. We now
have a complete answer to our original question. Indeed, starting from
given information consisting of the *position* of the car at every instant we
have found the *speed* of the car at every instant. A graph of our given
information is shown in Fig. 1.1 and the information which we have
found is in Fig. 1.2.

Figure 1.2

Speed

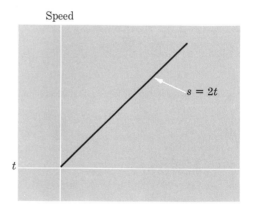

$s = 2t$

t

We have now carried out the solution of a prototype problem in the
differential calculus. The process of transforming the given graph in
Fig. 1.1, or equivalently the given relationship position = (time)^2, into
the graph in Fig. 1.2, or equivalently into the relationship speed =
2(time), is called *differentiation*. We used the example of the automobile
only for motivational purposes. It would be helpful if we thought of the
process of differentiation as one which converts a given graph or relation
into another graph or relation, in the way described, rather than as an
idea which is tied to such things as speeds, positions, accelerations, etc.

Exercises

1. Each of the following represents the position of a certain automobile at time t. In each case, graph the given relationship, then find the speed of the car at each time t by differentiation, then graph your answer.

   (a) $x = t^2 + 3$
   (b) $x = t^2 + t$
   (c) $x = t^2 + t + 3$
   (d) $x = t^3$
   (e) $x = 5$
   (f) $x = 5t^2$

2. By surveying your answers to Exercise 1, what general observations can you make about the process of differentiation? In particular, what is the effect on your answer of adding some constant to the given relation? Can you give a physical (i.e., in terms of automobiles) reason why this should be so? What is the effect of multiplying by a constant?

3. The acceleration of an automobile bears the same relation to its speed as the speed does to the position. Thus the instantaneous acceleration can be found by differentiation of the speed vs time relationship. Using your answers to Exercise 1, find and graph the instantaneous acceleration of each car as it depends on the time.

1.2. Integral Calculus

In the preceding section we learned how to handle, conceptually at least, the problem

> GIVEN   Position of car at every time
> FIND   Speed of car at every time

In this section we will be led to the fundamental ideas of the integral calculus by considering the converse problem

> GIVEN   The speed of a car at every time
> FIND   The position of the car at each time

The process which goes in the reverse direction is known as integration and is conceptually as well as practically rather more complex than differentiation. We will see, however, that the process is natural and inevitable if we wish to be able to handle the problem just posed.

Specifically, we will use the same automobile that we used in Section 1.1, but we will pretend that we do not know that its position at time t is t^2, only that its speed at time t is $2t$. Accepting this, we now try to find out how far the car traveled in its first second of motion. If the speed were constant during that first second, the problem would be easy—we would merely multiply the constant speed by 1 sec, getting the answer at once. Obviously, in this problem, the speed is not constant, so more sophisticated methods are called for. Our plan is to replace the given problem by a sequence of approximate problems, none of which is exactly the truth, and to solve these (much easier) approximate problems. We will then notice that as our approximations get closer and closer to the truth, our approximate answers get closer and closer to a certain number (1 ft), which we will then take as the exact solution of the problem.

In certain respects this approach is similar to the philosophy we used in differentiation. There, in order to compute an *instantaneous speed,* we made approximations to the truth by calculating instead the *average speed* over very small time intervals. As these intervals shrank we noticed that our approximations got closer and closer to a certain number, which we then identified as the desired instantaneous speed. The common feature of differentiation and integration, then, is this "reaching beyond" a whole sequence of approximate answers, which can be easily calculated in order to find an exact answer.

Figure 1.3

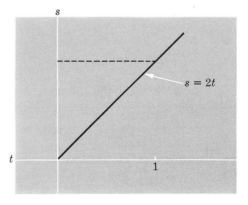

Returning to the problem at hand, let us replace it by a very crude approximate problem. Let us assume that throughout the 1-sec time period in question the car has constant speed, and that its constant speed is equal to its true speed at the end of the time period. In other words, instead of the real automobile whose speed at time t is $2t$, we consider a fictitious automobile whose speed throughout the first second is 2 ft/sec. In graphical terms, the true speed graph (solid line, Fig. 1.3) is replaced by a fictitious speed graph (dotted line, Fig. 1.3).

This is obviously a very poor approximation to the truth, but it has at least the advantage of being an easy problem to solve. Indeed, the distance traveled by our fictitious automobile in the first second is just

$$(2 \text{ ft/sec}) \times (1 \text{ sec}) = 2 \text{ ft}$$

Keeping in mind the right answer, which we know to be 1 ft, we see just how bad this approximation is. It does, however, point in the direction of better approximations. To see one of these, we look now at the

Second Approximation. Forgetting about our first fictitious car, we now replace the real automobile by a second fictitious one. This car has one constant speed in the first half-second and another constant speed in the next half-second. We take its constant speed in the first half-second to be equal to the speed of the true car at the end of that half-second, and its constant speed in the next half-second, similarly, to be the true speed at $t = 1$. Thus, we are considering a car which travels at 1 ft/sec for the first half-second, and at 2 ft/sec for the next half-second. Graphically, we replace the true speed graph (solid line, Fig. 1.4) by an approximate speed graph (dotted line, Fig. 1.4), which, while still poor, is clearly closer to the truth than the previous one. In this case, the distance traveled in the first second by our approximate automobile is

$$(1 \text{ ft/sec}) \times (\tfrac{1}{2} \text{ sec}) + (2 \text{ ft/sec}) \times (\tfrac{1}{2} \text{ sec}) = 1.5 \text{ ft}$$

still far from the truth, but better than before. It is worth noticing, at this point, that the two terms in our distance calculation in the preceding equation are equal to the areas of the shaded rectangles in Fig. 1.4, so that our approximate distance is the total shaded area.

Tenth Approximation. Skipping over a number of intermediate fictions, we consider the tenth approximation to the solution of our problem. Here, instead of splitting up the 1-sec time interval into two

pieces, we chop it into ten pieces. Our new fictitious automobile travels
at one constant speed for times between 0 sec and 0.1 sec, at another

Figure 1.4

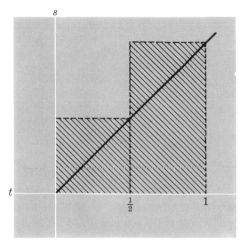

constant speed between 0.1 sec and 0.2 sec, etc. In each case, we choose
its constant speed to be the true speed of the real automobile at the end
of the "piece of time" in question. Therefore, for times between 0 sec and
0.1 sec, the car has a constant speed of 0.2 ft/sec, between 0.1 sec
and 0.2 sec it has a constant speed of 0.4 ft/sec, . . . , and between 0.9 sec
and 1.0 sec it has a constant speed of 2 ft/sec. In this case the true speed
graph (solid line, Fig. 1.5) is replaced by a much closer fictitious speed
graph (dotted line, Fig. 1.5).

To compute the distance traveled in this approximation, we just add
up the distances traveled in each tenth of a second

$$(0.2 \text{ ft/sec}) \times (0.1 \text{ sec}) + (0.4 \text{ ft/sec}) \times (0.1 \text{ sec}) + \cdots$$
$$+ (2.0 \text{ ft/sec}) \times (0.1 \text{ sec})$$
$$= 1.1 \text{ ft}$$

Evidently we are closing in on the right answer, but without knowing the right answer in advance, how can we find it? One clue can be
found in Fig. 1.5. The sum of ten terms which we used to compute our
tenth approximation to the distance traveled we easily see to be identi-

cal to the total shaded area of the rectangles shown. If we took one thousand subdivisions instead of ten, this total shaded area would then

Figure 1.5

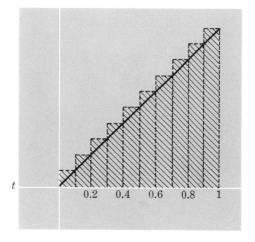

be very close indeed to the area of the triangle under the true speed graph. If we took one million subdivisions we would get still closer to the area of that triangle. One feels intuitively, then, that the answer we seek is the area of that triangle. This area is obviously $(\frac{1}{2}) \times (1 \text{ sec}) \times (2 \text{ ft/sec}) = 1$ ft, which, as we know, is indeed the right answer to our problem. The success of this intuitive approach, however, hinged critically on our knowledge of the way to compute the area of a triangle. What could we have done if the speed graph were something other than a straight line, so that the area under it were some irregular curved figure? In such a case we should fall back on analytical methods which, in fact, will turn out to serve as the *definition* of the word "area." Admittedly, these analytical methods are unnecessary in the present case because of the success of our intuition. Nevertheless, we carry them out to completion so that the general method will be clear. Therefore, we consider, finally, the

*n*th *Approximation.* We now split the time interval (0,1) into *n* pieces of equal size. In each of these subintervals our fictitious car will have constant speed, and the value of that constant speed will be equal to the true speed at the end of the time interval. Thus, between 0 and $1/n$ sec the speed is $2/n$ ft/sec, between $1/n$ and $2/n$ sec it is $4/n$ ft/sec, ... , between $(n-1)/n$ and 1 sec it is 2 ft/sec. The total distance traveled by such a car will be

$$\left(\frac{2}{n} \text{ ft/sec}\right) \times \left(\frac{1}{n} \text{ sec}\right) + \left(\frac{4}{n} \text{ ft/sec}\right) \times \left(\frac{1}{n} \text{ sec}\right) + \cdots$$

$$+ (2 \text{ ft/sec}) \times \left(\frac{1}{n} \text{ sec}\right)$$

$$= \frac{1}{n^2}(2 + 4 + 6 + \cdots + 2n) \text{ ft}$$

$$= \frac{2}{n^2}(1 + 2 + 3 + \cdots + n) \text{ ft}$$

In order to reduce this last expression to manageable form we need to know how to add up the first n positive integers. We claim that the sum of the integers 1, 2, 3, ... , n is $n(n+1)/2$. To prove this, let us temporarily designate this sum by the letter S, so that

$$S = 1 + 2 + 3 + \cdots + n$$

Writing the summands in reverse order, we also see that

$$S = n + (n-1) + (n-2) + \cdots + 1$$

Adding these last two equations together,

$$2S = (n+1) + (n+1) + (n+1) + \cdots + (n+1)$$
$$= n(n+1)$$

and the result claimed follows immediately.

Using this formula, our result for the distance traveled by the fictitious car in the nth approximation takes the simple form

$$\text{distance traveled} = \frac{2}{n^2} \cdot \frac{n(n+1)}{2} = 1 + \frac{1}{n} \text{ ft}$$

We see at once that this expression is very close to 1 ft, and that it can be made as close as we wish to 1 ft by choosing n, the number of subintervals, large enough.

By means of this very lengthy process of approximation we have finally found the distance traveled by our car in the first second. In a similar way we can find the distance traveled in the first two seconds, or indeed, in the first t seconds. We would, of course, find that the answer is t^2 ft. This procedure, whereby we take the graph of a certain relationship, chop up the interval into tiny pieces, add up the areas of each of the rectangles so formed, and thereby calculate the area under a curve, is called integration. As we present integration in this section, it is the converse of differentiation. As we present integration later, on a more rigorous basis, the foregoing will be less obvious, but still true.

In conclusion, let us observe that upon careful study of these typical problems of the differential and integral calculus at least two major concepts, each occurring in both examples, appear which seem worthy of further discussion. First, note that in both examples we started with a formula giving a certain property of the automobile at every instant of time and ended with another formula giving a different property of the automobile at every instant of time. This idea of a formula, which tells us one thing if we know another, needs considerable elaboration. This elaboration consists in formalizing the concept of function, which we do in Section 1.3.

Second, as we have noted, a curious feature of both problems is that we did not find the answer by doing a single calculation. We found it by doing a whole family of calculations, with each member of the family being, in itself, only an approximation to the true answer. We then took the crucial step of selecting for our answer a number which was not itself the result of any one of the calculations. This number was identified only as a number toward which our approximations were leading us. This idea also needs amplification, and leads to the notion of limit. These two concepts, "function" and "limit," form the pillars on which the calculus is erected.

Exercises

1. Try to formulate a reasonable definition of the area of a plane figure having arbitrarily curved boundaries.
2. Suppose that the speed of a certain car at time t is $\sqrt{1 - t^2}$. Graph this relationship for $0 \leq t \leq 1$. How far did the car travel in the first second?
3. By using the method of chopping up the time interval, write down the nth ap-

proximation to the answer of Exercise 2. Use this for $n = 5$ to get an approximate value of the number π numerically.

4.   For the automobile treated in the text, verify by computing the nth approximation that the car travels t^2 ft in the first t sec. Check this by calculating the
area of a suitable triangle.

1.3.   *The Concept of Function*

We wish now to make the idea of a function, which we have already used
informally in the preceding sections, more precise. Roughly speaking, a
function may be thought of as a rule of dependence, that is to say, as a
rule which tells how one variable depends upon another. In our examples
of the automobile the relation $x = t^2$ was one example of such a rule, since
it tells how one variable (position) depends upon another (time). The
relation speed $= 2t$, telling us how the speed depends upon the time, is
another example of a function.

If we adhere too closely, however, to the idea of a function as a rule of
dependence, we will pay a price later on in this work, where it becomes
desirable to use the function concept in its broadest sense. Since it is a bit
annoying to change definitions continually, we instead shall present the
definition of a function immediately in a very broad manner.

Let us return to the rule $x = t^2$. When looking at this rule, let us try
not to think of two "variables," for a moment, but of two sets of numbers. For the first set we take the set of all nonnegative real numbers, and
for the second set, in this particular case, we also take the set of nonnegative real numbers. Now we can think of the rule $x = t^2$ as a recipe that
attaches to every member of the first set a unique member of the second
set, namely, its square. To conjure up a pictorial image, we can think of
the two sets as abstract blobs and of the function as a collection of
arrows running from members of the blob on the left to members of the
blob on the right (Fig. 1.6).

In our example, the sets A and B in Fig. 1.6 happen to be identical.
The function f attaches to any member of A which we might happen to
pick up, its square over in the set B. As another example of a function,
suppose we consider two variables x and y which are related by the
equation $y = x^3$, provided that x lies between 1 and 4, with the relation-

ship undefined for other values of x. In this case the left-hand blob, or the set A, consists of all real numbers between 1 and 4, and, for the right-hand set B, we can take, for instance, all real numbers between 0 and 150.

Figure 1.6

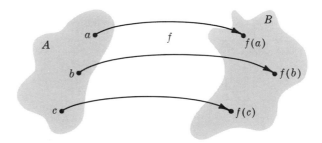

If we choose any member of the set A, then, the function f in this case assigns to it a unique member of the set B, namely, its cube.

We note that the function in this last example did not exhaust the set B. That is, there are some numbers in the set B which never got attached by the function to anything in the set A. The number 100, for example, is not the cube of anything at all in the set A. This is perfectly permissible. All that is required is that every member of A be attached to some unique member of B. Formally, we state the

> **DEFINITION**   Let A and B be two given sets. A function f from A to B is a rule which assigns to each member of A one and only one member of B. The set A is called the *domain* of the function and the set B is called the *range* of the function. If a is any member of the set A, the member of B which f assigns to a is denoted by the symbol $f(a)$ (read "f of a").

Examples
1.   If A is the set of all trees, and B is the set of all real numbers, then an example of a function f from A to B is the rule which assigns to every tree its height in feet.
2.   If A is the set of positive real numbers, and B is the set of positive real numbers, then an example of a function f from A to B is the rule

which assigns to each number in A its positive square root. In other words, for each x in A, $f(x) = \sqrt{x}$.

3.   If A is the set of all states in the United States, and B is the set of all real numbers, a function f from A to B is the rule which assigns to each state the number 633. Another function from this same A to this same B could be the rule which assigns to each state the year in which it entered the Union.

In most of our early work it will be clear from the context just what the domain and range of each function is. When this is so, these sets will not be stated explicitly. For instance, if the formula

$$f(x) = x^4$$

is given, then it may be assumed that this formula is valid for all real numbers x, unless we explicitly state the contrary. For a formula like

$$f(x) = \frac{1}{x}$$

one would normally assume that the set A is the set of all nonzero real numbers, and B is all the real numbers. In general, we make the convention that the set A is the largest set of real numbers for which the given formulas make sense, and B is all the real numbers, unless otherwise stated.

Even when we are dealing with numbers, it is not necessary for the function to be given by a single formula. For instance, the notation

$$f(x) = \begin{cases} 1/x & x \neq 0 \\ 5 & x = 0 \end{cases} \tag{1.2}$$

means that we are talking about the function which assigns to every number other than zero its reciprocal and to zero the number 5. A few other examples are

$$f(x) = \begin{cases} 1 + 2x & x < 1 \\ 4 & x = 1 \\ x^2 & x > 1 \end{cases} \tag{1.3}$$

$$f(x) = \begin{cases} p & \text{if } x = p/q, \text{ a positive rational fraction in lowest terms} \\ 0 & \text{otherwise} \end{cases} \quad (1.4)$$

$$f(x) = \begin{cases} 1 & \text{if } x \text{ is an odd integer} \\ -1 & \text{if } x \text{ is an even integer} \\ 0 & \text{otherwise} \end{cases} \quad (1.5)$$

It is useful here to develop some facility in manipulating functional relationships, and also to get accustomed to letters other than f to designate a function, and other than $f(x)$ to designate its value. If $f(x) = x^2$, then

$$f(x + 1) = (x + 1)^2 = x^2 + 2x + 1$$
$$f(xy) - f(x)f(y) = (xy)^2 - x^2y^2 = 0$$
$$f(x + y) - (f(x) + f(y)) = (x + y)^2 - (x^2 + y^2)$$
$$= 2xy$$

and, finally,

$$f(f(x)) = f(x)^2 = (x^2)^2 = x^4$$

If, furthermore, $g(x) = x^3$, then

$$f(x - 1) + g(x + 1) = (x - 1)^2 + (x + 1)^3$$

and

$$f(g(x)) = g(x)^2 = (x^3)^2 = x^6$$

If the domain and range of a function are both subsets of the real numbers then we can visualize the function by means of its graph, which is defined to be the totality of points $(x, f(x))$ in the x–y plane, as x runs over the domain of the function.

Exercises

1. Graph each of the functions (1.2) and (1.3). Can you draw the graph of (1.4)?
2. Identify the domains of each of the following functions.

    (a) $f(x) = \sqrt{1 - x^2}$

    (b) $g(x) = \dfrac{1}{x + 1}$

(c) $h(x) = (x^2 - 5x + 6)^{-1}$

(d) $u(x) = \dfrac{3x + 2}{\sqrt{x(1 + x)}}$

3. Suppose that $f(x) = 1 + x^2$, $g(x) = 1 - 2x^2$; find

    (a) $f(x) + g(x - 1)$
    (b) $f(g(x)) - g(f(x))$
    (c) $f(2t + 3) - 2f(t) - 3$
    (d) $2g(2z) + zg(2)$
    (e) $g(3^2) - g(3)^2$
    (f) $f(u + v) - uf(v) - vf(u)$
    (g) $f(\sqrt{x}) + \frac{1}{2}g(\sqrt{x})$
    (h) $\dfrac{f(x + h) - f(x)}{h}$
    (i) $\dfrac{g(x + h) - 2g(x) + g(x - h)}{h^2}$

4. Give an example of a function which is defined by one simple formula if $x \le 2$, and by another simple formula if $x > 2$, whose graph can nevertheless be drawn without ever lifting pencil from paper.

5. Express the area of a circle as a function of its circumference.

6. Express the perimeter of a square as a function of its area.

7. A cable car travels up a wire making an angle of $30°$ with the horizontal at the rate of r ft/sec. Find its height above the ground as a function of time.

8. We define a function d, whose domain is the set of positive integers, by saying that $d(n)$ is the number of positive integers which divide into n leaving no re-mainder. Make a table of $d(n)$ for $n = 1, 2, \ldots, 15$. How could you define a prime number in terms of this function? Make a list of all pairs of integers m, n among those for which you tabulated $d(n)$, for which it is true that $d(mn) = d(m)d(n)$, and another list of those pairs for which this is false (restrict yourself to pairs whose product is at most 15). Do you see any easy way to characterize the pairs for which it is true? Test your conjecture by ex-tending the table as you see fit.

9. For each positive real number x define $\varphi(x)$ to be the number of prime num-bers which do not exceed x. Calculate $\varphi(3)$, $\varphi(4.5)$, $\varphi(6\frac{3}{4})$, $\varphi(10)$. Graph $\varphi(x)$ for $1 \le x \le 15$. What is $\varphi(\varphi(8))$? $\varphi(\varphi(\varphi(8)))$?

10. Let f be the function which assigns to each triangle in the plane its area. What is the domain of f? Give three different sets any of which will serve as the range of f.

11. A certain function f from the real numbers to the real numbers satisfies $f(x + y) = f(x)f(y)$ for all x and y. Prove that $f(4) = f(1)^4$, that $f(\frac{1}{2}) = \pm \sqrt{f(1)}$, and that $f(0)$ is either 0 or 1.

1.4. The Concept of Limit

In this section we wish to make precise an idea which has already appeared in the automobile problems previously considered. There we saw, for instance, that the average speed of a certain car over a time interval $(1, 1 + h)$ was $2 + h$, and that as h got smaller, whether through positive or negative values, this number approached 2 as a limit. The essential feature of this number 2, which is shared by no other number in this problem, is that we can make $2 + h$ as close to it as we wish, by keeping h sufficiently near to zero. In the language which we are about to adopt, we would say that the limit of $2 + h$ as h approaches zero is 2. You may well wonder why we do not dispense with this circuitous argument, and just notice that if, in the expression $2 + h$ we simply replace h by zero, we see at once that it has the value 2.

To answer this we first remark that replacing h by zero is meaningless in this case because the expression $2 + h$ is not valid if $h = 0$. Recall that $2 + h$ represents the average speed of a car over the time interval from 1 to $1 + h$ sec. If $h = 0$, then we are talking about the average speed over the time interval from 1 sec to 1 sec. How could we compute this? Could we compute the distance traveled in no seconds and divide it by zero? The idea of a limit is introduced precisely to avoid such nonsensical operations, and it is defined in such a way that the limit of a certain expression as h approaches zero has nothing whatever to do with the value of the expression at $h = 0$. As a second remark, many expressions which we will have to treat in this book, and which have perfectly good limits as, say, h approaches zero, will not reveal those limits to the reader who merely replaces h by zero. For example, the function $(\sin x)/x$ approaches the limit 1 as x approaches zero, as we will see later, but merely replacing x by zero gives no clue to this.

To arrive at a useful definition of limit, we return to the peculiar property of the number 2 in the case of $2 + h$ when h is small and, thus guided, formulate the

First Definition of Limit. Let f be a given function. A number L is called the limit of $f(x)$ as x approaches x_0 if we can make $f(x)$ stay as close to L as we wish by keeping x sufficiently close to x_0 (but not equal to x_0 !!!). We then write

$$\lim_{x \to x_0} f(x) = L \tag{1.6}$$

or

$$f(x) \to L \qquad \text{as} \qquad x \to x_0 \tag{1.7}$$

The arrow $\to$ is read "approaches." For example, it is true that

$$\lim_{x \to 2} x^2 = 4 \tag{1.8}$$

because we can keep x^2 as close to 4 as we like by keeping x close enough to 2. If we want to keep x^2 within 1 unit of 4, we can do so by keeping x between 1.8 and 2.1, for instance. If we want x^2 to stay within 0.0001 units of 4, we can do that, too, by keeping x between 1.99995 and 2.00005, for example. The essential property of the number 4 in this case is that we can respond to any such challenge of closeness to 4 by specifying a certain interval about 2, such that if x stays in that interval, then x^2 will stay within the prescribed tolerance of 4.

In order to formulate a rigorous definition of limit we now need just a bit more notation to help us express our ideas of closeness symbolically. We first define a particular, very useful, function, known as the "absolute value" function. If x is any real number, the absolute value of x, written $|x|$, is defined to be x if x is positive, to be $-x$ if x is negative, and zero if x is zero. In other words, to find the absolute value of x, just ignore the sign of x. Thus, $|2| = 2$, $|-1| = 1$, $|-12| = 12$, $|7| = 7$, etc. The reason for the introduction of this function here is that if we think of the real numbers laid out in the usual way on the x axis, then $|a - b|$ is just the distance between a and b, and to say that a is near b we need only say that $|a - b|$ is small.

Exercises

1.   Draw a graph of $|x|$.
2.   Describe the set of real numbers x for which it is true that

        (a) $|x - 1| \leq 3$
        (b) $|x - 2| \leq 1$
        (c) $|x + 3| \leq 0$
        (d) $|x + 5| = 2$
        (e) $1 \leq |x - 1| \leq 2$
        (f) $0 < |x|$

(g) $0 < |x| < 1$

(h) $0 < |x - 1| < 1$

(i) $0 < |x + 4| < 2$

(j) $0 < |x - a| < \delta$

In each case shade the portion of the x axis in which the given relation is true.

3.   Find each of the following limits:

(a) $\lim_{x \to 3} (x^3 + 1)$

(b) $\lim_{x \to 0} 2^x$

(c) $\lim_{x \to 1} \dfrac{x^2 - 1}{x - 1}$

(d) $\lim_{x \to 0} \dfrac{x^3 + x^2}{x}$

(e) $\lim_{h \to 0} \dfrac{(x + h)^4 - x^4}{h}$

(f) $\lim_{x \to 1} (1 + x)^{30}$

Returning now to our definition of limit, how, in practice, would we go about testing a certain number L to see if it is the limit of $f(x)$ as $x \to x_0$? We should be able to keep $f(x)$ no further than 0.1 from L by keeping x close to (but not equal to) x_0, that is to say, by keeping

$$0 < |x - x_0| < \text{something small enough}$$

Or, if we would like $f(x)$ still closer to L, say

$$|f(x) - L| < 10^{-30}$$

we should be able to get that, too, by keeping x in a still smaller interval about x_0. We will say that the number L is indeed the limit we seek if we can respond successfully to *every* such challenge.

Second Definition of Limit. Let f be a given function. We say that

$$\lim_{x \to x_0} f(x) = L$$

if for every number $\epsilon > 0$ there is a number $\delta > 0$ such that we have

$$|f(x) - L| < \epsilon$$

whenever $0 < |x - x_0| < \delta$.

In this definition, the number ϵ plays the role of the challenge, and the number δ is our response to it. The condition $0 < |x - x_0|$ excludes consideration of the case $x = x_0$. L is the limit if and only if there is a response to every possible challenge. This kind of definition is admittedly difficult to work with in practice, but it is the end result of a long quest for a way to remove the idea of limit from the area of mysticism and to entrench it as a proper branch of mathematics. We will, in subsequent work, use this definition primarily to prove theorems about limits, a task for which it is very well adapted. Then we will use these theorems to help us in the actual task of evaluating troublesome limits. Naturally, in nontroublesome cases the usual mystical ideas will be quite sufficient.

As an example of the direct use of this definition, let us consider the function

$$f(x) = \begin{cases} x^2 & \text{if } x \neq 0 \\ 6 & \text{if } x = 0 \end{cases} \tag{1.9}$$

and we will prove that

$$\lim_{x \to 0} f(x) = 0 \tag{1.10}$$

Referring to the definition we see that what has to be shown is that if $\epsilon > 0$ is given there is a $\delta > 0$ such that $|f(x)| < \epsilon$ whenever $0 < |x| < \delta$. Suppose ϵ is given. To keep $|f(x)| < \epsilon$ we need

$$|x^2| < \epsilon$$

whenever $0 < |x| < \delta$. How can we find δ? If $|x| < \delta$, then

$$|x^2| < \delta^2$$

so $|x^2|$ will surely be $< \epsilon$ if δ^2 is $< \epsilon$, that is, if $\delta < \sqrt{\epsilon}$. Any $\delta < \sqrt{\epsilon}$ will do, so we can take, for instance, $\delta = \frac{1}{10}\sqrt{\epsilon}$. Once we have found this δ, say on a piece of scratch paper, we could then make a formal argument as follows:

To prove: $\lim_{x \to 0} f(x) = 0$

PROOF   Let $\epsilon > 0$ be given. Choose $\delta = \frac{1}{10}\sqrt{\epsilon}$. Then if $0 < |x| < \delta$,

$$|f(x) - 0| = |f(x)| = |x^2|$$
$$= |x|^2$$
$$< \delta^2$$
$$= \frac{\epsilon}{100}$$
$$< \epsilon$$

Thus, for every $\epsilon > 0$ there is indeed a $\delta > 0$ such that $|f(x) - 0| < \epsilon$, whenever $|x| < \delta$, which was to be shown.

This example underscores the irrelevancy of the value of the function at $x = x_0$ in determining the limit, since we never needed to look at the value 6 in (1.9).

As another example, we now discuss a situation in which a limit does not exist. Suppose we define

$$f(x) = \begin{cases} 1 & x \geq 0 \\ 0 & x < 0 \end{cases} \tag{1.11}$$

and consider the question of finding

$$\lim_{x \to 0} f(x)$$

We claim that the limit does not exist. Intuitively speaking, the reason it does not exist is because we cannot keep $f(x)$ close to some number by keeping x close to zero. Indeed, no matter how small an interval about zero we choose, it is bound to contain some positive x and some negative x and, therefore, some values of f which are $+1$ and some values which are zero.

To give a formal proof, based on the definition of limit, that this limit does not exist, one would assume that it does exist and obtain a contradiction. Indeed, if we suppose that the limit exists, then its value is either 1, 0, or some other number. Suppose the limit is 1. Then it is easy to see that if the number ϵ in the definition of limit is given as, say, $\frac{1}{2}$, we will be unable to find the number δ, for no matter how small we choose δ, the interval $0 < |x| < \delta$ will contain some negative numbers, and at these, the condition $|f(x) - 1| < \epsilon$ will be violated. We leave the other two cases as an exercise.

Exercises

1. Complete the formal proof that the function (1.11) does not have a limit at $x = 0$.

2. Find two functions f and g, neither of which has a limit at $x = 0$ but whose sum $f + g$ does have a limit there.

3. Let

$$f(x) = \begin{cases} 1 - x & x \leqq 1 \\ x & x > 1 \end{cases}$$

Does $\lim_{x \to 1} f(x)$ exist? Why?

4. Let

$$f(x) = \begin{cases} x & x \leqq 1 \\ 2 - x & x > 1 \end{cases}$$

Does $\lim_{x \to 1} f(x)$ exist? Why?

5. Find $\delta > 0$ such that $|x^2| < \frac{1}{10}$ whenever $0 < |x| < \delta$.

6. Find $\delta > 0$ such that $|x^2 - 9| < \frac{1}{10}$ whenever $0 < |x - 3| < \delta$. (Don't work too hard! Will $\delta = 10^{-40}$ do the job? Then why not use it?)

7. Given $\epsilon > 0$, find $\delta > 0$ such that $|x^2 - 1| < \epsilon$ whenever $|x - 1| < \delta$.

8. Find a function with no limit at any point. Prove your answer.

9. Prove that if

$$\lim_{x \to 1} f(x) = L$$

then

$$\lim_{x \to 0} f(x + 1) = L$$

State and prove the appropriate generalization of this result.

10. Show that if

$$\lim_{x \to 2} f(x) = 3$$

then

$$\lim_{x \to 2} \{f(x) + x\} = 5$$

Using our precise definition of limit we will now prove some theorems about limits which will be useful in what follows. The main tool used in proving these theorems is the "triangle inequality" satisfied by the absolute value function, which we state as a

LEMMA   Let a and b be real numbers. Then

$$|a + b| \leqq |a| + |b| \tag{1.12}$$

PROOF   We have

$$(|a| + |b|)^2 - |a + b|^2 = a^2 + 2|a||b| + b^2 - (a^2 + 2ab + b^2)$$
$$= 2(|ab| - ab)$$

If a and b have the same sign, this is zero. If they have opposite signs, it is positive or zero. Hence, in all cases it is nonnegative,
which is to say that

$$(|a| + |b|)^2 - |a + b|^2 \geqq 0$$

which was to be shown.

The triangle inequality (1.12) is made obvious by the remark that if
a and b have the same sign, the two sides of (1.12) are evidently equal,
while if they have opposite signs, cancellation occurs on the left side but
not on the right.

We can now prove that the limit of the sum of two functions is equal
to the sum of their limits, if the latter exist.

THEOREM 1.1.   Suppose

$$\lim_{x \to x_0} f(x) = A \qquad \text{and} \qquad \lim_{x \to x_0} g(x) = B$$

both exist. Then

$$\lim_{x \to x_0} (f(x) + g(x))$$

exists and is equal to $A + B$.

PROOF   Let $\epsilon > 0$ be given. We have to find a $\delta > 0$ such that

$$|f(x) + g(x) - (A + B)| < \epsilon$$

for all x such that $0 < |x - x_0| < \delta$.

Now using the hypothesis that $\lim_{x \to x_0} f(x)$ exists and is equal to A, we
know that we can find a number δ_1 such that

$$|f(x) - A| < \frac{\epsilon}{2} \qquad \text{whenever} \qquad 0 < |x - x_0| < \delta_1 \tag{1.13}$$

Using the hypothesis that $\lim_{x \to x_0} g(x)$ exists and is equal to B, we know that we can find a number δ_2 such that

$$|g(x) - B| < \frac{\epsilon}{2} \qquad \text{whenever} \qquad 0 < |x - x_0| < \delta_2 \qquad (1.14)$$

We now claim that the smaller of the two numbers δ_1, δ_2 will serve as the δ we seek. For suppose

$$0 < |x - x_0| < \delta = \text{smaller of } (\delta_1, \delta_2)$$

Then (1.13) and (1.14) hold simultaneously, and so for such x

$$\begin{aligned}
|f(x) + g(x) - (A + B)| &= |(f(x) - A) + (g(x) - B)| \\
&\leq |f(x) - A| + |g(x) - B| \\
&< \frac{\epsilon}{2} + \frac{\epsilon}{2} \\
&= \epsilon
\end{aligned}$$

as required, completing the proof.

We now show that the limit of a product of two functions behaves as one might expect.

THEOREM 1.2.   If

$$\lim_{x \to x_0} f(x) = A \qquad \text{and} \qquad \lim_{x \to x_0} g(x) = B$$

both exist, then

$$\lim_{x \to x_0} f(x)g(x)$$

exists and is equal to AB.

PROOF   Let a number $\epsilon > 0$ be given. We must find a number $\delta > 0$ such that

$$|f(x)g(x) - AB| < \epsilon$$

for all x such that $0 < |x - x_0| < \delta$. But

$$
\begin{aligned}
&|f(x)g(x) - AB| \\
&= |A(g(x) - B) + (f(x) - A)(g(x) - B) + B(f(x) - A)| \\
&\leqq |A||g(x) - B| + |f(x) - A||g(x) - B| + |B||f(x) - A|
\end{aligned}
$$

Since $g(x) \to B$, we can make the first and second terms as small as we wish by keeping x close enough to x_0, and since $f(x) \to A$ we can make the third term as small as we please similarly. Hence, by keeping x in a small enough neighborhood of x_0 we can make the whole sum as small as we wish, which was to be shown.

Exercise

Prove that if both of the statements

$$
\lim_{x \to x_0} f(x) = A \quad \text{and} \quad \lim_{x \to x_0} f(x) = B
$$

are true, then $A = B$. That is, show that a function cannot have two different limits at the same point x_0.

We now wish to broaden our definition of a limit in order to include such an assertion as

$$
\lim_{x \to \infty} \left(1 + \frac{1}{x} \right) = 1 \tag{1.15}
$$

This statement does not mean that there is such place as infinity, and when x gets there the value of the expression $1 + 1/x$ is 1. It only means that when x is very large, the number $1 + 1/x$ is near 1, and we can make it as close to 1 as we wish by keeping x large enough. Formally, we state the

DEFINITION We say that

$$
\lim_{x \to \infty} f(x) = A
$$

if, given $\epsilon > 0$, we can find a number M such that

$$|f(x) - A| < \epsilon$$

for all $x > M$.

Let us now prove, using this definition, that (1.15) is indeed true. Suppose a number $\epsilon > 0$ is given. We have to find a number M such that

$$\left|\left(1 + \frac{1}{x}\right) - 1\right| < \epsilon$$

whenever $x > M$. But evidently

$$\left|\left(1 + \frac{1}{x}\right) - 1\right| = \left|\frac{1}{x}\right|$$

and to get this to be $< \epsilon$ all we have to do is keep $x > 1/\epsilon$. In other words, we have shown that if $\epsilon > 0$ is given, then we can take the number M appearing in the definition to be $1/\epsilon$, completing the proof.

Exercises

1.   Formulate a good definition of

$$\lim_{x \to -\infty} f(x) = A$$

2.   Find the following limits.

(a) $\displaystyle\lim_{x \to \infty} \frac{x^2 + 3x - 1}{2x^2 - x + 1}$

(b) $\displaystyle\lim_{x \to -\infty} \frac{(x + 1)^5}{x^5 + 1}$

(c) $\displaystyle\lim_{x \to \infty} \frac{x + 1}{(x - 3)^3}$

(d) $\displaystyle\lim_{x \to -\infty} \frac{1}{x}$

(e) $\displaystyle\lim_{x \to \infty} (1 + 2^{-x})$

(f) $\displaystyle\lim_{x \to \infty} 3$

(g) $\displaystyle\lim_{x \to -\infty} \frac{x + 1}{1 - x}$

(h) $\displaystyle\lim_{x \to \infty} \frac{\sqrt{x}}{1 + x^2}$

3. Why did we need a separate definition of limit as $x \to \infty$? What was wrong with our previous definition in this case?

4. Evaluate the following limits.

   (a) $\lim\limits_{x \to 2} 3^{x-2}$

   (b) $\lim\limits_{x \to 0} \dfrac{(1 + x^2)^2 - 1}{3x^2}$

   (c) $\lim\limits_{h \to 0} \dfrac{1}{h}\left\{\dfrac{1}{x + h} - \dfrac{1}{x}\right\}$

   (d) $\lim\limits_{h \to 0} \dfrac{(\sqrt{2} + h)^4 - (4 + h)}{h}$

Review Problems for Chapter 1

1. Let $f(x)$ be defined for all real x, and let $g(x) = f(2x) - f(x)$. Show that $g(x)$ is zero somewhere.

2. For what values of x is the larger of the two numbers

$$1 + x, \quad x^2 - 2x + 1$$

   the second one?

3. Make careful sketches of the graphs of each of the following functions.

   (a) $g(x) = $ the smaller of x and x^2.
   (b) $h(x) = $ the larger of $x^2 - 1$ and $x - 1$.
   (c) $f(x) = $ the largest integer which is $\leq x$.
   (d) $f(x) = $ the first digit after the decimal point in the number x.
   (e) $f(x) = $ the distance from x to the nearest integer.

   In each case your graph should go up at least $x = 15$.

4. For each of the functions in Problem 3, find the limit of the function as $x \to 7$, or else prove that the limit does not exist.

5. Do you know of any function which satisfies the equation

$$f(xy) = f(x) + f(y)$$

   for $x > 0$, $y > 0$?

6. Show that

$$\frac{|x - y|}{2} + \frac{x + y}{2}$$

   is equal to the larger of the two numbers x and y. Find a similar expression which is equal to the smaller of x and y.

The Derivative
Geometrical Aspects of Differentiation
Continuity and Differentiability
The Integral
Properties of the Integral
The Integral as a Function of its Upper Limit
Rolle's Theorem and the Mean-Value Theorem

2

Theory of Differentiation and Integration

2.1. The Derivative

Recalling our automobile problem in Chapter 1, we promised at that time to elaborate the concepts that were used to solve that problem, and we have so far treated the fundamental ideas of functions and limits. In Chapter 2 we discuss the actual processes that we used to find the speed from the position, in the first case, and the position from the speed, in the second case. These are the processes of differentiation and integration, respectively, and the development of their theoretical foundations forms the basis of our discussion. In Chapter 3 we will discuss the actual mechanics of these processes and develop a formidable analytical structure for carrying out these basic operations on a wide variety of functions. For the present, though, we shall not concern ourselves with these technical questions, but will concentrate only on the conceptual aspects.

To begin with differentiation, let us return to the automobile problem once more, remembering that its position at time t was

$$x = t^2 \tag{2.1}$$

and we recast our discussion of finding its speed into the language of functions and limits.

First, we recognize that Eq. (2.1) states that x is a function of t. We call this function $x(t)$, and so we write

$$x(t) = t^2 \tag{2.2}$$

To find the speed at time t we looked next at the average speed over the time interval $t, t + h$. The distance traveled in that time interval was just $x(t + h) - x(t)$, so this average speed was

$$\frac{x(t + h) - x(t)}{h} = \frac{(t + h)^2 - t^2}{h}$$

$$= 2t + h$$

We finally observed that as h got small this could be made arbitrarily close to $2t$, or, using the language of limits, we would say that

$$\lim_{h \to 0} (2t + h) = 2t$$

and thereby take $2t$ for our answer.

To summarize, we found that for the particular function $x(t)$ in (2.1) or (2.2) the limit

$$\lim_{h \to 0} \frac{x(t + h) - x(t)}{h}$$

existed and had the value $2t$. We wish now to remove this operation from the world of automobiles, positions, speeds, times, etc., and put it into the world of mathematics. We, therefore, formulate a definition of a derivative of a function by saying that whenever we have a function defined for which a limit like the one above exists, we will call that limit the derivative of the function.

DEFINITION   Let f be a given function. If for a certain fixed number t the limit

$$\lim_{h \to 0} \frac{f(t + h) - f(t)}{h} \tag{2.3}$$

exists, then its value is called the derivative of the function f at the point t and is written $f'(t)$.

It seems necessary for us to stress, at this point, the distinction between limits and derivatives. It is true that a derivative is a limit, but it
is a limit of a very special type, namely, one of the form (2.3), where f is
a given function. Thus, while every derivative involves taking a limit, it
is surely false that every limit is a derivative. We remark further that the
limit in (2.3) is taken as $h \to 0$, and so it is one of the "hard" limits, i.e.,
where we cannot simply replace h by 0 and get an answer. If we did replace h by 0, the ratio in (2.3) would assume the form 0/0 and we would
have learned nothing about the limit. It should also be borne in mind that
when we have a limit such as $h \to 0$, the definition of a limit requires us
to look at small positive and small negative values of h. Consequently,
the existence of the limit in (2.3) is a statement about the behavior of the
function a little to the left *and* a little to the right of the point t. Naturally, we do not imply that the limit (2.3) always exists. In fact, in
many cases arising in practice it does not, and in such situations we say
that the function f does not have a derivative at the point t.

For a given function f, then, the set of points in its domain will be
divided up into two subsets, those points at which f has a derivative (at
which f is differentiable) and those at which it does not. If we call the
first subset, i.e., the collection of all points at which is differentiable, the
set D', then we can manufacture a new function, whose domain is D': at
each point t of D', our new function has the value $f'(t)$. In other words,
we are considering the function whose value at each point is the derivative of f at that point. This function is called f'. The process of obtaining f' from f, i.e., of computing the limit (2.3), is called differentiation.
We illustrate these ideas by computing f' for a few simple functions f.

Examples
1.   Let $f(x) = 3$ for all x. Then

$$\frac{f(x + h) - f(x)}{h} = \frac{3 - 3}{h} = 0$$

and so

$$\lim_{h \to 0} \frac{f(x + h) - f(x)}{h} = \lim_{h \to 0} 0 = 0$$

Hence, the derivative of this function, which everywhere has a constant value, is zero. Evidently, any function whose value is everywhere
the same will have a derivative which is everywhere zero.

2.   Let $f(x) = 4x$ for all x. Then

$$\frac{f(x + h) - f(x)}{h} = \frac{4(x + h) - 4x}{h}$$

$$= 4$$

Thus,

$$f'(x) = \lim_{h \to 0} \frac{f(x + h) - f(x)}{h}$$

$$= \lim_{h \to 0} 4$$

$$= 4$$

Therefore, for this function f, whose graph is a straight line of slope 4, we find, directly from the definition of the derivative, that its derivative is $f'(x) = 4$ for all x.

3.   Let $f(x) = |x|$ for all x. With this function we have to be rather careful in computing the derivative. First, we will calculate that derivative for a fixed *positive* value of x. In this case, if h is small enough,

$$\frac{f(x + h) - f(x)}{h} = \frac{|x + h| - |x|}{h}$$

$$= \frac{x + h - x}{h} \qquad \text{(because } x \text{ and } x + h \text{ are positive)}$$

$$= 1$$

Thus, if x is positive,

$$f'(x) = \lim_{h \to 0} \frac{f(x + h) - f(x)}{h}$$

$$= \lim_{h \to 0} 1$$

$$= 1$$

and we have found the derivative of this function for all positive x. Now suppose x is negative. Then, if h is small enough (how small?), we have

$$\frac{f(x+h) - f(x)}{h} = \frac{|x+h| - |x|}{h}$$

$$= \frac{-(x+h) - (-x)}{h}$$

$$= -1 \qquad \text{(because } x \text{ and } x+h \text{ are negative)}$$

and taking the limit, as before, we find that $f'(x) = -1$ for all negative x.

It remains only to consider the case $x = 0$. We claim that the function has no derivative at $x = 0$. Indeed, consider the quotient

$$\frac{f(h) - f(0)}{h} = \frac{|h| - |0|}{h}$$

$$= \frac{|h|}{h}$$

If h is small and positive, this quotient is $+1$, while if h is small and negative, the quotient is -1. Hence, the limit of this quotient as $h \to 0$ does not exist, and from the definition of the derivative, we conclude that the given function does not have a derivative at the origin. To summarize our discussion of the function $f(x) = |x|$, we have found that

$$f'(x) = \begin{cases} 1 & \text{if } x > 0 \\ -1 & \text{if } x < 0 \\ \text{undefined} & \text{if } x = 0 \end{cases}$$

hence, the domain of the function f' is the set of nonzero real numbers.

4. Suppose $f(x) = 1/x$ ($x \neq 0$). Here we cannot even contemplate the derivative at $x = 0$ because the function itself is not defined there. Hence, suppose x is a fixed, nonzero, real number. Then

$$\frac{f(x+h) - f(x)}{h} = \frac{1/(x+h) - 1/x}{h}$$

$$= -\frac{1}{x(x+h)}$$

It follows that

$$f'(x) = \lim_{h \to 0} \frac{f(x + h) - f(x)}{h}$$

$$= \lim_{h \to 0} - \frac{1}{x(x + h)}$$

$$= -\frac{1}{x^2}$$

and so the derivative of this function is $-x^{-2}$ for all nonzero values of x.

Exercises

1. For each of the functions below, find the derivative and specify carefully its domain of definition.

    (a) $f(x) = 3x^2 + 2$
    (b) $f(x) = (3x - 2)^2$
    (c) $f(x) = x^{-2}$

    (d) $f(x) = \begin{cases} 2x - 1 & x \leq 2 \\ 3x + 4 & x > 2 \end{cases}$

    (e) $f(x) = \begin{cases} x^2 - x + 1 & x \leq 1 \\ 2x^2 - 3x + 2 & x > 1 \end{cases}$ (careful!)

    (f) $f(x) = |x + 1|$
    (g) $f(x) = ax + b$
    (h) $f(x) = ax^2 + bx + c$

    (i) $F(x) = \dfrac{1}{x + 3}$

2. For each of the preceding functions make graphs of the function and of its derivative. Compare the graphs of each function with that of its derivative, noticing how the values of the derivative reflect the slope of the graph of the given function.

3. Give an example of a function which has a derivative everywhere but at exactly two points; three points; n points.

4. Give an example of a function which has no derivative at any point.

There is another terminology for the derivative which is used as often as the one already given. If y and x are two variables which are related by a function f, so that

$$y = f(x)$$

then we say that y is a function of x, that x is the independent variable, and that y is the dependent variable. Then the derivative of $f(x)$ (i.e., of y) is also called

$$\frac{dy}{dx} = f'(x)$$

and is read "the derivative of y with respect to x." Naturally, there is nothing magic about the letters, if

$$z = h(q)$$

describes the dependence of a variable z on a variable q, then

$$\frac{dz}{dq} = h'(q)$$

is the derivative of z with respect to q.

2.2. *Geometrical Aspects of Differentiation*

So far we have viewed differentiation as an entirely analytical process, aside from dropping an occasional hint that the slope of a curve was somehow involved. That is to say, our point of view has been that we are somehow given a function, and that we then compute the limit of a certain curious quotient, thereby finding the derivative. We shall not retreat from this position one inch, for that is precisely what a derivative is. Using this rigorous definition of derivative, we can now define the slope of a curve. It is essential to recognize that we are defining a new concept "slope of curve" in terms of a known concept "derivative" and *not* vice versa. Those who regard the idea of slope of a curve as already known are invited to try to give a definition of it without using the concepts of differentiation or other undefined terms such as "tangent."

DEFINITION   Let $y = f(x)$ be a given curve. By the slope of the curve at the point (x_0, y_0) on the curve we mean the number $f'(x_0)$ if f' exists at that point. Otherwise, the slope is not defined at the point.

Now it remains for us only to show why this is a reasonable way to define the slope of a curve. If f is a given function, consider the graph $y = f(x)$, which might look like the curve shown in Fig. 2.1.

Figure 2.1

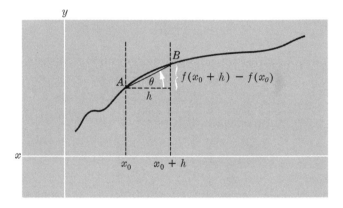

Let $x = x_0$ be some fixed abscissa, and consider the ratio

$$\frac{f(x_0 + h) - f(x_0)}{h} \tag{2.4}$$

which we recognize as the ratio whose limit we would calculate in order to find $f'(x_0)$. Referring to Fig. 2.1, we notice that the numerator of this ratio is the vertical side of a certain triangle and that the denominator of the ratio is the horizontal side of that same triangle. It follows that the value of the ratio is the tangent of the angle θ shown. In other words, the quotient (2.4) is precisely the slope of the *chord AB* of the curve. Now as h approaches zero, either through positive or negative values, the direction of this chord changes and (if our function is differentiable) approaches a certain limiting direction. The line in this limiting direction is called the tangent line to the curve at the point x_0, and the slope of this tangent line, which by construction is just the limit of (2.4) as h approaches zero, is called the slope of the curve at the point x_0.

Examples

1. Calculate the slope of the curve (i.e., the slope of the tangent line to the curve) $y = 3x^2$ at the point $x = 1, y = 3$.

    Here the required slope is

    $$f'(1) = \lim_{h \to 0} \frac{f(1 + h) - f(1)}{h}$$

    $$= \lim_{h \to 0} \frac{3(1 + h)^2 - 3(1)^2}{h}$$

    $$= \lim_{h \to 0} (6 + 3h)$$

    $$= 6$$

2. Find the equation of the tangent line to the curve $y = 3x^2$ at the point $x = 1, y = 3$.

    In Example 1 we found the slope of the curve at this point to be 6. Hence, the equation of the tangent line is of the form

    $$y = 6x + b$$

    To find b we require the line to pass through the point (1,3), getting

    $$3 = 6 \cdot 1 + b$$

    whence $b = -3$, and the answer to the problem is $y = 6x - 3$. The reader should graph the curve and the tangent line just found to see that it "looks" like a self-respecting tangent line should look.

Exercises

1. Show by differentiation that the slope of the line $y = mx + b$ is m, so that our present definition of slope in terms of derivatives reduces to the familiar result in the case of a straight line.
2. Find the equation of the tangent line to the curve $y = (x - 2)^2$ at the point $x = 2$; at the point $x = x_0$.
3. Find the point on the curve $y = x(1 - x)$ at which the slope is zero.

4.   Find a function whose graph has slope zero at every point where the slope is defined, even though the function is not constant.

5.   At what point on the parabola $y = ax^2$ is the tangent line parallel to the line $y = x$?

6.   If $f(x) = x^2 - x + 2$ find

$$\frac{f(x + h) - f(x)}{h}$$

when

(a) $x = 1, h = 1$
(b) $x = 0, h = 1$
(c) $x = 0, h = \frac{1}{2}$
(d) $x = 0, h = h$

7.   In Exercise 6 above find a δ such that

(a) $\left| \dfrac{f(h) - f(0)}{h} + 1 \right| < \dfrac{1}{2}$, when $0 < |h| < \delta$

(b) $\left| \dfrac{f(1 + h) - f(1)}{h} - 1 \right| < \dfrac{1}{4}$, when $0 < |h| < \delta$

(c) $\left| \dfrac{f(h) - f(0)}{h} + 1 \right| < 10^{-7}$, when $0 < |h| < \delta$

(d) $\left| \dfrac{f(h) - f(0)}{h} + 1 \right| < \epsilon$, when $0 < |h| < \delta$

8.   For each of the following functions compute

$$\frac{f(x + h) - f(x)}{h}$$

(a) $f(x) = \dfrac{1}{x}$

(b) $f(x) = \dfrac{x + 2}{x + 1}$

(c) $f(x) = \dfrac{3x + 2}{2x - 1}$

(d) $f(x) = \dfrac{ax + b}{cx + d}$

(e) $f(x) = x^3$

9.   In each case of Exercise 8 take the limit $h \to 0$ and thereby find $f'(x)$.

2.3. Continuity and Differentiability

At this point we make a slight digression to introduce an extremely important property of certain functions, and to relate it to differentiability insofar as possible. The property in question is known as continuity and, roughly speaking, a function is continuous at a point if its graph does not take a jump at that point. More loosely, $f(x)$ is continuous if its graph can be drawn without lifting the pencil from the paper. The curve in Fig. 2.2 is continuous. The one in Fig. 2.3 is continuous except at the

Figure 2.2

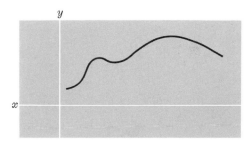

three points where the curve is broken, and at those points it is discontinuous.

Figure 2.3

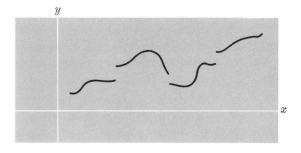

To formulate a precise definition of continuity at a point x we notice that the key property of a continuous function is that when x changes just a little, $f(x)$ changes just a little, whereas if f is discontinuous at a point, then no matter how little we disturb x, $f(x)$ may take a violent jump. Accordingly, our formal definition will say that f is continuous at the point $x = x_0$ if $f(x)$ stays near $f(x_0)$ when x stays near x_0.

> **DEFINITION**   The function f is continuous at the point x_0 if x_0 is in the domain of f, and, given any number $\epsilon > 0$, we can find a number $\delta > 0$ such that
>
> $$|f(x) - f(x_0)| < \epsilon \qquad (2.5)$$
>
> for all values of x in the domain of f such that $|x - x_0| < \delta$.

If a function is continuous at every point of a certain set, then we say that it is continuous on the set. Thus we speak of functions which are continuous on the interval (0,1), i.e., on the set of all x such that $0 < x < 1$, to mean that such functions are continuous at every point of that interval. Another way to define continuity, which is fully equivalent to the definition already given, is to say that f is continuous at x_0 if

$$\lim_{x \to x_0} f(x) = f(x_0) \qquad (2.6)$$

Recall that in the definition of a limit one looks at values of the function very near to the point x_0 but not *at* the point x_0. Then it will be noted that Eq. (2.6) really says that after inspecting the values of the function near to x_0 we are not shocked at the value of f at x_0.

We leave as exercises for the reader the proofs that if f and g are both continuous at x_0, then so are $f \pm g$ and fg. We turn next to the relationship between continuity and differentiability. In a nutshell, that relation is simply that if a function has a derivative, the function must be continuous, while if it is continuous, it need not have a derivative. We have already seen, for instance, that the function $f(x) = |x|$, which is obviously continuous everywhere, has no derivative at $x = 0$. The same will be true of any function whose graph has sharp points on it, namely, at each of those points the function will be continuous but will not have a derivative. In the other direction, however, we have the following

> **THEOREM 2.1.**   Suppose the derivative of f exists at the point x_0. Then f is continuous at x_0.

> PROOF   Since $f'(x_0)$ exists, for every $\epsilon > 0$ we can find a $\delta > 0$

such that

$$\left| \frac{f(x_0 + h) - f(x_0)}{h} - f'(x_0) \right| < \epsilon$$

for all h such that $0 < |h| < \delta$. But this means that for such h

$$\mp h(f'(x_0) - \epsilon) < f(x_0 + h) - f(x_0) < \pm h(\epsilon + f'(x_0))$$

and since both sides of this inequality go to zero with h, it is clear that $f(x_0 + h)$ is near $f(x_0)$ if h is small.

Exercises

1. Give an example of a function which is continuous everywhere except at the points $x = 1, 2, 3, \ldots, n$.
2. Prove that if f and g are continuous, so is $f + g$.
3. Show that if f and g are discontinuous, $f + g$ can still be continuous, though of course, it need not be.
4. Under what circumstances is the reciprocal of a continuous function continuous?
5. It is true, though we cannot prove it here, that there are functions that are continuous *everywhere* and have derivatives *nowhere*. Give, however, a simple formula that represents a function that is continuous throughout the interval $0 \leq x \leq 1$, which fails to be differentiable at exactly n distinct points. Graph this function.
6. Describe the points at which each of the following functions is continuous and those at which they are discontinuous.

   (a) $\dfrac{1}{x^2}$

   (b) $\dfrac{1}{x + 1}$

   (c) $\begin{cases} \dfrac{x^2 - 4}{x - 2} & \text{if } x \neq 2 \\ 4 & \text{if } x = 2 \end{cases}$

   (d) $|x + 3|$

2.4.   The Integral

Differentiation is, as we have seen, a process that associates with a given function f another function f', its derivative. Integration can be used to reverse this process, and thereby to find the function if its derivative is given. Our theoretical development of the integral will be the natural generalization of the chopping-up process by which we found the position of the automobile in Section 1.2 from its speed. The differences between our present discussion and that of Section 1.2 are as follows. First, we do not use words like "speed," "position," and so on but define the integral for any given function instead. Second, whereas in Section 1.2 we always chopped up the interval into pieces of equal size, we no longer make that restriction here. Third, in Section 1.2 we took for the constant value of the speed in each little piece the actual value of the speed at the end of that piece, whereas here we will use the actual value of the function at some point in the piece which need not be an endpoint. These differences are minor and are insignificant when compared with the conceptual similarities between our general approach to integration and the problem-oriented approach we took previously.

We suppose that we are given a function f defined for x in the interval (a,b), and initially we will suppose that the values of f are nonnegative numbers, though this assumption will be relaxed later. For this given function f and interval (a,b) we will compute a certain number, called the integral of f over the interval (a,b), and written

$$\int_a^b f(x)\,dx$$

Intuitively, one can think of this number as being the area under the graph of the curve $y = f(x)$, above the x axis, and between the vertical lines $x = a$ and $x = b$. We emphasize at this stage of the argument that such a remark as the preceding is intended only as an aid to visualization of what follows, and cannot serve as a rigorous definition of the integral. The reason for this is roughly comparable to the reason why we cannot define a derivative as a slope: because we do not know what the slope of a curve means until we have an analytical definition of derivative. Similarly, while the use of the term "area" conjures up an immediate pictorial image of the integral and is therefore of didactic value, we really do not know what is meant by the area under an arbitrary curve and will not be able to know until we have an analytical definition of the integral.

With these *caveats* out of the way, we proceed to construct the integral. Having fixed the function f and the interval (a,b) of the x axis, our first step will be to subdivide the interval into many subintervals. Next, inside of each subinterval we will choose and fix a point. Inside of each subinterval we will then think of our function as being constant, with a constant value equal to its true value at the point we selected. Multiplying that constant value by the width of the subinterval will give us an approximation to the area under the curve in that subinterval. Adding up all of these approximations over all the subintervals will give us an approximation to the total area. We then take a peculiar kind of limit of these approximate areas, namely, a limit as the size of the largest subinterval (and so of all of them) shrinks to zero. If this limit exists, we will call it the integral of f over (a,b).

To begin with the subintervals, we define the idea of a *partition*. By a partition P of the interval (a,b) we mean a collection of points x_0, x_1, $x_2, \ldots, x_n$ lying interior to the interval, where the leftmost point x_0 is equal to a, the left endpoint of the large interval, and the rightmost point x_n is equal to b. In other words, a partition of (a,b) is defined by a collection of points satisfying

$$a = x_0 < x_1 < x_2 < x_3 < \cdots < x_{n-1} < x_n = b$$

By the *norm* of a partition P we mean the size of the largest subinterval determined by the points of the partition, that is, the largest of the numbers

$$x_1 - a, \; x_2 - x_1, \; x_3 - x_2, \ldots, \; b - x_{n-1}$$

We denote the norm of a partition P by the symbol $\mu(P)$. The smallness of $\mu(P)$ measures the fineness of the partition, or the density with which we have scattered the points of the partition about the interval (a,b).

Example

We can partition the interval $0 \leq x \leq 1$, for instance, by taking

$$x_0 = 0; \; x_1 = \tfrac{1}{4}; \; x_2 = \tfrac{1}{2}; \; x_3 = \tfrac{15}{16}; \; x_4 = 1$$

For this particular partition of the interval (0,1) the norm is

$$\mu(P) = \text{largest of } (\tfrac{1}{4} - 0, \tfrac{1}{2} - \tfrac{1}{4}, \tfrac{15}{16} - \tfrac{1}{2}, 1 - \tfrac{15}{16})$$
$$= \text{largest of } (\tfrac{1}{4}, \tfrac{1}{4}, \tfrac{7}{16}, \tfrac{1}{16})$$
$$= \tfrac{7}{16}$$

To refine a partition of a certain interval is to add more points to it. Thus, a refinement of the partition in the example above is the partition

$$x_0 = 0; \; x_1 = \tfrac{1}{4}; \; x_2 = \tfrac{1}{2}; \; x_3 = \tfrac{3}{4}; \; x_4 = \tfrac{15}{16}; \; x_5 = 1$$

whose norm is $\tfrac{1}{4}$. Notice that refining a partition does not necessarily lower the norm and will not if the new points are added in the "wrong place."

Now let f be a given function defined on the interval (a,b). We propose to define its integral, and thereby the area indicated in Fig. 2.4.

Figure 2.4

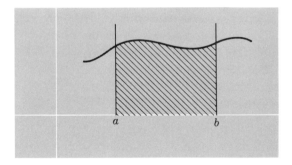

To do this we begin by choosing a partition P of the interval. Suppose this partition is

$$P: a = x_0 < x_1 < x_2 < \cdots < x_{n-1} < x_n = b$$

Let us now fix this partition P. Next, interior to the first subinterval (x_0, x_1) we select and fix a point t_1. Similarly, somewhere between x_1 and x_2 we fix a point t_2, between x_2 and x_3 a point t_3, etc., finally selecting t_n between x_{n-1} and b.

We then consider the rectangle whose base is the segment (x_0, x_1) of the x axis and whose height is $f(t_1)$. Its area is $(x_1 - x_0)f(t_1)$ (see Fig. 2.5).

The next rectangle has for its base the interval (x_1, x_2) and for its height $f(t_2)$. Its area is $(x_2 - x_1)f(t_2)$. Similarly, we consider the entire family of rectangles whose bases are the segments of the x axis determined by our partition P and whose heights are the values of the function f at the

Figure 2.5

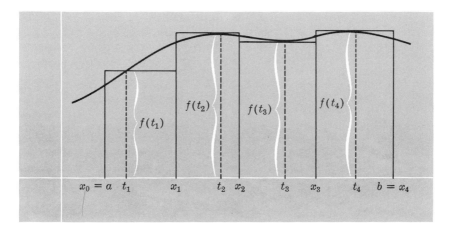

points $t_1, t_2, t_3, \ldots, t_n$ which we chose and which lie inside those subintervals. The total area of all of these rectangles is given by the expression

$$R(P) = (x_1 - a)f(t_1) + (x_2 - x_1)f(t_2) + (x_3 - x_2)f(t_3) + \cdots \\ + (b - x_{n-1})f(t_n)$$

This sum, whose value depends upon the particular partition P we are using as well as upon the intermediate points $t_1, t_2, \ldots$, is called a *Riemann sum* for the function f and the interval (a,b). Its value should be regarded as an approximation to the area under the curve, which will be a good approximation if the partition is fine (has small norm). To find the integral of the function f we now need to take the limit of these Riemann sums as the partitions get finer and finer.

DEFINITION   We say that the number I is the integral of the function f over the interval (a,b), and write

$$I = \int_a^b f(x)\, dx$$

if, given any number $\epsilon > 0$, we can find a number $\delta > 0$ such that we have

$$|R(P) - I| < \epsilon$$

for *all partitions* P whose norm is less than δ and *all* choices of the points $t_1, t_2, \ldots$, in such partitions.

In other words, the integral is I if every partition of small norm gives a Riemann sum whose value is nearly I, and if we can keep the Riemann sums as close to I as we wish by keeping the norm of the partition small enough.

Exercises

1.   Choose two different three-point partitions of the interval $(0,1)$, not counting the endpoints among the three. For each of these choose two sets of interior points t_1, t_2, t_3, t_4. Write down and evaluate numerically the four Riemann sums which you can now form to approximate the integral

$$\int_0^1 x \, dx$$

What is the exact value of this integral? Make a graph showing the exact value of the integral as a shaded area and each of the four approximate values which you computed.

2.   Identify each of the following as a Riemann sum for a certain integral. In each case, write down the integral, sketch the graph of the function which is being integrated, and shade in the approximate area which is represented by the Riemann sum.

(a) $\frac{1}{50}\left(\left(\frac{1}{49}\right)^2 + \left(\frac{2}{49}\right)^2 + \left(\frac{3}{49}\right)^2 + \cdots + \left(\frac{48}{49}\right)^2 + 1\right)$

(b) $\frac{1}{20}\left(\frac{1}{1} + \frac{1}{1 + \frac{1}{20}} + \frac{1}{1 + \frac{2}{20}} + \frac{1}{1 + \frac{3}{20}} + \cdots + \frac{1}{1 + 1}\right)$

(c) $\frac{1}{10}(2 + 2^{1.1} + 2^{1.2} + \cdots + 2^{1.9} + 2^2)$

(d) $1 + \frac{1}{2} + \frac{1}{3} + \frac{1}{4} + \cdots + \frac{1}{n}$

(e) $\frac{1}{30}(1 + 1 + 1 + 1 + \cdots + 1)$

(f) $\frac{1}{5}((1 + 3)^2 + (1 + 3.2)^2 + (1 + 3.4)^2 + \cdots + (1 + 4)^2)$

3. Find the approximate values of each of the following integrals by forming and evaluating numerically a five-point Riemann sum.

(a) $\int_2^3 x^2\, dx$

(b) $\int_{-1}^1 |x|\, dx$

(c) $\int_0^4 2^x\, dx$

(d) $\int_0^1 (1 - t)^2\, dt$

(e) $\int_4^7 \frac{1}{x}\, dx$

2.5. *Properties of the Integral*

In this section we discuss certain basic properties of

$$\int_a^b f(x)\, dx \qquad\qquad (2.7)$$

as defined in the previous section. One of the most important questions that should concern us now is the existence of the limit which defines the integral. So far all we have said is that if the limit of the Riemann sums exists, then the value of that limit is called the integral. This idea would not be very useful if the limit did not exist very often. Hence, our first task should be to describe a large family of functions, including almost all of those occurring in applications, for which it is true that the limit exists, that is, for which it is true that the function is integrable. The fundamental theorem in this area is the assertion that *every continuous function is integrable.* The proof of this theorem is quite long and we shall not give it here, though we shall use the result repeatedly. It will be a consequence of this theorem and of the results of this section that not only are continuous functions integrable but also those functions that have only a finite number of finite discontinuities. In practice, the kind of functions that may not have an integral will, therefore, be the unbounded ones. For example, the function

$$f(x) = \begin{cases} 1/x & x \neq 0 \\ 5 & x = 0 \end{cases}$$

does not have an integral on the interval (0,1). One may think of this as meaning that the area under the graph of this function is infinite.

THEOREM 2.2. Suppose that f and g are integrable over (a,b). Then so is $f + g$, and we have

$$\int_a^b (f(x) + g(x))\, dx = \int_a^b f(x)\, dx + \int_a^b g(x)\, dx \tag{2.8}$$

PROOF   A Riemann sum approximating the left-hand side of (2.8) is

$$(f(t_1) + g(t_1))(x_1 - a) + (f(t_2) + g(t_2))(x_2 - x_1) + \cdots$$
$$+ (f(t_n) + g(t_n))(b - x_{n-1}) \tag{2.9}$$

which is evidently equal to

$$[f(t_1)(x_1 - a) + f(t_2)(x_2 - x_1) + \cdots + f(t_n)(b - x_{n-1})]$$
$$+ [g(t_1)(x_1 - a) + g(t_2)(x_2 - x_1) + \cdots + g(t_n)(b - x_{n-1})] \tag{2.10}$$

Our hypotheses state that each of the two quantities in the brackets approaches a limit. Hence, (2.9), being the sum of these, must approach the sum of these two limits.

THEOREM 2.3. If f is integrable over (a,b) and c is a real number, then cf is integrable over (a,b) and

$$\int_a^b cf(x)\, dx = c \int_a^b f(x)\, dx \tag{2.11}$$

PROOF   The proof is immediate, upon writing down an approximating Riemann sum for the integral on the left.

THEOREM 2.4. Let f be defined for $a \leq x \leq b$. Let c be a number lying between a and b, and suppose that f is integrable over (a,c) and over (c,b), that is, suppose that each of the integrals

$$\int_a^c f(x)\, dx, \quad \int_c^b f(x)\, dx$$

exists. Then f is integrable over the whole interval (a,b), and we have

$$\int_a^b f(x)\, dx = \int_a^c f(x)\, dx + \int_c^b f(x)\, dx \qquad (2.12)$$

PROOF   Let us choose a partition P_1 of the interval (a,c) and a partition P_2 of the interval (c,b). Approximate the first integral on the right of (2.12) by a Riemann sum based on the partition P_1 and approximate the second integral on the right by an approximating Riemann sum based on the partition P_2. The sum of these two Riemann sums is a Riemann sum for the integral on the left-hand side of (2.12) because the set of points consisting of those in P_1 and those in P_2 (i.e., the members of the union of P_1 and P_2) constitutes a partition of the whole interval (a,b). Since each of the Riemann sums on the right approaches a limit by hypothesis, the theorem is proved.

Geometrically speaking, Theorem 2.3 asserts that the area under a curve from a to c plus the area from c to b is equal to the area from a to b. We have so far defined the integral only for functions f whose values were nonnegative numbers, and we promised that this assumption would, sooner or later, be dropped. We do so now by defining the integral of a function whose values may be positive or negative. First, consider a function whose values are all nonpositive numbers. If f is such a function, we define its integral by the relation

$$\int_a^b f(x)\, dx = - \int_a^b -f(x)\, dx \qquad (2.13)$$

Since, in the integral on the right a function with only nonnegative values appears, this definition reduces the case considered to the one we already treated. In case of a function which assumes some positive, some negative, and some zero values, we suppose that we can split up the interval of integration (a,b) into subintervals, in each of which the function f maintains constant sign. We can then, following the spirit of Theorem 2.3, define the integral over (a,b) to be the sum of the integrals over each of these subintervals of constant sign. For example,

$$\int_0^2 (x - x^2)\, dx = \int_0^1 (x - x^2)\, dx + \int_1^2 (x - x^2)\, dx \qquad (2.14)$$

and in each integral on the right the integrand (function being integrated) has constant sign.

Finally, we notice that the integral

$$\int_a^b f(x)\,dx$$

has been so far defined only in the case where $a < b$. If $a > b$, we define

$$\int_a^b f(x)\,dx = -\int_b^a f(x)\,dx \qquad (2.15)$$

so that, for example,

$$\int_2^1 x\,dx = -\int_1^2 x\,dx$$

An immediate consequence of (2.15) is that

$$\int_a^a f(x)\,dx = 0$$

which says that the area over an interval of zero length is zero.

THEOREM 2.5.   Suppose f is integrable over (a,b) and that M is a number with the property that

$$|f(x)| \leqq M$$

for all x in the interval (a,b). Then

$$\left| \int_a^b f(x)\,dx \right| \leqq M(b - a) \qquad (2.16)$$

PROOF   A Riemann sum approximating the integral of f is

$$f(t_1)(x_1 - a) + f(t_2)(x_2 - x_1) + \cdots + f(t_n)(b - x_{n-1})$$

If we take the absolute value of this sum, and remember that according to the triangle inequality, the absolute value of a sum of numbers cannot exceed the sum of their absolute values, we find that the absolute value of this Riemann sum cannot exceed

$$M(x_1 - a) + M(x_2 - x_1) + M(x_3 - x_2) + \cdots + M(b - x_{n-1})$$
$$= M\{x_1 - a + x_2 - x_1 + x_3 - x_2 + \cdots + b - x_{n-1}\}$$
$$= M(b - a)$$

which was to be shown.

As an example of the use of Theorem 2.5, consider the integral

$$\int_0^1 (x^3 + x^2 + x + 1)\, dx$$

Now for all x in the interval $(0,1)$ it is surely true that the integrand does not exceed 4. Thus taking $M = 4$, we find that the integral in question is at most equal to $4(1 - 0) = 4$. The actual value of this integral happens to be $\frac{25}{12}$, so our estimate is quite conservative.

THEOREM 2.6.   Let k be a real number. Then

$$\int_a^b k\, dx = k(b - a). \tag{2.17}$$

PROOF   This is obvious geometrically because the graph of the integrand is a horizontal straight line, and (2.17) is just telling us how to compute the area of a rectangle. Analytically, it is equally obvious, for every Riemann sum has the value $k(b - a)$.

Exercises

1.   Write each of the following integrals in terms of integrals whose integrands are nonnegative functions:

(a) $\int_1^1 x\, dx$

(b) $\int_0^3 (4 - t^2)\, dt$

(c) $\int_{-5}^{-2} \frac{1}{x}\, dx$

(d) $\int_{-1}^1 (1 - 2^x)\, dx$

2.   For each of the integrals in the preceding problem, find a positive number which is surely not exceeded by the absolute value of the integral.

2.6.   *The Integral as a Function of its Upper Limit*

Suppose that we are given a function f which is defined for $a \leq t \leq b$ and is integrable there. Then we know that the integral

$$\int_a^b f(t)\,dt$$

is a certain number which represents the area under the curve $y = f(t)$ between $t = a$ and $t = b$. In this section we propose to regard the number b which appears as the upper limit of integration as a variable rather than as a constant. Our objective in so doing is to lay the groundwork for showing that integration is, in a sense, the opposite of differentiation, a fact which was probably quite clear when we were calculating with automobiles in Chapter 1, but may be rather abstruse now that we have adopted our rather formal definition of an integral as a limit of Riemann sums.

Thus, suppose that instead of computing all of the area under our given curve we wish to compute only some of it. More precisely, instead of calculating the area from a to b, let us find only the area from a to x, where x is some intermediate number. This area is evidently represented by the integral

$$\int_a^x f(t)\,dt$$

The value of this integral will, of course, depend on the value of x which we choose, that is to say, the value of this integral is a function of x. Let us call this function $F(x)$, so that

$$F(x) = \int_a^x f(t)\,dt$$

Evidently, $F(a) = 0$. In this manner, starting with a given function f we construct another function F by integration from a to x.

Example
Suppose we start with $f(t) = t$ for $0 \leqq t \leqq 1$. Then

$$F(x) = \int_0^x t \, dt$$

represents the area shaded (Fig. 2.6).

Figure 2.6

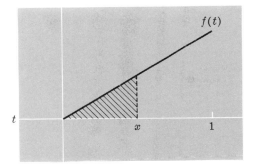

Since this is a right triangle whose base and altitude are both equal to x, we have

$$F(x) = \frac{x^2}{2}$$

It is reasonable to inquire, at this stage, about the converse of this operation. If someone were to hand us the F, how would we find the f from which it came? The answer is that we would differentiate $F(x)$ in order to find $f(x)$, and this fact constitutes the precise statement of the inverse relationship which exists between differentiation and integration. This fact is also responsible for a method of evaluating integrals, which does not make any use whatever of the cumbersome Riemann sums where it is applicable. In view of the far-reaching importance of this result, it is not surprising that it is called

THE FUNDAMENTAL THEOREM OF THE CALCULUS

Let a function f be defined for $a \leq x \leq b$ and be integrable and continuous there. Let

$$F(x) = \int_a^x f(t)\, dt \tag{2.18}$$

Then F has a derivative for all x in the interval, and that derivative is f.

PROOF   To prove this theorem we take the definition of F in (2.18) and differentiate it directly from the definition of a derivative. Thus, we consider, for some fixed value of x_0, the difference quotient

$$\frac{F(x_0 + h) - F(x_0)}{h} = \frac{1}{h} \left\{ \int_a^{x_0+h} f(t)\, dt - \int_a^{x_0} f(t)\, dt \right\} \tag{2.19}$$

By Theorem 2.4 this becomes

$$\frac{F(x_0 + h) - F(x_0)}{h} = \frac{1}{h} \int_{x_0}^{x_0+h} f(t)\, dt \tag{2.20}$$

and we wish to show that as h approaches zero, this number approaches $f(x_0)$. Roughly speaking, this will be true because when h is small the interval of integration $(x_0, x_0 + h)$ is small, and so the integrand $f(t)$ does not change much and is, therefore, approximately constant, the constant being $f(x_0)$. If $f(t)$ were exactly constant then the right-hand side of (2.20) would be exactly $f(x_0)$. To prove that the limit is $f(x_0)$, suppose $\epsilon > 0$ is given. Since f is continuous, there is a number δ such that

$$|f(t) - f(x_0)| < \epsilon \tag{2.21}$$

whenever $|t - x_0| < \delta$. Choose such a δ and fix it. Now, since x_0 is fixed, $f(x_0)$ is just some constant, and so

$$f(x_0) = f(x_0) \cdot 1$$

$$= f(x_0) \cdot \frac{1}{h} \int_{x_0}^{x_0+h} 1\, dt \qquad \text{(by Theorem 2.6)} \tag{2.22}$$

$$= \frac{1}{h} \int_{x_0}^{x_0+h} f(x_0)\, dt \qquad \text{(Theorem 2.6 again)}$$

Therefore, from (2.20) and (2.22)

$$\frac{F(x_0 + h) - F(x_0)}{h} - f(x_0) = \frac{1}{h}\left\{\int_{x_0}^{x_0+h} f(t)\, dt - \int_{x_0}^{x_0+h} f(x_0)\, dt\right\}$$

$$= \frac{1}{h}\int_{x_0}^{x_0+h} \{f(t) - f(x_0)\}\, dt \qquad \text{(by Theorem 2.2)} \qquad (2.23)$$

According to (2.21), the quantity which is being integrated in (2.23) is, in absolute value, at most ϵ throughout the range of integration if $|h| < \delta$. Hence, we can use Theorem 2.5, taking $M = \epsilon$, and, thereby, deduce that

$$\left|\frac{1}{h}\int_{x_0}^{x_0+h} \{f(t) - f(x_0)\}\, dt\right| \leqq \frac{1}{h}\cdot\epsilon\cdot h$$

$$= \epsilon$$

Hence, from (2.23), we conclude that whenever $|h| < \delta$,

$$\left|\frac{F(x_0 + h) - F(x_0)}{h} - f(x_0)\right| < \epsilon$$

which is to say that

$$\lim_{h\to 0} \frac{F(x_0 + h) - F(x_0)}{h} = f(x_0)$$

i.e.,

$$F'(x_0) = f(x_0)$$

which was to be shown.

Exercises

1. Show by an example that the conclusion of the fundamental theorem may be false if f is not continuous.
2. What was the need for the curious calculation in (2.22)?
3. Evaluate

(a) $\dfrac{d}{dx}\displaystyle t^2\, dt$

(b) $\dfrac{d}{dx}\displaystyle\int_2^3 t^2\, dt$

(c) $\dfrac{d}{du}\displaystyle\int_5^u x^4\, dx$

2.7.   *Rolle's Theorem and the Mean-Value Theorem*

We can regard the fundamental theorem of the calculus as a partial answer to the following question: If a function f is given, how can we find a function F whose derivative is f? The answer given by the fundamental theorem is that if f is continuous, then such a function F is

$$F(x) = \int_a^x f(t)\, dt$$

It will be noted that there is some freedom involved in the choice of the fixed lower limit of integration. No matter how we fix the lower limit, so long as it lies within the domain of f, we find a function whose derivative is f. It is noteworthy, however, that any two of the functions so found can differ only by a constant. Indeed, if F and G are two such functions obtained by using different lower limits, say

$$F(x) = \int_\alpha^x f(t)\, dt$$

and

$$G(x) = \int_\beta^x f(t)\, dt$$

then

$$F(x) - G(x) = \int_\alpha^x f(t)\, dt - \int_\beta^x f(t)\, dt$$

$$= \int_\alpha^\beta f(t)\, dt$$

which is indeed a constant.

As an example, if we take the function f which is equal to 1 for all x, then one function whose derivative is f, by the fundamental theorem is

$$F(x) = \int_0^x 1\, dt = x$$

while another is

$$G(x) = \int_{1/2}^{x} 1 \, dt = x - \tfrac{1}{2}$$

Evidently, $F(x)$ and $G(x)$ differ only by a constant.

What we have shown so far is that any two functions *of the particular form*

$$\int_{a}^{x} f(t) \, dt$$

can differ only by a constant. But how can we be sure that any function whose derivative is f must be of this form? For example, in the case where $f(x) = 1$ for all x the fundamental theorem tells us that the function given by $F(x) = x + c$ has f for its derivative, no matter what the constant c is. Could there, however, be another function whose derivative is this f, a function which is not of the type $x + c$, but is something more complicated? The reader may well suspect that the answer is no and that we have indeed found *all* functions whose derivative is f. The proof of this fact is not trivial, and we prove it here both because of its own intrinsic interest and because some of the tools which we will develop along the way will be useful in our later work. The proof will be done in its entirety except for the very first step, which is the most difficult, and so we content ourselves merely with the statement, but not the proof of

ROLLE'S THEOREM Let f be defined for $a \leqq x \leqq b$. If f is

    (a) continuous for $a \leqq x \leqq b$
    (b) differentiable for $a < x < b$
and if
    (c) $f(a) = f(b)$
then there is a point ξ such that
    (d) $a < \xi < b$ and
    (e) $f'(\xi) = 0$

Remarks. Behind the formidable façade of the statement of this theorem lurks a trivially simple idea: "What goes up, and comes down, must turn around somewhere." Notice that hypothesis (c) says that the value of the function is the same at both endpoints of the interval. The conclusion (e) says that there is a point somewhere (unspecified) in the interval where the derivative is zero, that is, where the tangent line to the curve is horizontal—where the curve turns around. Thus, the theorem merely claims that if a function has the same value at both ends of a certain interval, and is suitably smooth in between, then somewhere between those endpoints is a point where the derivative of the function is zero. While this statement is quite easy to grasp, the proof is rather lengthy and is omitted.

Exercises

1.   Show by an example that hypotheses (a) and (b) are necessary.
2.   If $f(x) = x - x^2$, $a = 0$, $b = 1$, show that the hypotheses are satisfied, and find the point ξ of Rolle's theorem.
3.   Show by examples that the point ξ need not be unique, and indeed that there may be any finite number of such points, or infinitely many of them.
4.   Show by example that hypothesis (c) is necessary.

Using Rolle's theorem we can now prove a result which will be most useful in our work. It also asserts that there is somewhere in a certain interval a point ξ with certain properties. The properties, however, are somewhat different from those in Rolle's theorem.

THEOREM 2.7 (*The Mean-Value Theorem of the Differential Calculus*).   Let f be continuous for $a \leqq x \leqq b$ and differentiable for $a < x < b$. Then there is a number ξ such that $a < \xi < b$ and

$$\frac{f(b) - f(a)}{b - a} = f'(\xi) \tag{2.24}$$

Remarks. To see what this theorem means geometrically, consider Fig. 2.7. The slope of the *chord* joining the endpoints of the graph of the curve is evidently

$$\frac{f(b) - f(a)}{b - a}$$

Thus the left-hand side of (2.24) of the mean-value theorem is the slope of the chord joining the endpoints of the graph. However, $f'(x)$, for every x, is the slope of the curve itself at the point x, that is to say, it is the slope of the tangent line to the curve at x. Hence, the right-hand side of (2.24) is the slope of the tangent to the curve at some point ξ. The theorem, therefore, asserts that somewhere between a and b there is a point on the curve at which the slope of the curve is the same as the slope of the chord, or equivalently, there is a point where the tangent line is parallel to the chord. Such a point is shown in Fig. 2.7.

Figure 2.7

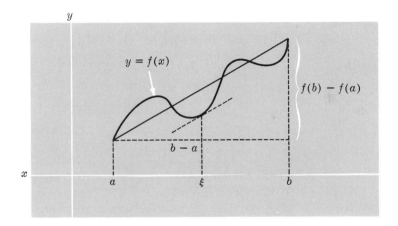

PROOF OF THE MEAN-VALUE THEOREM   We wish to prove the mean-value theorem by using Rolle's theorem. We cannot do this directly, for our function $f(x)$ does not satisfy the crucial hypothesis of Rolle's theorem which requires it to have the same value at both ends of the interval (a,b). We are, therefore, forced to carry out a slight trick, and change the function f to a somewhat different function which does have the same value at both endpoints. We then apply Rolle's theorem to that altered function and get the desired result.

To carry out this modification of f, we must subtract a certain straight line from it. Let us consider

$$G(x) = f(x) - kx$$

and determine the constant k in such a way as to make $G(a) = G(b)$. But this means that

$$f(a) - ka = f(b) - kb$$

so

$$k = \frac{f(b) - f(a)}{b - a}$$

Therefore, we consider the modified function

$$G(x) = f(x) - \frac{f(b) - f(a)}{b - a} x$$

and we know, by construction, that $G(a) = G(b)$. Therefore, by Rolle's theorem, there is a point ξ in (a,b) where $G'(\xi) = 0$. But, by direct differentiation,

$$G'(x) = f'(x) - \frac{f(b) - f(a)}{b - a}$$

and replacing x by ξ we see that the statement $G'(\xi) = 0$ is identical with (2.24), completing the proof.

Using the mean-value theorem we can prove that a function whose derivative is zero must be a constant. This is another result that sounds obvious but whose proof requires all of the apparatus that we have so far built up.

THEOREM 2.8.   Let f be continuous for $a \leqq x \leqq b$ and suppose that $f'(x) = 0$ for *all* x in the interval (a,b). Then $f(x)$ is constant throughout that interval.

PROOF   Let x_1 and x_2 be any two distinct points of the interval (a,b). Then

$$f(x_2) - f(x_1) = (x_2 - x_1)f'(\xi) \tag{2.25}$$

where ξ is somewhere between x_1 and x_2, by the mean-value theorem.

We do not know the exact value of ξ, but, whatever it is, our hypothesis that f' is zero everywhere assures us that f' is zero at ξ. Then, by (2.25), $f(x_2) = f(x_1)$. We have shown, then, that at any two distinct points, f has the same value. This clearly implies that f has the same value everywhere, i.e., that f is constant.

We are now in a position to answer the problem raised at the beginning of this section by showing that if somehow we can find one function whose derivative is f, then we can find every function whose derivative is f by adding constants to it.

THEOREM 2.9. Two functions with the same derivative differ by a constant.

PROOF Suppose that f and g have the same derivative, so that

$$f'(x) = g'(x)$$

for all x in the interval considered. Then the derivative of $f - g$ is $f' - g'$, that is, $f - g$ has a derivative that is everywhere zero. Hence, by Theorem 2.8 $f - g$ is constant, as claimed.

This result is of the greatest importance for the evaluation of integrals without the computation of Riemann sums. The combination of this last theorem with the fundamental theorem of the calculus produces a method for calculating integrals that shows how we find the value of the integral if we can find any function whose derivative is the integrated function. Before giving a general discussion of this method, let us discover it by doing a particular example.

Suppose we wish to evaluate

$$\int_0^1 t \, dt \tag{2.26}$$

We then define

$$F(x) = \int_0^x t \, dt \tag{2.27}$$

and, by the fundamental theorem, we know that $F'(x) = x$. Another function with that same derivative is

$$G(x) = \frac{x^2}{2}$$

as we can check by direct differentiation. Hence, by Theorem 2.8, F and

G differ by a constant, and, therefore,

$$F(x) = \tfrac{1}{2}x^2 + C \qquad (2.28)$$

where C is some constant. To find the constant, notice that from (2.27), $F(0) = 0$, and substituting $x = 0$ in (28), we find that $C = 0$. Therefore,

$$F(x) = \tfrac{1}{2}x^2 \qquad (2.29)$$

Our problem, however, was to evaluate the integral (2.26). When we compare (2.26) with (2.27), our answer is evidently $F(1)$, which from (2.29) is $\tfrac{1}{2}$, the answer we require. The success of this method hinges upon our ability to produce a function whose derivative is equal to the integrand in the desired integral. In practical problems the method may be obvious, easy, difficult, or impossible, but where it is possible it is the easiest way to perform integration.

Let us now formulate our method more generally. Suppose it is required to evaluate the integral

$$\int_a^b f(t)\, dt \qquad (2.30)$$

Then define

$$F(x) = \int_a^x f(t)\, dt \qquad (2.31)$$

and notice that the desired integral (2.30) is just $F(b)$. Now, if f is continuous, we know from the fundamental theorem that $F' = f$. Suppose that in some way we can find any other function G with the same derivative,

$$G'(x) = f(x)$$

Then by Theorem 2.9,

$$F(x) - G(x) = C \qquad (2.32)$$

for some constant C. To evaluate C note that from (2.31), $F(a) = 0$. Putting $x = a$ in (2.32),

$$C = -G(a)$$

and substituting this in (2.32)

$$F(x) = G(x) - G(a) \qquad (2.33)$$

Finally, if we let $x = b$ in (2.33), we find the required integral

$$\int_a^b f(t)\, dt = G(b) - G(a) \tag{2.34}$$

We summarize this discussion in the form of a simple recipe given by

THEOREM 2.10. In order to evaluate $\int_a^b f(t)\, dt$, where f is a continuous function:

    (1) Find any function G whose derivative is f.
    (2) The answer is

$$\int_a^b f(t)\, dt = G(b) - G(a).$$

Exercises

1. Given that the derivative of x^n is nx^{n-1}, find a function whose derivative is

    (a) x^2
    (b) $x^3 + 1$
    (c) $(x + 1)^2$
    (d) $3x^5 - 7x^4 + x + 1$
    (e) x^n $(n \neq -1)$

2. Find the integral of each function in Exercise 1 from $x = 0$ to $x = 1$.
3. If f is a given function, what is

$$\int_a^b f'(t)\, dt?$$

4. For each of the following functions, in the interval shown, find a value of ξ which satisfies the mean-value theorem.

    (a) $f(x) = x^2$ (0,1)
    (b) $f(x) = (x - 1)^2$ (0,1)
    (c) $f(x) = x^2 + 3x - 2$ (0,2)
    (d) $f(x) = ax + b$ (c,d)

5. Calculate

    (a) $\int_1^2 (x^2 - 3x + 1)\, dx$

(b) $\int_{-1}^{1} (x^2 + x + 2) \, dx$

(c) $\int_{0}^{3} (x - 1)^3 \, dx$

(d) $\int_{a}^{b} (x + 1) \, dx$

(e) $\int_{1}^{3} (x^4 - 3x^3 + x^2 - x + 2) \, dx$

(f) $\int_{0}^{1} (a_0 + a_1 x + a_2 x^2 + a_3 x^3) \, dx$

6. Assume that the derivative of x^a is ax^{a-1}. Apply the mean-value theorem to $f(x) = x^{1/5}$ on the interval (2.32 and 2.33) and thereby show that

$$2 + \tfrac{1}{165} \leqq \sqrt[5]{33} \leqq 2 + \tfrac{1}{80}$$

7. Prove the mean-value theorem of the integral calculus: If f is continuous on (a,b), then there is a point ξ such that $a < \xi < b$ and

$$\int_{a}^{b} f(t) \, dt = (b - a) f(\xi)$$

[Hint: Apply Theorem 2.7 to the function

$$F(x) = \int_{a}^{x} f(t) \, dt.]$$

Rules for Differentiation
Elementary Integrals
Logarithmic Functions
The Exponential Function
The Trigonometric Functions
Inverse Functions
Monotone Functions
The Inverse Trigonometric Functions
The Mechanics of Integration: Integration by Parts
The Mechanics of Integration: Integration by Substitution
The Mechanics of Integration: Rational Functions

3

The Machinery of
Differentiation and Integration

3.1. Rules for Differentiation

We are now in possession of the theoretical apparatus which is necessary
in order to make use of the calculus. Our next task is to acquire facility
in carrying out the fundamental operations of the calculus, differentiation and integration. We would like to build up, in this chapter, the
machinery required in order to permit differentiation and integration of
a vast number of different kinds of functions, more or less at sight. The
basic pattern by which this will be accomplished is that we will learn how
to differentiate a few elementary functions, and we will also prove some
theorems which show how to differentiate more complicated functions in
terms of these elementary functions.

We begin with the differentiation of algebraic functions. Suppose n is
a nonnegative integer, and let $y(x) = x^n$. Then

$$\frac{dy}{dx} = \lim_{h \to 0} \frac{(x + h)^n - x^n}{h}$$

$$= \lim_{h \to 0} \frac{1}{h} \left\{ x^n + nx^{n-1}h + \frac{n(n-1)}{2} x^{n-2}h^2 + \cdots - x^n \right\}$$

$$= \lim_{h \to 0} \left\{ nx^{n-1} + \frac{n(n-1)}{2} x^{n-2}h + \cdots \right\}$$

$$= nx^{n-1}$$

since each term after the first has a factor of h and, therefore, approaches zero as h goes to zero. Thus, for $n \geq 0$, the derivative of x^n is nx^{n-1}. We wish to extend the range of validity of this formula to the negative integers and to the rational numbers. We could do this by a suitable direct calculation, but it is preferable at this point to begin with the statement of some of our labor-extending theorems referred to earlier. These theorems will, in particular, give the desired extension of our rule for differentiating powers of x.

THEOREM 3.1.   Let f and g be two functions, and let f' and g' be their derivatives. Then

$$(f + g)' = f' + g' \tag{3.1}$$

$$(cf)' = cf' \quad (c, \text{ a constant}) \tag{3.2}$$

$$(fg)' = fg' + f'g \tag{3.3}$$

$$\left(\frac{f}{g}\right)' = \frac{gf' - fg'}{g^2} \quad (\text{if } g \neq 0) \tag{3.4}$$

PROOF   Rules (3.1) and (3.2) are trivial and follow directly from the definition of a derivative and the corresponding theorems for limits. Rule (3.3) shows us how to differentiate the product of two functions if we know the derivative of each of them. To prove it, we have

$$\frac{d}{dx}(fg)$$

$$= \lim_{h \to 0} \frac{f(x + h)g(x + h) - f(x)g(x)}{h}$$

$$= \lim_{h \to 0} \frac{f(x + h)g(x + h) - f(x + h)g(x) + f(x + h)g(x) - f(x)g(x)}{h}$$

$$= \lim_{h \to 0} \left\{ f(x+h) \frac{g(x+h) - g(x)}{h} + g(x) \frac{f(x+h) - f(x)}{h} \right\}$$

$$= \lim_{h \to 0} f(x+h) \lim_{h \to 0} \frac{g(x+h) - g(x)}{h} + \lim_{h \to 0} g(x) \lim_{h \to 0} \frac{f(x+h) - f(x)}{h}$$

$$= f(x)g'(x) + f'(x)g(x)$$

The proof of rule (3.4), which shows how to differentiate the quotient of two functions if the derivative of each of them is known, uses a similar trick:

$$\frac{d}{dx} \left(\frac{f}{g} \right)$$

$$= \lim_{h \to 0} \frac{1}{h} \left\{ \frac{f(x+h)}{g(x+h)} - \frac{f(x)}{g(x)} \right\}$$

$$= \lim_{h \to 0} \frac{1}{h} \left\{ \frac{g(x)f(x+h) - f(x)g(x+h)}{g(x)g(x+h)} \right\}$$

$$= \lim_{h \to 0} \frac{1}{h} \left\{ \frac{g(x)f(x+h) - g(x)f(x) + g(x)f(x) - g(x+h)f(x)}{g(x)g(x+h)} \right\}$$

$$= \lim_{h \to 0} \frac{1}{g(x)g(x+h)} \left\{ g(x) \frac{f(x+h) - f(x)}{h} - f(x) \frac{g(x+h) - g(x)}{h} \right\}$$

$$= \frac{1}{g^2(x)} \left\{ g(x)f'(x) - f(x)g'(x) \right\}$$

Let us now use these rules to show that the derivative of x^n is nx^{n-1} when n is a *negative* integer. Hence, let $y(x) = x^{-m}$, where m is now non-negative. Using (3.4) with $f = 1, g = x^m$, we find that

$$\frac{d}{dx}(x^{-m}) = \frac{d}{dx} \left(\frac{1}{x^m} \right)$$

$$= \frac{x^m(1)' - 1(x^m)'}{x^{2m}}$$

$$= \frac{0 - mx^{m-1}}{x^{2m}}$$

$$= -mx^{-m-1}$$

which was to be shown. We are now able to differentiate any function which is either a polynomial or a quotient of polynomials.

Examples

1.   Find the derivative of

$$7x^{11} - 2x^2 + 3x$$

We have

$$(7x^{11} - 2x^2 + 3x)' = (7x^{11})' + (-2x^2)' + (3x)' \qquad \text{[by (3.1)]}$$
$$= 7(x^{11})' - 2(x^2)' + 3(x)' \qquad \text{[by (3.2)]}$$
$$= 7(11x^{10}) - 2(2x) + 3(1)$$
$$= 77x^{10} - 4x + 3$$

2.   Find the derivative of

$$\frac{x^2 + 5}{x^3 - 6}$$

Here we use the quotient rule (3.4) and find

$$\frac{d}{dx}\left(\frac{x^2 + 5}{x^3 - 6}\right) = \frac{(x^3 - 6)\dfrac{d}{dx}(x^2 + 5) - (x^2 + 5)\dfrac{d}{dx}(x^3 - 6)}{(x^3 - 6)^2}$$
$$= \frac{(x^3 - 6)(2x) - (x^2 + 5)(3x^2)}{(x^3 - 6)^2}$$
$$= \frac{-x^4 - 15x^2 - 12x}{(x^3 - 6)^2}$$

3.   Find the derivative of

$$4x^2 + \frac{3}{x} + \frac{7}{x^4}$$

This requires the use of our formula for differentiating powers of x where the powers are negative. We find

$$\frac{d}{dx}\left(4x^2 + \frac{3}{x} + \frac{7}{x^4}\right) = \frac{d}{dx}(4x^2 + 3x^{-1} + 7x^{-4})$$

$$= 4(2x) + 3(-x^{-2}) + 7(-4x^{-5})$$

$$= 8x - \frac{3}{x^2} - \frac{28}{x^5}$$

Exercises

Find the derivatives of the following functions.

(a) $x^4 - x$

(b) $8x^2 + \dfrac{1}{x}$

(c) $7x^3 - 3x + 2 + \dfrac{1}{x^4}$

(d) $ax^2 + \dfrac{b}{x} + \dfrac{c}{x^3}$

(e) $(x + a)^3$

(f) $\dfrac{x + 1}{x - 1}$

(g) $\dfrac{x^2 + 3}{(x - 1)^2}$

(h) $x^3 + \dfrac{1}{x + 4}$

(i) $\dfrac{1}{x^7 + x^6 + 2}$

(j) $\dfrac{x^5 + x^2 + 6}{x^6 + x + 1}$

(k) $\dfrac{ax + b}{cx + d}$

(l) $\dfrac{ax^2 + bx + c}{dx^2 + ex + f}$

(m) $x^{10} + 3x^7 + \dfrac{1}{x^2 + 2}$

(n) $3x^4 - x - \dfrac{1}{(x + 1)^3}$

(o) $\dfrac{x^m + 1}{x^{m+1} + 1}$

(p) $\dfrac{x^p + x^q}{x^p - x^q}$

Our next problem concerns the differentiation of a function of a function. If we were asked to find the derivative of

$$(x^3 + 1)^{35} \tag{3.5}$$

for example, we could expand the 35th power by the binomial theorem and then differentiate the resulting polynomial term-by-term as above. It is tempting, however, to note that we already know how to differentiate the 35th power of x, and so could the derivative of (3.5) be just

$$35(x^3 + 1)^{34}?$$

The answer is that the correct derivative is slightly more complicated. The correct derivative of the function in (3.5) is

$$35(x^3 + 1)^{34}(3x^2)$$

The additional factor of $3x^2$ arises because it is not x that is being raised to the 35th power in (3.5), but $x^3 + 1$, and so the derivative of $x^3 + 1$ has to be included. More generally, if u is any function of x, then the derivative of u^{35} is $35u^{34}u'$, where u' means, as usual, the derivative of u with respect to x. We may now replace the 35th power by a more general function and ask for the derivative of $f(u)$, where u is some function of x, the assumption being that we know the derivative of f and of u with respect to x. The answer is given by Theorem 3.2 which is variously called either the chain rule or the composite function rule.

THEOREM 3.2.   Let f and u be two continuously differentiable* functions such that the range of u is a subset of the domain of f, i.e., such that $f(u(x))$ makes sense. Then

$$\frac{d}{dx}f(u) = f'(u)\frac{du}{dx} \tag{3.6}$$

PROOF   First, by the mean-value theorem

$$f(u(x + h)) - f(u(x)) = (u(x + h) - u(x))f'(\xi)$$

where ξ is somewhere between $u(x)$ and $u(x + h)$. Dividing by h,

$$\frac{f(u(x + h)) - f(u(x))}{h} = \frac{u(x + h) - u(x)}{h}f'(\xi)$$

As h approaches zero the first factor on the right approaches $u'(x)$. Also, as h approaches zero, the point ξ is "trapped" between $u(x + h)$ and $u(x)$ and $u(x + h)$ approaches $u(x)$. Hence, the num-

---

* That is, f and u have derivatives f' and u' which are continuous.

ber ξ approaches $u(x)$ also and so the second factor on the right approaches $f'(u(x))$, proving the theorem.

Examples

1. Differentiate

$$(x^3 + 2x^2 + 10)^{40}.$$

The chain rule tells us that

$$\frac{d}{dx}(\text{something})^{40} = 40(\text{something})^{39}\frac{d}{dx}(\text{something})$$

and so

$$\frac{d}{dx}(x^3 + 2x^2 + 10)^{40} = 40(x^3 + 2x^2 + 10)^{39}\frac{d}{dx}(x^3 + 2x^2 + 10)$$

$$= 40(x^3 + 2x^2 + 10)^{39}(3x^2 + 4x)$$

2. Differentiate

$$\left(x + \frac{1}{x}\right)^{-5}$$

In this case we find from the chain rule that

$$\frac{d}{dx}\left(x + \frac{1}{x}\right)^{-5} = -5\left(x + \frac{1}{x}\right)^{-6}\frac{d}{dx}\left(x + \frac{1}{x}\right)$$

$$= -5\left(x + \frac{1}{x}\right)^{-6}\left(1 - \frac{1}{x^2}\right)$$

3. Find the derivative of

$$\left(\frac{x^2 + 1}{x^3 - 1}\right)^{10}$$

Here we use the chain rule followed by the quotient rule and get

$$\frac{d}{dx}\left(\frac{x^2 + 1}{x^3 - 1}\right)^{10} = 10\left(\frac{x^2 + 1}{x^3 - 1}\right)^{9}\frac{d}{dx}\left(\frac{x^2 + 1}{x^3 - 1}\right)$$

$$= 10\left(\frac{x^2 + 1}{x^3 - 1}\right)^{9}\left(\frac{(x^3 - 1)\frac{d}{dx}(x^2 + 1) - (x^2 + 1)\frac{d}{dx}(x^3 - 1)}{(x^3 - 1)^2}\right)$$

$$= 10\left(\frac{x^2 + 1}{x^3 - 1}\right)^9\left(\frac{(x^3 - 1)(2x) - (x^2 + 1)(3x^2)}{(x^3 - 1)^2}\right)$$

$$= 10\left(\frac{x^2 + 1}{x^3 - 1}\right)^9\left(\frac{-x^4 - 3x^2 - 2x}{(x^3 - 1)^2}\right)$$

Exercises

1.   In each of the three examples above, identify the functions f and u which appear in the statement of the chain rule.

2.   Differentiate each of the following functions.

(a) $(x^{10} + x^{-2})^{12}$

(b) $(x^a + x^b)^c$

(c) $\left(\dfrac{3x^2 + 2x + 1}{x^2 + 3}\right)^{30}$

(d) $\left(5x^6 + 2 + \dfrac{1}{x^2 - 1}\right)^{-3}$

(e) $\left(\dfrac{1}{x^5 + 2} - 3\right)^{11} + \left(\dfrac{x^5}{3 - x} + 1\right)^{11}$

(f) $(ax^2 + bx + c)^n$

(g) $\left(\dfrac{ax + b}{cx + d}\right)^n$

(h) $f(x^2)g(x^3)$

(i) $f(x)^3 g(x)^2$

(j) $f\left(x + \dfrac{1}{x}\right)$

(k) $f(g(x^2))$

(l) $f(ax + b)^n$

(m) $f(x)^2 + g(x)^2$

(n) $f(ax^2 + bx + c)g(dx + e)$

(o) $\left\{\dfrac{f(ax + b)}{g(cx + d)}\right\}^n$

Before proving the chain rule we had shown that the formula

$$\frac{d}{dx}(x^n) = nx^{n-1}$$

is valid if n is any integer, positive or negative. Using the chain rule we can show that this formula remains valid if n is a fraction, that is, a rational number. For suppose we let

$$y = x^{p/q} \tag{3.7}$$

where p and q are integers $q \neq 0$.

To find the derivative of y with respect to x we notice that

$$y^q = x^p$$

and we now differentiate both sides of this equation *with respect to x.* By the chain rule, the derivative of the left-hand side is $qy^{q-1}y'$, while the derivative of the right-hand side is px^{p-1}. Hence,

$$qy^{q-1}y' = px^{p-1}$$

and so

$$y' = \frac{p}{q} x^{p-1} y^{-q+1}$$

Finally, we substitute for y using (3.7), and get

$$y' = \frac{p}{q} x^{p-1} x^{(p/q)(-q+1)}$$

$$= \frac{p}{q} x^{(p/q)-1}$$

which was to be shown.

In summary, we have shown that the formula

$$\frac{d}{dx}(x^a) = ax^{a-1} \tag{3.8}$$

is true when a is either an integer or a fraction. We will see later that it remains true when a is any real number.

For example, we can now differentiate $\sqrt{x}$, for

$$\frac{d}{dx}\sqrt{x} = \frac{d}{dx}x^{1/2}$$

$$= \tfrac{1}{2}x^{-1/2}$$

$$= \frac{1}{2\sqrt{x}}$$

Combining these results with the chain rule permits us to differentiate fractional powers of polynomials and of ratios of polynomials, such as

$$\frac{d}{dx}(3x^5 + 1)^{-4/3} = -\frac{4}{3}(3x^5 + 1)^{-7/3}\frac{d}{dx}(3x^5 + 1)$$

$$= -\frac{4}{3}(3x^5 + 1)^{-7/3}(15x^4)$$

$$= -20(3x^5 + 1)^{-7/3}x^4$$

Exercises

1. Differentiate each of the following functions.

(a) $x^{3/4} + 3\sqrt{x}$

(b) $\sqrt{2x^2 + 3x + 5}$

(c) $\left(3x^{10} + \frac{1}{x}\right)^{1/5}$

(d) $\left(\sqrt{x} + \frac{1}{\sqrt{x}}\right)^{10}$

(e) $f(x^{1/3})$

(f) $f(5x)^{1/7}$

(g) $\sqrt{f(x^2)}$

(h) $f(\sqrt{x})^2$

(i) $\dfrac{(x^{2/3} + x^{3/4})^{1/4}}{(1 + x^4)^3}$

(j) $\left\{\dfrac{1}{f(1/x)}\right\}^5$

2. Given that the derivative of $\sin x$ is $\cos x$ find the derivatives of

(a) $\sin \sqrt{x}$

(b) $\sin x^2$

(c) $(\sin x)^{12}$

(d) $\sin 5x$

(e) $(3 + 4 \sin 2x + \sin 4x)^7$

(f) $\sqrt{1 - \sin x}$

(g) $\sin\left(x + \frac{1}{x}\right)$

3. Show that

(a) $\dfrac{d}{dx}\displaystyle\int_a^{g(x)} f(t)\,dt = f(g(x))g'(x)$

(b) $\dfrac{d}{dx}\displaystyle\int_{f(x)}^{g(x)} h(t)\,dt = h(g(x))g'(x) - h(f(x))f'(x)$

4. Find

(a) $\dfrac{d}{dx}\displaystyle\int_1^x 2^t\,dt$

(b) $\dfrac{d}{dx}\displaystyle\int_{3-4x}^{2+x} (t^4 + 6t^2 + 1)^{32}\,dt$

(Assume the results of Exercise 3 above.)

3.2. *Elementary Integrals*

According to Theorem 2.10 of Chapter 2, every time we learn how to differentiate some function, we learn how to integrate another, namely, its derivative. For instance, to say that

$$\frac{d}{dx}(x^3 + x^2) = 3x^2 + 2x$$

is to say that a function whose derivative is $3x^2 + 2x$ is $G(x) = x^3 + x^2$, and, therefore, that

$$\int_a^b (3x^2 + 2x)\,dx = G(b) - G(a)$$

$$= b^3 + b^2 - a^3 - a^2$$

In general, since

$$\frac{d}{dx}(x^n) = nx^{n-1}$$

we have also

$$\frac{d}{dx}\left(\frac{x^{n+1}}{n+1}\right) = x^n \tag{3.9}$$

PROOF   Let a be a fixed positive number, and define a new function G by

$$G(x) = L(ax) - L(x) \tag{3.12}$$

Then, differentiating (3.12) we get

$$G'(x) = aL'(ax) - L'(x)$$
$$= a\left(\frac{1}{ax}\right) - \frac{1}{x}$$
$$= 0$$

Since the derivative of $G(x)$ is everywhere zero, $G(x)$ must be everywhere a constant C. To evaluate the constant C, note that since $L(1) = 0$ we find by putting $x = 1$ in (3.12) that

$$G(x) = C = L(a) - L(1) = L(a)$$

Hence $G(x) = L(a)$ for all x, and referring back to the definition (3.12) of $G(x)$ we have shown that $L(ax) - L(x) = L(a)$ for all x. This is just what we had to prove.

We have so far shown that if we consider the area under the curve $y = 1/t$ between $t = 1$ and $t = x$, and if we call that area $L(x)$, then the function $L(x)$ has the property (3.11). It may be remarked (somewhat frivolously) that it would be very useful to have a table of values of this function $L(x)$. Suppose we had such a table. Then in order to multiply together any two positive numbers we would only need to add! If we wished to multiply 2.43 by 3.77, for instance, we could look in our table and find $L(2.43)$ and $L(3.77)$, add these two numbers together, and then find in the table a number t such that $L(t)$ is that latter sum. According to (3.11), the number t would be the desired product 2.43×3.77, and we have indeed done multiplication by using only addition and the table. At this point the reader should have no doubts about the title of such a table, but if he does, reference may be made to the title of this section.

THEOREM 3.4.   If x is any positive number and α is any real number then

$$L(x^\alpha) = \alpha L(x) \tag{3.13}$$

PROOF   Using (3.11),

$$L(x^2) = L(x) + L(x) = 2L(x)$$

Then

$$L(x^3) = L(x^2 x) = L(x^2) + L(x)$$
$$= 2L(x) + L(x)$$
$$= 3L(x)$$

We have now proved the theorem in the two special cases $\alpha = 2$ and $\alpha = 3$. By continuing in this way we can prove it for any fixed positive integer n. (If this statement annoys you, read Section 6.3 now.) Let us suppose that this has been done. Then we prove the theorem when n is a negative integer. First, since

$$x^n x^{-n} = 1$$

we have

$$L(x^n x^{-n}) = L(1) = 0$$
$$= L(x^n) + L(x^{-n})$$

and so

$$L(x^n) = -L(x^{-n})$$
$$= -(-n)L(x) \qquad \text{(if } n \text{ is negative)}$$
$$= nL(x)$$

which proves the theorem when α is any integer. Now suppose α is a fraction, say $\alpha = p/q$, where p, q are integers, $q \neq 0$. Since

$$(x^{p/q})^q = x^p$$

we find that

$$qL(x^{p/q}) = L(x^p) = pL(x)$$

where

$$L(x^{p/q}) = \frac{p}{q} L(x)$$

as required. The theorem is now proved for all rational numbers α

and, therefore, follows for real numbers because $L(x)$, being differentiable, is continuous.

THEOREM 3.5.   The function $L(x)$ is negative when $0 < x < 1$, positive when $x > 1$ and increases steadily without bound as x increases.

PROOF   (a) If $0 < x < 1$, then

$$L(x) = \int_1^x \frac{1}{t} \, dt = - \int_x^1 \frac{1}{t} \, dt < 0$$

and so $L(x)$ is negative for such x.

(b) $L(x)$ is positive when $x > 1$ obviously from (3.10).

(c) To show that $L(x)$ increases steadily as x increases, suppose $x_2 > x_1$. Then

$$L(x_2) - L(x_1) = \int_1^{x_2} \frac{1}{t} \, dt - \int_1^{x_1} \frac{1}{t} \, dt = \int_{x_1}^{x_2} \frac{1}{t} \, dt > 0$$

hence, $L(x_2) > L(x_1)$.

(d) $L(x)$ increases without bound, because from the relation

$$L(2^n) = nL(2)$$

and the fact that $L(2)$ is positive, we see that by making n large, $L(2^n)$ can be made as large as we please.

Using these facts about $L(x)$, we can sketch its graph, which is shown in Fig. 3.1.

Figure 3.1

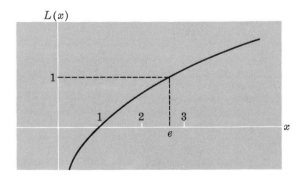

It is a consequence of Theorem 3.5 that there is precisely one value of x at which $L(x)$ has the value 1. This number is called e, and has the numerical value $2.71828.\ldots$ If in Eq. (3.13) we choose $x = e$, and use the relation $L(e) = 1$, we find that

$$L(e^\alpha) = \alpha$$

and so

$$e^{L(e^\alpha)} = e^\alpha$$

and writing t for e^α on both sides of this equation we find

THEOREM 3.6.   For all $t > 0$,

$$e^{L(t)} = t \tag{3.14}$$

In words: $L(t)$ is the power to which e must be raised in order to produce t. This is precisely the conventional definition of the logarithm of t to the base e. Henceforth, instead of writing $L(t)$, then, we will write $\log t$. Other notations which are often used are $\log_e t$ and $\ln t$. Logarithms to the base e are called natural logarithms. Indeed, what could be more natural than the use of (3.10) to define a function whose derivative is $1/x$?

To summarize our discussion of this section, we say the definition of the natural logarithm function is

$$\log x = \int_1^x \frac{1}{t}\,dt$$

and its derivative is

$$\frac{d}{dx}(\log x) = \frac{1}{x}$$

We also have the evaluation of the integral

$$\int_a^b \frac{1}{t}\,dt = \log b - \log a$$

Exercises

1.   What is the relationship between the two numbers $\log x$ and $\log_{10} x$? Between $\log x$ and $\log_b x$?

2.   Find the derivatives of each of the following functions.

(a) $\log_{10} x$

(b) $\log_b x$

(c) $\sqrt{\log x}$

(d) $\log (1 + x^2)$

(e) $\log \left(\dfrac{1 + x}{1 - x} \right)$

(f) $(\log x)^2 + \dfrac{3}{\log x}$

(g) $f(\log x)$

(h) $\log f(x)$

3.4.   The Exponential Function

An exponential function is a function of the form

$$f(x) = a^x \tag{3.15}$$

where a is some positive constant. "The" exponential function is the special case where $a = e$, the base of natural logarithms,

$$f(x) = e^x \tag{3.16}$$

The graph of an exponential function in the case $a > 1$ is shown in Fig. 3.2.

Figure 3.2

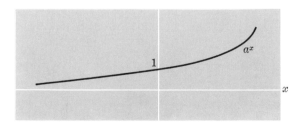

The exponential function has an interesting property with respect to differentiation, namely, the fact that it is its own derivative. To see this we let

$$y = e^x$$

Then

$$\log y = x$$

and differentiating both sides with respect to x we obtain

$$\frac{y'}{y} = 1$$

which says that $y' = y$, as claimed. Hence,

$$\frac{d}{dx}(e^u) = e^u \frac{du}{dx} \tag{3.17}$$

by the chain rule.

It is not only true that the exponential function is its own derivative, but also it is essentially the only function with that property. Suppose we are given any function y with the property that $y' = y$. Then we claim that $y = Ae^x$, where A is some constant. Indeed, if such a function y is given, consider the function

$$g(x) = ye^{-x}$$

Its derivative is

$$g'(x) = y'e^{-x} - ye^{-x}$$
$$= (y' - y)e^{-x}$$
$$= 0$$

Since the derivative of $g(x)$ is everywhere zero, $g(x)$ is a constant A, which is to say that $y = Ae^x$, as claimed.

More generally, if we have a function whose derivative is k times itself

$$y' = ky \tag{3.18}$$

then that function must be of the form Ae^{kx} for some constant A. The proof of this is similar to the above and is left to the reader. These properties of the exponential function are responsible for many natural occurrences of the function in science, for Eq. (3.18) can be interpreted as stating that the rate of change of y is proportional to y itself, and such phenomena are of frequent occurrence in nature. The classical example of this kind of behavior is afforded by the growth of bacterial cultures where if we make the reasonable hypothesis that the number of reproductions taking place at any instant in the culture is proportional to the number of bacteria present, then the function $y(t)$ which represents the number of bacteria present at time t, satisfies Eq. (3.18) where the differentiation is with respect to the time. Hence, under this assumption, the number of bacteria in the culture at time t can be expected to grow exponentially, i.e., according to the law Ae^{kt}.

Returning to the more general exponential function a^x, where a is not necessarily equal to e, we can find how to differentiate it by letting

$$y = a^x$$

taking logarithms

$$\log y = x \log a$$

and differentiating with respect to x, we get

$$\frac{y'}{y} = \log a$$

Hence, we have shown that

$$\frac{d}{dx}(a^x) = a^x \log a$$

and so, of course,

$$\frac{d}{dx}(a^u) = a^u \log a \frac{du}{dx} \tag{3.19}$$

by the chain rule.

As usual, by reading our differentiation formulas backwards we find integration formulas. Some of these are

$$\int_a^b e^x \, dx = e^x \Big]_a^b \tag{3.20}$$

$$\int_c^d a^x \, dx = \frac{a^x}{\log a} \Big]_c^d \tag{3.21}$$

The machinery of logarithms and exponentials also permits us to differentiate an apparently new class of functions. We already know how to differentiate a variable to a constant power

$$\frac{d}{dx}(u^a) = au^{a-1}u'$$

and a constant to a variable power [see (3.19) above]. Neither of these formulas covers the seemingly more difficult case of a variable to a variable power, such as, for example, x^x. We can always do such problems however, by methods we have already developed, after taking logarithms. Thus, to differentiate x^x we would let

$$y = x^x.$$

Taking logarithms of both sides,

$$\log y = x \log x$$

and differentiating both sides with respect to x gives

$$\frac{y'}{y} = x\left(\frac{1}{x}\right) + (1) \log x$$

$$= 1 + \log x$$

Hence,

$$y' = (1 + \log x)y$$

or, finally,

$$\frac{d}{dx}(x^x) = (1 + \log x)x^x \tag{3.22}$$

Exercises

1.   Differentiate each of the following functions.

   (a) $e^{\sqrt{x}}$
   (b) $2^{(x^2+1)}$
   (c) e^{e^x}
   (d) $3^{(1+x)/(1-x)}$
   (e) $2^{(\log x + x)}$
   (f) $x^{\log x}$

(g) $x^{1/\log x}$

(h) $(x^2 + 1)^{(x^2+1)}$

(i) $f(e^x)$

(j) $f(x)^{g(x)}$

2. How do you explain the strange answer which you got to part (g) above?
3. Sketch a graph of the function (3.15) if a is a positive number less than 1.
4. Show that $e^{x+y} = e^x e^y$.
5. Find the area under the exponential curve from $x = 0$ to $x = \log 2$.
6. Perform each of the following integrations.

(a) $\int_0^2 e^{4x} \, dx$

(b) $\int_0^1 (1 - e^{-x})^2 \, dx$

(c) $\int_0^1 (2^x + 2^{-x})^2 \, dx$

(d) $\int_{-1}^1 (3 + x^2 + 2e^{3x}) \, dx$

Certain combinations of exponential functions which occur frequently in practice are the so-called hyperbolic functions. These are defined by

$$\sinh x = \text{hyperbolic sine of } x = \frac{e^x - e^{-x}}{2}$$

$$\cosh x = \text{hyperbolic cosine of } x = \frac{e^x + e^{-x}}{2}$$

The hyperbolic functions tanh x, coth x, sech x, csch x are formed from sinh x and cosh x just as their trigonometric counterparts are formed from sin x and cos x.

The picturesque names of these functions are in part due to the fact that they satisfy certain identities which are reminiscent of those satisfied by their trigonometric namesakes. For instance

$$\cosh^2 x - \sinh^2 x = \left(\frac{e^x + e^{-x}}{2}\right)^2 - \left(\frac{e^x - e^{-x}}{2}\right)^2$$

$$= \tfrac{1}{4}(e^{2x} + 2 + e^{-2x}) - \tfrac{1}{4}(e^{2x} - 2 + e^{-2x})$$

$$= 1$$

As a final remark about the hyperbolic functions we discuss briefly the idea of an even function or an odd function. A function f is *even* if for every x in its domain, $-x$ is also in its domain, and the equation

$$f(x) = f(-x)$$

holds for all x in the domain. Examples of even functions are 1, x^2, x^4, any polynomial in x involving only even powers of x, $\cosh x$ (check this!), etc. A function is *odd* if

$$f(-x) = -f(x)$$

for all x in its domain. Examples of odd functions are polynomials involving only odd powers of x, and $\sinh x$.

Some functions are neither even nor odd, such as polynomials which contain both even and odd powers of x. The exponential function e^x is neither even nor odd. Nevertheless, any function can be written as the sum of two functions, one of which is even and the other of which is odd. Indeed, the equation

$$f(x) = \tfrac{1}{2}(f(x) + f(-x)) + \tfrac{1}{2}(f(x) - f(-x)) \qquad (3.23)$$

is obviously an identity, but the first term is evidently an even function and the second function is odd, no matter what $f(x)$ is. Accordingly we sometimes speak of the first term in (3.23) as the "even part of f" and of the second term as the "odd part of f." Using this terminology it is clear that $\cosh x$ is the even part of e^x and $\sinh x$ is the odd part.

Exercises

1. How would you recognize from the graph of a function whether it was even, or odd, or neither?
2. What is the even part of 2^x? of $1 + 2x + x^2 + 3x^3$? The odd part?
3. Graph the functions $\sinh x$, $\cosh x$, $\tanh x$.
4. Evaluate the limit of $\tanh x$ as x approaches infinity.
5. Prove the identities
    (a) $\sinh (x + y) = \sinh x \cosh y + \cosh x \sinh y$
    (b) $\sinh 2x = 2 \sinh x \cosh x$
    (c) $\cosh 2x = \cosh^2 x + \sinh^2 x$

6. Find the derivatives of

       (a) $\sinh x$

       (b) $\cosh x$

       (c) $\tanh x$

       (d) $\cosh(\sqrt{x^2 + 1})$

       (e) $\{\sinh(\sqrt{x})\}^{11}$

       (f) $\cosh \dfrac{x+1}{x-1} \sinh x$

       (g) $\cosh 5x + 6\left(\cosh \dfrac{1}{x}\right)^3$

7. Show that

       (a) $\sinh(\log x) = \dfrac{x^2 - 1}{2x}$

       (b) $\cosh(\log x) = \dfrac{x^2 + 1}{2x}$

Knowing the derivative of e^x, we can evaluate an interesting limit. We have

$$\frac{d}{dx}(e^x) = \lim_{h \to 0} \frac{e^{x+h} - e^x}{h}$$

$$= \lim_{h \to 0} \frac{e^x e^h - e^x}{h}$$

$$= e^x \lim_{h \to 0} \frac{e^h - 1}{h}$$

Since the derivative is e^x, it must be that

$$\lim_{h \to 0} \frac{e^h - 1}{h} = 1$$

This tells us that when h is small e^h is approximated by $1 + h$.

3.5. The Trigonometric Functions

We assume that the elementary properties of the trigonometric functions $\sin x$, $\cos x$, $\tan x$, etc., are known. For those readers who may not be accustomed to measuring angles in radians we include first a description of radian measure. Consider a circle of radius R, and a central angle θ in that circle (Fig. 3.3).

The radian measure of the angle θ is equal to the length of the arc of the circle between the arms of the angle divided by R. Thus the radian

Figure 3.3

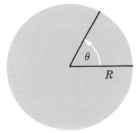

measure of $360°$ is 2π, of $180°$ is π, of $90°$ $\pi/2$, of $60°$ $\pi/3$, and so on. In this way we can make an angle correspond to every number between 0 and 2π.

We can also make an angle correspond to a number larger than 2π or to a negative number. If any real number x is given, we add or subtract integer multiples of 2π until the resulting number lies between 0 and 2π. The angle that corresponds to x is the angle that corresponds to this latter number between 0 and 2π. For example, if $x = 9\pi$, we subtract multiples of 2π, arriving finally at π, and, therefore, 9π and π correspond to the same angle, namely, a half-circle, or $180°$. Given $x = -\pi/2$, we add 2π to x, obtaining $3\pi/2$ or $270°$ as the angle which corresponds to x. In this way, to every real number x there corresponds a unique angle. Evidently, we can convert degree measure to radian measure by multiplying the given number of degrees by $2\pi/360° = \pi/180°$.

Exercises

1. How many degrees are in 1 radian?
2. An automobile whose tires have radius 2 ft travels 100 miles. If the air inlet valve of one of the tires was at the top of the tire initially, where was it at the end of the trip? (This problem is due to Professor E. Calabi.)

We shall assume, unless explicitly stated otherwise, that all angles are measured in radians throughout this book. Now suppose x is a given real number. We wish to define the function

$$f(x) = \sin x$$

First, by adding or subtracting integer multiples of 2π, bring x into the range $0 \leqq x < 2\pi$. Place a circle of radius 1 at the origin of coordinates and measure the angle x counterclockwise from the positive real axis. The y coordinate of the point where the sector arm meets the circumference of the circle is defined as $\sin x$ (Fig. 3.4).

Figure 3.4

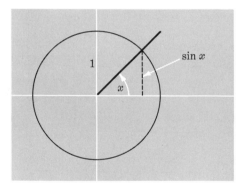

The abcissa of this point is defined to be $\cos x$, and the other trigo-nometric functions are defined as usual in terms of these. A graph of the curve $y = \sin x$ is shown in Fig. 3.5.

Figure 3.5

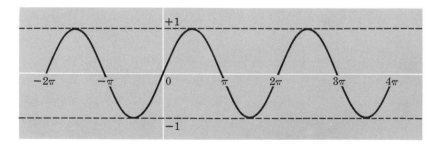

Exercise

Carefully sketch the graphs of $y = \cos x$, $y = \tan x$.

Our present concern with the trigonometric functions rests with our need to discuss their derivatives and integrals. In order to do this we must first evaluate a certain limit. After we have this we will be able to differentiate $\sin x$ and $\cos x$, and the derivatives of the remaining trigonometric functions will follow from the quotient rules of differentiation. The limit in question asserts that when x is very small, $\sin x$ is nearly equal to x, the approximation getting better as x gets smaller.

THEOREM 3.7.

$$\lim_{x \to 0} \frac{\sin x}{x} = 1 \qquad (3.24)$$

PROOF   Reference to Fig. 3.6, in which arc AC is an arc of a circle of radius unity centered at O, shows that

$$\text{Area of } \triangle OAC < \text{Area of sector } OAC < \text{Area of } \triangle ODC$$

Figure 3.6

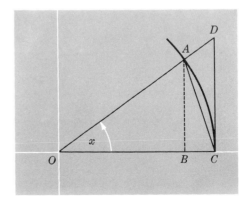

When we use formulas for the areas of triangles and circular sectors, this means that

$$\tfrac{1}{2}\overline{AB} \cdot \overline{OC} < \tfrac{1}{2}\overline{OA}^2 \cdot x < \tfrac{1}{2}\overline{DC} \cdot \overline{OC}$$

Since the radius of the circle is $\overline{OC} = 1$, it follows that $\overline{AB} = \sin x$ and $\overline{DC} = \tan x$, where

$$\tfrac{1}{2}\sin x < \tfrac{1}{2}x < \tfrac{1}{2}\tan x$$

Dividing by $\tfrac{1}{2}\sin x$, and supposing that x is small and positive,

$$1 < \frac{x}{\sin x} < \frac{1}{\cos x}$$

or, finally, inverting

$$\cos x < \frac{\sin x}{x} < 1 \tag{3.25}$$

If x had been small and negative instead of small and positive, then dividing by $\tfrac{1}{2}\sin x$ would have reversed all the signs of inequality, but the final "inverting" would have reversed them again, and so the result (3.25) would hold in that case also. Now let x approach zero. Then $\cos x$ approaches 1, and so in (3.25) $(\sin x)/x$ is sandwiched between something which is approaching 1 and 1 itself and, therefore, has no choice but to approach 1 also, which was to be shown.

It is now easy to evaluate one more limit which we need, namely,

$$\lim_{x \to 0} \frac{1 - \cos x}{x} = 0 \tag{3.26}$$

For since

$$\sin^2 x + \cos^2 x = 1$$

it follows that

$$1 - \cos x = \frac{\sin^2 x}{1 + \cos x}$$

and so

$$\frac{1 - \cos x}{x} = \frac{\sin x}{x}\frac{\sin x}{1 + \cos x}$$

If we let x approach zero, the first term on the right approaches 1 and the second approaches zero, and the desired result (3.26) follows.

We can now differentiate all of the trigonometric functions. We begin by finding the derivative of $\sin x$. We have

$$\frac{d}{dx}(\sin x) = \lim_{h \to 0} \frac{\sin(x + h) - \sin x}{h}$$

$$= \lim_{h \to 0} \frac{\sin x \cos h + \cos x \sin h - \sin x}{h}$$

$$= \lim_{h \to 0} \left\{ \sin x \frac{\cos h - 1}{h} + \cos x \frac{\sin h}{h} \right\}$$

$$= \sin x \lim_{h \to 0} \frac{\cos h - 1}{h} + \cos x \lim_{h \to 0} \frac{\sin h}{h}$$

$$= \cos x$$

by (3.24) and (3.26). We could find the derivative of $\cos x$ in the same way but it is easier to note that

$$\frac{d}{dx}(\cos x) = \frac{d}{dx}\left[\sin\left(\frac{\pi}{2} - x \right) \right]$$

$$= -\cos\left(\frac{\pi}{2} - x \right)$$

$$= -\sin x.$$

If we use the quotient rule for differentiation, we can get the derivatives of the remaining trigonometric functions. For example,

$$\frac{d}{dx}(\tan x) = \frac{d}{dx}\left(\frac{\sin x}{\cos x} \right)$$

$$= \frac{\cos x \cos x - \sin x(-\sin x)}{\cos^2 x}$$

$$= \frac{1}{\cos^2 x}$$

$$= \sec^2 x$$

Of course, with the aid of the chain rule for differentiation we can also compute the derivatives of trigonometric functions of things other than x itself. Thus

$$\frac{d}{dx}(\sin e^{-x})^2 = 2 \sin e^{-x} \frac{d}{dx}(\sin e^{-x})$$

$$= 2 \sin e^{-x} \cos e^{-x} \frac{d}{dx}(e^{-x})$$

$$= 2 \sin (e^{-x}) \cos (e^{-x})(-e^{-x})$$

$$= -e^{-x} \sin (2e^{-x}) \qquad \text{(Why?)}$$

Again, since differentiation and integration are inverse operations, we also know how to integrate the trigonometric functions. The area under the first arch of the curve $y = \sin x$ is

$$\int_0^{\pi} \sin x \, dx = -\cos x \Big]_0^{\pi}$$

$$= -\cos \pi - (-\cos 0)$$

$$= 1 + 1 = 2$$

To calculate

$$\int_a^b \sin 2x \, dx$$

we need a function whose derivative is $\sin 2x$. Such a function is $-\frac{1}{2} \cos 2x$ and so

$$\int_a^b \sin 2x \, dx = \tfrac{1}{2}(\cos 2a - \cos 2b)$$

Exercises

1. Differentiate the following functions.

   (a) $\sin (\log x)$
   (b) $\log (\sin x)$
   (c) $e^{\sqrt{\sin x}}$
   (d) $\cot (1 + \sec x)$
   (e) $\csc x$
   (f) $(\cos 8x)^{14}$

(g) $\dfrac{1 + \sin^3 3x}{1 - \cos^3 x}$

(h) $\sin (\sin x)$

(i) $f(\sin^2 x)$

(j) $\sin^2 f(x)$

(k) $\sqrt{1 + \cos 2^{-x}}$

(l) $[\sin (3x + 2) + \cos (4x - 1)]^{11}$

2. Perform the following integrations.

(a) $\displaystyle\int_0^{\pi/2} \cos x \, dx$

(b) $\displaystyle\int_\pi^{2\pi} (1 - \sin x) \, dx$

(c) $\displaystyle\int_0^1 \sin \pi x \, dx$

(d) $\displaystyle\int_0^{\pi/2} 2 \sin x \cos x \, dx$

(e) $\displaystyle\int_0^{\pi/2} \sin^2 x \, dx$

(f) $\displaystyle\int_0^1 (x - e^x + \cos 3x) \, dx$

(g) $\displaystyle\int_{-1}^1 (e^x + 2e^{-2x} + \sin x) \, dx$

(h) $\displaystyle\int_2^3 \left(\dfrac{1}{x} + 4 \sin 2x\right) dx$

(i) $\displaystyle\int_0^1 (1 - \cos x)^2 \, dx$

(j) $\displaystyle\int_0^{\pi/2} \cos^2 x \, dx$

3.6.   *Inverse Functions*

One feels intuitively that the functions x^2 and $\sqrt{x}$ are inverse to each other in the sense that what one of them does, the other undoes. If we start with a positive number x, square it, and then take the positive square root of the answer, we are back where we started from, at x. To put it more formally, we would say that if $f(x) = x^2$ and $g(x) = \sqrt{x}$, then, if $x > 0$,

$$f(g(x)) = x$$

We wish to generalize this idea of a pair of functions which bear an inverse relationship to each other. To do this it is essential that we think carefully of the domains and the ranges of the functions involved.

Suppose we are given a function whose domain is a certain set D and whose range is a set R. Thus, to every object x in D, f assigns an object $f(x)$ in R. We now wish to find another function, the *inverse* of f, which will undo the work which f did. If we denote this inverse function temporarily by the letter g, the function g will have to take an object in R back again to the object in D from which f brought it. The situation may be illuminated by the abstract art of Fig. 3.7.

Figure 3.7

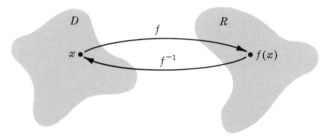

A difficulty should be at once apparent. Suppose some object in R came from two different places in D. For instance, if $f(x) = x^2$ is defined for all the real numbers (D), we can take the nonnegative numbers for R. Then, the number 4 in R comes from two places in D, namely, from -2 and from 2. To which one of these will the inverse function carry it back? To avoid this difficulty, the concept of inverse function is not defined where such ambiguity exists.

The kind of function, then, which can have an inverse function is a function which takes every value at most once. To formalize these ideas, we introduce the term "image." The image of the domain of a function is the totality of values which the function takes. That is, if f is defined on a set D, the image of D under the function f is the totality of objects

$f(x)$ in R, as x runs over the domain D. The image is sometimes denoted symbolically by $f(D)$. It is, in a sense, the smallest set that could be used for the range of the function, since every object in the image actually appears as a function value. The image of the real line under the function $f(x) = x^2$ is the set of nonnegative real numbers. The image of the real line under the function $f(x) = \sin x$ is the interval $-1 \leq x \leq 1$.

DEFINITION   Let f be defined on a set D, and let $f(D)$ denote the image of D under f. We say that f is 1–1 (one-to-one) if every object in $f(D)$ comes from exactly one object in D. That is, f is 1–1 if whenever $a \neq b$ we have $f(a) \neq f(b)$.

The function $f(x) = x$ from the real line to itself is 1–1. The function given by $f(x) = x^2$ from the nonnegative real numbers to the nonnegative real numbers is 1–1. The function f whose values are $f(x) = x^2$ from the real numbers to the nonnegative real numbers is not 1–1.

DEFINITION   Let f be 1–1 from its domain D to its image $f(D)$. The inverse function of f, written f^{-1}, is the function whose domain is $f(D)$, and which assigns to each object y there, the unique object x in D such that $f(x) = y$.

If x is in D, then,

$$f^{-1}(f(x)) = x,$$

while if y is in $f(D)$,

$$f(f^{-1}(y)) = y.$$

Example

If D is the set of all real numbers and $f(x) = e^x$, then $f(D)$ is the set of positive real numbers. The function f is 1–1, for if $f(a) = f(b)$, then $e^a = e^b$, and so $e^{a-b} = 1$. Thus $a - b = 0$, and $a = b$. Hence, e^x has an inverse function. This inverse function is defined on the positive real numbers and takes real values. It has the property that

$$f^{-1}(e^x) = x$$

Evidently, the inverse function of e^x is $\log x$ because we already know that

$$\log e^x = x \qquad \text{and} \qquad e^{\log x} = x$$

the first being valid for all real x (i.e., x in D), the second being valid for positive real x [i.e., for x in $f(D)$].

   In the case of a function which is defined on a set of real numbers, the property of being 1–1 has a simple graphical interpretation. Clearly, f is 1–1 if and only if the graph of $f(x)$ crosses every horizontal line once at most.

Exercises

1.   For each of the functions below determine whether an inverse function exists. If not, try to shrink the domain of definition of the function so that an inverse function will exist. Then determine that inverse function. Give the domain and the image of each function considered.

   (a) $f(x) = x^3$ for all real x.
   (b) $f(x) = e^{x^2}$ for all real x.
   (c) $f(x) = x - x^2$ for $0 \leq x \leq 1$.
   (d) $f(x) = \tan x$ for $0 \leq x \leq 2\pi$.
   (e) $f(x) = 1$ for all real x.

2.   Let D, R be two sets of real numbers and suppose $f: D \to R$ and $g: R \to D$ are a pair of inverse functions. Suppose further that f and g are each differentiable throughout their respective domains. Show that $f'(x)$ and $g'(x)$ are never zero. What does this mean graphically? [Hint: Differentiate the relation $f(g(x)) = x$.]

3.7.   Monotone Functions

Let f be a function defined on a certain set S of real numbers and taking real values. We say that f is *increasing* on S if whenever $x_1 < x_2$, x_1 and x_2 being in S, we have

$$f(x_1) < f(x_2)$$

Graphically, this just means that the graph of f goes up from left to right as we pass through the set S. We say that f is *nondecreasing* on S

if under the same conditions

$$f(x_1) \leq f(x_2)$$

In the obvious way we also define the terms "decreasing" and "non-increasing."

Example

If S is the set of all real numbers, e^x, x, x^3 are all increasing functions. The function f such that $f(x) = 2$ for all x is both nonincreasing and nondecreasing; e^{-x} decreases for all real x; x^2 increases on the set S of nonnegative real numbers, and decreases on the set S of nonpositive real numbers; xe^{-x} increases on the interval $(0,1)$ and decreases for $x > 1$.

A function is said to be *monotone* if it has any one of the four properties just defined. For differentiable functions there is a very useful test for monotonicity which is given by

THEOREM 3.8. A differentiable function f is nondecreasing on the interval $a < x < b$ if and only if $f'(x) \geq 0$ there. It is nonincreasing if and only if $f'(x) \leq 0$.

PROOF   The statement of the theorem can easily be visualized in terms of slopes. To prove it, suppose first that $f'(x) \geq 0$ for $a < x < b$. If we choose two points in the interval $x_1 < x_2$, then by the mean-value theorem

$$f(x_2) - f(x_1) = (x_2 - x_1)f'(\xi)$$

where ξ is somewhere between x_1 and x_2. Since f' is nonnegative throughout the interval it is nonnegative at ξ; hence, $f(x_2) - f(x_1)$ is nonnegative, which proves that $f(x_2) \geq f(x_1)$, and, therefore, that f is nondecreasing.

Conversely, suppose f is nondecreasing. We must show that $f'(x) \geq 0$ for all x in the interval. But

$$f'(x) = \lim_{h \to 0} \frac{f(x + h) - f(x)}{h}$$

If $h > 0$, $f(x + h) \geqq f(x)$, and so

$$\frac{f(x + h) - f(x)}{h} \geqq 0$$

while if $h < 0$, $f(x + h) \leqq f(x)$ and

$$\frac{f(x + h) - f(x)}{h} \geqq 0$$

again. Hence, $f'(x)$ is the limit of a quantity which is always non-negative, and so it must be nonnegative also, which was to be shown.

Our immediate application of the idea of monotonicity will be to the determination of inverse functions. Evidently a function which is increasing on a certain interval can take no value twice on that interval, and therefore it will have an inverse function. In this connection, Theorem 3.8 can provide a useful tool for determining whether or not a given function has an inverse.

Exercises

For each of the following functions determine the intervals of the real axis on which the function increases and those on which it decreases.

1. (a) $\sin (x^2)$
    (b) e^{x^2}
    (c) $x^3 - 3x^2 - x + 1$
    (d) xe^{-x^2}
    (e) $(1 - x)^n$
    (f) $(x^2 - x + 1)e^x$

2. If f and g are increasing, is $f + g$? Is fg?

3.8.   *The Inverse Trigonometric Functions*

In this section we consider the definition and the differentiation of the inverses of the trigonometric functions. A rudimentary examination of the graph of the function $\sin x$, for example, shows that it cannot have an inverse function since, as x ranges over the real numbers, $\sin x$ takes every value between -1 and 1 infinitely often. In order to define an inverse of sin x, therefore, it is necessary to restrict the domain of the function so that it takes each value just once. There are, of course, many ways to do this. The one which seems to be conventional is to take the new domain to be the interval $-\pi/2 \leq x \leq \pi/2$, in which sin x takes every value between -1 and 1 exactly once. Accordingly, we define a new function Sin x (distinguished from sin x by the capital S) by

$$\text{Sin } x = \begin{cases} \sin x & \text{if } -\pi/2 \leq x \leq \pi/2 \\ \text{undefined} & \text{otherwise} \end{cases}$$

The function Sin x has an inverse function, and this inverse function is referred to variously as $\sin^{-1} x$ or arcsin x. The function $\sin^{-1} x$ is defined for x in the interval $-1 \leq x \leq 1$, and its value is the unique number between $-\pi/2$ and $\pi/2$, whose sine is x.

Thus, $\sin^{-1} 1 = \pi/2$, $\sin^{-1} 0 = 0$, $\sin^{-1}(-\tfrac{1}{2}) = -\pi/6$, etc. The graph of the function $\sin^{-1} x$ is shown in Fig. 3.8. Clearly, we have

Figure 3.8

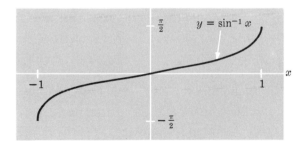

$$\sin^{-1}(\text{Sin } x) = x \qquad \left(-\frac{\pi}{2} \leq x \leq \frac{\pi}{2}\right)$$

and

$$\text{Sin }(\sin^{-1} x) = x \qquad (-1 \leq x \leq 1)$$

Next we propose to find the derivative of the function $\sin^{-1} x$. To do this let us put

$$y = \sin^{-1} x$$

and observe that

$$\text{Sin } y = x$$

If we differentiate both sides of this last equation with respect to x, we get

$$(\cos y)y' = 1$$

and so

$$y' = \frac{1}{\cos y}$$

It remains to express this answer in terms of x. To do this we must find $\cos y$ if $\sin y = x$. From the triangle in Fig. 3.9 we see at once that $\cos y = \sqrt{1 - x^2}$ and so

$$\frac{d}{dx}(\sin^{-1} x) = \frac{1}{\sqrt{1 - x^2}} \qquad (-1 < x < 1) \qquad (3.27)$$

is the required derivative.

Figure 3.9

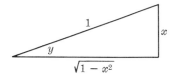

The derivative at $x = 1$ or $x = -1$ is not defined because the function is not defined for $x < -1$ or $x > 1$. It is clear from (3.27), however, that the slope of the curve gets large without bound as x gets near $+1$ or -1, and this can also be observed in the graph in Fig. 3.8.

Example
Differentiate $\sin^{-1}(e^{-x^2})$
     We find

$$\frac{d}{dx}[\sin^{-1}(e^{-x^2})] = \frac{1}{\sqrt{1 - e^{-2x^2}}}\frac{d}{dx}(e^{-x^2})$$

$$= \frac{1}{\sqrt{1 - e^{-2x^2}}}e^{-x^2}\frac{d}{dx}(-x^2)$$

$$= \frac{-2xe^{-x^2}}{\sqrt{1 - e^{-2x^2}}}$$

Exercises

Give careful definitions of each of the inverse functions appearing below and prove the differentiation formulas given.

1. $\dfrac{d}{dx}(\cos^{-1} x) = -\dfrac{1}{\sqrt{1 - x^2}}$

2. $\dfrac{d}{dx}(\tan^{-1} x) = \dfrac{1}{1 + x^2}$

3. $\dfrac{d}{dx}(\sec^{-1} x) = \dfrac{1}{x\sqrt{x^2 - 1}}$

4. $\dfrac{d}{dx}(\csc^{-1} x) = -\dfrac{1}{x\sqrt{x^2 - 1}}$

5. $\dfrac{d}{dx}(\cot^{-1} x) = -\dfrac{1}{1 + x^2}$

Differentiate the following.

6. $\cos^{-1} \dfrac{x}{1 + x^2}$

7. $\tan^{-1} e^{\sqrt{x}}$

8. $e^{\sin^{-1} x}$

9. $\log \sin^{-1} x$

10. $(\cos^{-1} \sqrt{x})^2$

11. $f(\sin^{-1} x)$

12. $\sin^{-1} (1 - x)$

13. $\dfrac{\sin^{-1} x}{\cos^{-1} x}$

3.9. The Mechanics of Integration: Integration by Parts

At this stage in our work we are able to differentiate at sight a vast array of functions. Among these are

$$x^a, \quad \sin x, \quad \cos x, \quad \ldots, \quad \log x, \quad a^x, \quad \sin^{-1} x, \quad \cos^{-1} x, \ldots$$

Further, if f and g are any two functions which we can differentiate, then automatically we can also differentiate

$$cf, \quad f + g, \quad f - g, \quad fg, \quad \frac{f}{g}, \quad f(g), \quad f^g$$

and so on.

Since we know how to differentiate all of these functions, there are also many functions which we can integrate, namely, the derivatives of any of these. As soon as we are told, for example, that

$$\frac{d}{dx}(\sin^{-1} x) = \frac{1}{\sqrt{1 - x^2}}$$

we know immediately that

$$\int_a^b \frac{dx}{\sqrt{1 - x^2}} = \sin^{-1} b - \sin^{-1} a \qquad (-1 < a \leq b < 1)$$

since a problem in integration is solved as soon as we can find a function whose derivative is the integrand.

It might be expected, then, that the integral of almost any function that one can reasonably imagine can be performed in explicit terms. This is not, in fact, the case. There are many very innocent-looking integrals whose values cannot be expressed in terms of our basic elementary functions. An example of such an integral is

$$\int_5^7 e^{x^2}\, dx$$

Integration is, therefore, more troublesome to handle than differentiation, the reason being that there are no analogs of the labor-extending theorems of differentiation. If we can integrate f and g, we can also integrate cf, $f + g, f - g$, but we know nothing at all about the integrals of $fg, f/g, f(g)$, and so on. Thus it should not be surprising that we can integrate e^x and x^2 but not e^{x^2} in terms of our elementary functions.

Despite this, there are a few techniques which can be useful in the evaluation of integrals. Some of these are rather widely applicable, and others are applicable to only a few situations. We discuss here three of the more widely applicable methods of integration, namely, the method of integration by parts, of integration by substitution, and the integration of rational functions.

For later convenience we introduce a new symbol, the *indefinite integral* (in contrast to the integral which we have been studying, the definite integral). This is written

$$\int f(t)\, dt$$

and differs from the definite integral only in the absence of limits of integration. The meaning of the indefinite integral is just this: $\int f(t)\, dt$ stands for a function whose derivative is $f(t)$. Thus

$$\int t^3\, dt = \frac{t^4}{4}$$

means that the derivative of the function on the right is t^3. It is also true that

$$\int t^3\, dt = \frac{t^4}{4} + 18$$

and indeed that

$$\int t^3\, dt = \frac{t^4}{4} + C$$

where C is any constant. The reader will be untroubled by ambiguity if he will always read the statement

$$\int f(t)\, dt = F(t)$$

with the words "a function whose derivative is f is F."
    Evidently,

$$\int (f + g)\, dt = \int f\, dt + \int g\, dt$$

and

$$\int cf\, dt = c \int f\, dt$$

The relationship between the indefinite and the definite integrals is that

$$\int_a^b f(t)\, dt = \left[\int f(t)\, dt\right]_a^b$$

no matter which $\int f(t)\, dt$ we choose, according to Theorem 2.9.

Let us turn now to integration by parts. We consider first the product rule for differentiation

$$\frac{d}{dx}(fg) = fg' + f'g$$

This says that a function whose derivative is $fg' + f'g$ is fg, i.e., that

$$\int (fg' + f'g)\, dx = fg$$

or finally that

$$\int (fg')\, dx = fg - \int f'g\, dx \qquad (3.28)$$

This is the rule for integration by parts. In the language of definite integrals it says that

$$\int_a^b f(t)g'(t)\, dt = f(t)g(t)\Big]_a^b - \int_a^b f'(t)g(t)\, dt$$

$$= f(b)g(b) - f(a)g(a) - \int_a^b f'(t)g(t)\, dt$$

As it stands, the rule (3.28) is just a lifeless assertion of a fact. In skilled hands (it does require those!) it can be a powerful tool for evaluating integrals. The trick is the following. Suppose we are asked to evaluate the integral

$$\int_a^b h(t)\, dt \qquad (3.29)$$

where h is some given function. In order to use (3.28) we would break up h into the product of two functions, one of which we call f and the other g'. Equation (3.28) will be useful in evaluating (3.29) if the integral of $f'g$ is easier to do than the integral of fg' was, for it then tells us how to express the integral (3.29) which we seek, in terms of something known,

$$fg\,\Big]_a^b$$

and another integral

$$\int_a^b f'g\, dt$$

which is easier than the one we started with. The key step in the process is the original breaking up of the given function h into the product of an f and a g'. This should be done in such a way that f is a function which looks easier after it is differentiated and g' is the derivative of something easy.

Example 1.
It is required to calculate

$$\int_0^1 xe^x \, dx$$

Offhand we do not know of any function whose derivative is xe^x, so we cannot do the integral at sight. To integrate by parts, we will want to regard xe^x as the product of two functions, one of which looks easier after differentiation and the other of which is the derivative of something obvious. Since e^x is oblivious to the processes of integration and differentiation, it can serve in either capacity. The factor x is obviously simpler after differentiating (when it becomes 1), so we choose it to be the function f, and we take e^x for the function g'. After we have made this choice, the rest is mechanical; we write down the two functions just chosen

$$f(x) = x$$
$$g'(x) = e^x$$

and from these two we compute f' and g

$$f'(x) = 1$$
$$g(x) = e^x$$

Equipped with all four of these functions, we substitute directly into (3.28) and find

$$\int_0^1 xe^x \, dx = xe^x \Big]_0^1 - \int_0^1 e^x \, dx$$

$$= e - \int_0^1 e^x \, dx$$

We have indeed gained something, for the integral on the right is easy

$$\int_0^1 e^x \, dx = e^x \Big]_0^1 = e - 1$$

and so

$$\int_0^1 xe^x \, dx = e - (e - 1) = 1$$

is the required answer. The success of the method evidently depends critically upon the cleverness of the factorization of the given integrand.

Example 2.
Find a function whose derivative is $x \log x$.
    Here we are asked for

$$\int x \log x \, dx$$

We wish now to factor the integrand $x \log x$ into the product of two functions, one of which looks much easier after differentiating, and the other of which is the derivative of something easy. Since we do not know of a function whose derivative is $\log x$, we have little choice. We must take $\log x$ as the function f to be differentiated, and x for g'. Now if

$$f(x) = \log x$$
$$g'(x) = x$$

then

$$f'(x) = \frac{1}{x}$$

and

$$g(x) = \frac{x^2}{2}$$

Substituting into (3.28), we find

$$\int x \log x \, dx = \frac{1}{2}x^2 \log x - \int \frac{1}{x} \frac{x^2}{2} \, dx$$

$$= \tfrac{1}{2}x^2 \log x - \tfrac{1}{2} \int x \, dx$$

Again our labor is rewarded (this always happens in textbooks) because clearly

$$\int x \, dx = \tfrac{1}{2}x^2$$

and so

$$\int x \log x \, dx = \frac{x^2}{2} \log x - \frac{1}{2} \frac{x^2}{2}$$

$$= \frac{x^2}{2} \log x - \frac{1}{4} x^2.$$

Thus, in answer to our original question, a function whose derivative is $x \log x$ is $\frac{1}{2} x^2 \log x - \frac{1}{4} x^2$. Naturally, by Theorem 2.8, any function whose derivative is $x \log x$ can differ from this particular one only by a constant. The answer to this kind of a problem can and should be checked by differentiation of the alleged answer.

Exercises

1. Find functions whose derivatives are each of the following, and check by differentiation.

   (a) $x^2 \log x$
   (b) $x^2 e^x$
   (c) $x \cos x$
   (d) $x^2 \cos x$
   (e) $\log x$
   (f) $\sin^3 x$
   (g) $x^3 e^{x/2}$
   (h) $(\log x)^2$

2. Evaluate the following definite integrals.

   (a) $\int_0^1 x e^{ax} \, dx$

   (b) $\int_0^{\pi/6} x \cos ax \, dx$

   (c) $\int_1^2 (x + 1)^2 \log x \, dx$

   (d) $\int_0^1 x^2 \sin \frac{\pi}{2} x \, dx$

   (e) $\int_0^1 e^x \cos x \, dx$

3.10. The Mechanics of Integration: Integration by Substitution

As in the discussion of integration by parts in Section 3.9, our introduction of the method of substitution begins by plucking out of the air a certain identity and then showing how this identity can be used to help do some difficult integrals.

This time we begin with the composite function rule (chain rule) for differentiation

$$\frac{d}{dx}\varphi(\psi(x)) = \varphi'(\psi(x))\psi'(x)$$

In the language of indefinite integrals, this tells us that

$$\int \varphi'(\psi(x))\psi'(x)\,dx = \varphi(\psi(x))$$

or in the language of definite integrals, that

$$\int_\alpha^\beta \varphi'(\psi(x))\psi'(x)\,dt = \varphi(\psi(\beta)) - \varphi(\psi(\alpha)) \tag{3.30}$$

On the other hand, it is obvious that

$$\int_{\psi(\alpha)}^{\psi(\beta)} \varphi'(t)\,dt = \varphi(\psi(\beta)) - \varphi(\psi(\alpha)) \tag{3.31}$$

Comparing (3.30) and (3.31) we see that the two left-hand sides must be equal and so

$$\int_{\psi(\alpha)}^{\psi(\beta)} \varphi'(t)\,dt = \int_\alpha^\beta \varphi'(\psi(x))\psi'(x)\,dx \tag{3.32}$$

In this equation, however, the function φ itself never appears, only its derivative φ'. Hence, we change the name of the function φ' on both sides of (3.32) and call it f instead. For symmetry we change the name of ψ also, calling it g. Then (3.32) becomes

$$\int_{g(\alpha)}^{g(\beta)} f(t)\,dt = \int_\alpha^\beta f(g(x))g'(x)\,dx \tag{3.33}$$

Finally, suppose that g is monotonic, either increasing or decreasing. Then g has an inverse function g^{-1}, and so if we write b for $g(\beta)$ and a for $g(\alpha)$, then $\beta = g^{-1}(b)$ and $\alpha = g^{-1}(a)$. Thus (3.33) takes the form

$$\int_a^b f(t)\, dt = \int_{g^{-1}(a)}^{g^{-1}(b)} f(g(x))g'(x)\, dx \tag{3.34}$$

which is the foundation of the method of integration by substitution. It tells us how to transform a given integral (the left-hand side) into another (the right-hand side) which may be easier to handle. The choice of $g(x)$ is completely arbitrary except that it must be monotonic. A clever choice of $g(x)$ will often reduce a complicated integral to an easier one. There is no need to memorize the formula (3.34), but only to understand the sequence of steps involved in carrying out the process implied by (3.34). These are:

(a) Suppose it is required to evaluate the integral $\int_a^b f(t)\, dt$.

(b) Choose a monotonic function $g(x)$ [this is usually done in such a way that $f(g(x))$ is easier to look at than $f(t)$ was].

(c) In the given integral, replace $f(t)$ by $f(g(x))$, that is, replace the letter t wherever it occurs in the integrand by $g(x)$.

(d) Replace dt by $g'(x)\, dx$

(e) Replace the limits by the values of x which correspond to the given limits on t.

Examples

1.   To evaluate

$$\int_2^3 te^{t^2}\, dt$$

(a) Take $g(x) = \sqrt{x}$. (Isn't e^x easier to look at than e^{t^2}?)

(b) Replace te^{t^2} by $\sqrt{x}\, e^x$ [i.e., replace $f(t)$ by $f(\sqrt{x})$].

(c) Replace dt by $(1/2\sqrt{x})\, dx$.

(d) Replace the limits $t = 2$, $t = 3$ by $x = 4$, $x = 9$ (because t is being replaced by $\sqrt{x}$).

After doing all of this we find that

$$\int_2^3 t e^{t^2}\, dt = \int_4^9 \sqrt{x}\, e^x \frac{1}{2\sqrt{x}}\, dx$$

$$= \tfrac{1}{2}\int_4^9 e^x\, dx$$

$$= \tfrac{1}{2}(e^9 - e^4)$$

2.   Find the value of the integral

$$\int_1^2 \cos\,(\log t)\,\frac{dt}{t}$$

(a) Write $t = e^x$ [i.e., take $g(x) = e^x$].
(b) Replace $t^{-1} \cos\,(\log t)$ by

$$e^{-x} \cos\,(\log e^x) = e^{-x} \cos x$$

(c) Replace dt by $e^x\, dx$.
(d) Replace the limits $t = 1, t = 2$ by $x = 0, x = \log 2$.
Then

$$\int_1^2 \cos\,(\log t)\,\frac{dt}{t} = \int_0^{\log 2} e^{-x} \cos x\, e^x\, dx$$

$$= \int_0^{\log 2} \cos x\, dx$$

$$= \sin x \, \Big]_0^{\log 2}$$

$$= \sin\,(\log 2)$$

3.   Find a function whose derivative is $e^{\sqrt{x}}$.
Such a function is evidently

$$f(x) = \int_0^x e^{\sqrt{t}}\, dt$$

To do the integral, let $t = v^2$. Then we must replace $e^{\sqrt{t}}$ by e^v, dt by $2v\, dv$, and the limits $0, x$ by $0, \sqrt{x}$, respectively. The required integral then becomes

$$f(x) = \int_0^{\sqrt{x}} e^v 2v\, dv = 2 \int_0^{\sqrt{x}} v e^v\, dv$$

We do this last integral by parts:

$$f(x) = 2ve^v \Big]_0^{\sqrt{x}} - 2 \int_0^{\sqrt{x}} e^v \, dv$$

$$= 2\sqrt{x}\, e^{\sqrt{x}} - 2e^v \Big]_0^{\sqrt{x}}$$

$$= 2\sqrt{x}\, e^{\sqrt{x}} - 2e^{\sqrt{x}} + 2$$

Since we were asked only for "a" function whose derivative is $e^{\sqrt{x}}$ we may ignore the last constant 2 if we wish, and give

$$f(x) = 2e^{\sqrt{x}}(\sqrt{x} - 1)$$

as our answer.

Exercises

1.   Evaluate the following integrals.

(a) $\int_0^1 e^{\sqrt{t}} \dfrac{dt}{\sqrt{t}}$

(b) $\int_0^1 \log(1 + t)\, dt$

(c) $\int_0^1 (e^{ax} - e^{bx})\, dx$

(d) $\int_0^{\pi/2} (\sin \theta)^{15} \cos \theta \, d\theta$

(e) $\int_0^1 e^{-x} \cos e^{-x} \, dx$

(f) $\int_a^b x \cos x^2 \, dx$

(g) $\int_4^{\pi/2} \sin 2x \log(\sin x)\, dx$

(h) $\int_0^1 \sqrt{x^2 + 3x + 1}\,(2x + 3)\, dx$

(i) $\int_0^1 x(4x^2 + 5)^{3/2} \, dx$

(j) $\int_0^1 \dfrac{t\, dt}{\sqrt{3t^2 + 2}}$

(k) $\int_0^1 \frac{dx}{(ax + b)^6}$

(l) $\int_0^1 (3t^5 + 8)^{4/3} \, t^4 \, dt$

2.   Find functions having each of the following for derivatives, and check your answers by differentiation.

   (a) $\log{(l + a)}$
   (b) $x\sqrt{ax^2 + b}$
   (c) $x^2 \sin x^3$
   (d) $(\cos x)^n \sin x$

   There is a particular kind of substitution which is useful in a large class of integrals, namely, in those integrals which involve expressions like

$$a^2 + x^2, \qquad a^2 - x^2, \qquad \sqrt{a^2 + x^2}$$

etc. These are the trigonometric substitutions $x = a \cos \theta$, $x = a \sin \theta$, etc., and their usefulness derives from the trigonometric identities

$$\cos^2 x + \sin^2 x = 1; \qquad 1 + \tan^2 x = \sec^2 x$$

and so forth. Consider, for example, the integral

$$\int_0^1 \frac{dx}{\sqrt{9 - x^2}}$$

Here we would put $x = 3 \sin \theta$. Then

$$\frac{1}{\sqrt{9 - x^2}} = \frac{1}{\sqrt{9 - 9 \sin^2 \theta}}$$

$$= \frac{1}{3\sqrt{1 - \sin^2 \theta}}$$

$$= \frac{1}{3 \cos \theta}$$

and we also replace dx by $3 \cos \theta \, d\theta$ and the limits 0,1 by 0, $\sin^{-1} \frac{1}{3}$, respectively. Then the given integral becomes

$$\int_0^1 \frac{dx}{\sqrt{9 - x^2}} = \int_0^{\sin^{-1}(1/3)} \frac{3 \cos \theta \, d\theta}{3 \cos \theta}$$

$$= \int_0^{\sin^{-1}(1/3)} d\theta$$

$$= \sin^{-1} \frac{1}{3}$$

In general, the appearance of the expression $a^2 - x^2$ suggests the substitution $x = a \sin \theta$ if $|x| \leq a$ throughout the range of integration, while $a^2 + x^2$ suggests $x = a \tan \theta$ or $x = a \sinh \theta$. In integrals involving $a^2 - x^2$ where $|x| \geq a$ throughout the range of integration, the substitution $x = a \sin \theta$ is clearly impossible, but $x = a \cosh \theta$ will often help.

Example
To calculate

$$\int_0^1 \frac{dx}{\sqrt{16 + x^2}}$$

put $x = 4 \sinh \theta$. Then

$$16 + x^2 = 16 + 16 \sinh^2 \theta$$
$$= 16(1 + \sinh^2 \theta)$$
$$= 16 \cosh^2 \theta$$

Also, dx is replaced by

$$\frac{d}{d\theta}(4 \sinh \theta) \, d\theta = 4 \cosh \theta \, d\theta$$

The new limits of integration are determined by the relations

$$0 = 4 \sinh \theta_0$$
$$1 = 4 \sinh \theta_1$$

That is, the new limits are $\theta_0 = 0$, $\theta_1 = \sinh^{-1} \frac{1}{4}$. Hence, the given integral is

$$\int_0^1 \frac{dx}{\sqrt{16 + x^2}} = \int_0^{\sinh^{-1}(1/4)} \frac{4 \cosh \theta}{4 \cosh \theta} \, d\theta$$

$$= \int_0^{\sinh^{-1}(1/4)} d\theta$$

$$= \sinh^{-1} \tfrac{1}{4}$$

Exercises

1.   Prove that

$$\sinh^{-1} x = \log (x + \sqrt{1 + x^2})$$

and, therefore, that

$$\sinh^{-1}\frac{1}{4} = \log\frac{1 + \sqrt{17}}{4}$$

(Hint: If $y = \sinh^{-1} x$, $x = \sinh y$, and so $2x = e^y - e^{-y}$. Solve a quadratic equation to find e^y.)

2. Calculate the following integrals.

(a) $\int_0^1 \sqrt{9 - x^2}\, dx$

(b) $\int_6^7 \frac{x\, dx}{\sqrt{x^2 - 16}}$

(c) $\int_0^1 \frac{dx}{a^2x^2 + b^2}$

3.11. *The Mechanics of Integration: Rational Functions*

By a rational function we mean a quotient of two polynomials. Thus

$$\frac{3x - 2}{(x + 4)^3(x - 3)}; \qquad \frac{x^2 + 5x + 6}{(x - 1)^5 x^4}$$

are both rational functions. In this section we are concerned with integrals of rational functions, that is, with integrals of the form

$$\int_a^b \frac{P(t)}{Q(t)}\, dt$$

where P and Q are polynomials in t.

We accept without proof the fact that if a polynomial $Q(x)$ is zero at a certain value of x, say $x = a$, then $Q(x)$ has $x - a$ as a factor. Thus, $x^2 - 3x + 2$ vanishes at $x = 2$ and has $x - 2$ as a factor:

$$x^2 - 3x + 2 = (x - 2)(x - 1)$$

It follows that if all the points at which a polynomial vanishes are real, then we can completely factor the polynomial into factors of the first degree (linear factors).

For instance, if we know that $x^3 - 3x^2 - x + 3$ vanishes at $x = 1$, $x = 3$, and $x = -1$, then immediately we have

$$x^3 - 3x^2 - x + 3 = (x - 1)(x - 3)(x + 1)$$

The importance of factorization in integration problems arises from the following kind of trick:

$$\frac{1}{x^2 - 3x + 2} = \frac{1}{(x - 2)(x - 1)}$$

$$= \frac{1}{x - 2} - \frac{1}{x - 1}$$

which implies that

$$\int \frac{dx}{x^2 - 3x + 2} = \int \frac{dx}{x - 2} - \int \frac{dx}{x - 1}$$

$$= \log (x - 2) - \log (x - 1)$$

Evidently, as soon as we can write the integrand as a sum of reciprocals of polynomials of degree 1, the integration can be done by inspection. As another example, the relation

$$\frac{1}{x^3 - 3x^2 - x + 3} = \frac{1}{(x - 1)(x - 3)(x + 1)}$$

$$= -\frac{1}{4} \frac{1}{x - 1} + \frac{1}{8} \frac{1}{x - 3} + \frac{1}{8} \frac{1}{x + 1}$$

gives the evaluation of the integral

$$\int \frac{dx}{x^3 - 3x^2 - x + 3} = \frac{1}{4} \log (x - 1) + \frac{1}{8} \log (x - 3) + \frac{1}{8} \log (x + 1)$$

What is needed, then, is a systematic way to arrive at the expression of the reciprocal of a polynomial as a sum of reciprocals of polynomials of the first degree. This is possible only when all of the roots of the polynomial are real and distinct, that is, when the polynomial in question can be factored into linear, nonrepeated, factors. It is possible also to handle other situations, but the theory gets rather complicated, and we omit it here. After giving a procedure for the reciprocal of a polynomial it will be very easy to take care of the case where the numerator of the integrand is any polynomial at all.

Suppose then that it is required to do an integral of the form

$$\int_a^b \frac{dx}{P(x)}$$

where $P(x)$ is a polynomial whose roots are all *real and distinct.* We first prove that such a polynomial and its derivative cannot have roots in common.

LEMMA 1.   If the roots $a_1, a_2, \ldots, a_n$ of the polynomial P are all distinct, then P' cannot vanish at any of the points $a_1, \ldots, a_n$ where P does.

PROOF   Since $P(a_1) = 0$, we have $P(x) = (x - a_1)Q(x)$ where Q is a polynomial. Then

$$P'(x) = (x - a_1)Q'(x) + Q(x)$$

and so $P'(a_1) = Q(a_1)$. If $P'(a_1) = 0$, then $Q(a_1) = 0$, so $Q(x)$ has the factor $(x - a_1)$ also. But then $P(x)$ has the factor $(x - a_1)^2$, contradicting the hypothesis that $P(x)$ has no repeated roots.

LEMMA 2.   A polynomial of degree n which vanishes at $n + 1$ distinct points is everywhere zero.

PROOF   This is obvious if $n = 1$. Suppose now that we have a polynomial $P(x)$ of degree 2, vanishing at three distinct points. By Rolle's theorem $P'(x)$, of degree 1, vanishes at least once between each pair of roots of $P(x)$, and, therefore, at least twice, contradicting the result already proved for $n = 1$ unless P vanishes everywhere. We continue in this way, reducing each value of n to the preceding one by differentiation, and obtaining a contradiction at each stage by the use of Rolle's theorem, thereby proving the theorem for every value of n.

THEOREM 3.9.   Let the polynomial $P(x)$, of degree n, vanish at n real, distinct points $a_1, a_2, \ldots, a_n$. Then, for all x

$$\frac{1}{P'(a_1)} \frac{P(x)}{x - a_1} + \frac{1}{P'(a_2)} \frac{P(x)}{x - a_2} + \cdots + \frac{1}{P'(a_n)} \frac{P(x)}{x - a_n} = 1$$

$$(3.35)$$

PROOF   Since $P(x)$ is divisible by each $x - a_j$, every term on the left is a polynomial of degree $n - 1$. Hence, the left-hand side is of degree $n - 1$. At each of the n points $a_1, \ldots, a_n$ the value of the left-hand side is 1 since every term is zero except one, and that term has the value 1. Hence, the difference between the left side of (3.35) and the right side of (3.35) is a polynomial of degree $n - 1$ which vanishes at n points, and so vanishes everywhere, which was to be shown.

We now return to the original problem. In order to do the integral

$$\int \frac{dx}{P(x)}$$

we have from (3.35)

$$\frac{1}{P(x)} = \frac{1}{P'(a_1)} \frac{1}{x - a_1} + \frac{1}{P'(a_2)} \frac{1}{x - a_2} + \cdots + \frac{1}{P'(a_n)} \frac{1}{x - a_n} \tag{3.36}$$

and so

$$\int \frac{dx}{P(x)} = \frac{1}{P'(a_1)} \log (x - a_1) + \cdots + \frac{1}{P'(a_n)} \log (x - a_n) \tag{3.37}$$

Example

If $P(x) = x^3 - 6x^2 + 11x - 6$, we find that $P(x) = 0$ at the points $a_1 = 1$, $a_2 = 2$, $a_3 = 3$; also, since $P'(x) = 3x^2 - 12x + 11$, we have

$$P'(a_1) = P'(1) = 2$$
$$P'(a_2) = P'(2) = -1$$
$$P'(a_3) = P'(3) = 2$$

Substituting in (3.37), we find

$$\int \frac{dx}{x^3 - 6x^2 + 11x - 6}$$
$$= \frac{1}{2} \log (x - 1) - \log (x - 2) + \frac{1}{2} \log (x - 3) \tag{3.38}$$

We have so far considered only those rational functions whose numerator is 1. To extend this method to the case where some polynomial appears in the numerator is easy. If the polynomial in the denominator satisfies the conditions of Theorem 3.9, then we go ahead and make the "partial fraction" expansion (3.37), ignoring the numerator, then multiply through the entire expression by the numerator, then perform the long divisions indicated, then integrate.

As an example, we consider an integral with the same denominator as (3.38):

$$\int \frac{x^2 + 7x + 2}{x^3 - 6x^2 + 11x - 6} \, dx \tag{3.39}$$

The first step is to apply (3.36) to the denominator as before,

$$\frac{1}{x^3 - 6x^2 + 11x - 6} = \frac{1}{2} \frac{1}{x - 1} - \frac{1}{x - 2} + \frac{1}{2} \frac{1}{x - 3}$$

Next, we multiply through by the numerator, getting

$$\frac{x^2 + 7x + 2}{x^3 - 6x^2 + 11x - 6}$$
$$= \frac{1}{2} \frac{x^2 + 7x + 2}{x - 1} - \frac{x^2 + 7x + 2}{x - 2} + \frac{1}{2} \frac{x^2 + 7x + 2}{x - 3} \tag{3.40}$$

We are now confronted with three long division problems. First, dividing $x - 1$ into $x^2 + 7x + 2$ we find that

$$\frac{x^2 + 7x + 2}{x - 1} = x + 8 + \frac{10}{x - 1}$$

In a similar way we obtain

$$\frac{x^2 + 7x + 2}{x - 2} = x + 9 + \frac{20}{x - 2}$$

$$\frac{x^2 + 7x + 2}{x - 3} = x + 10 + \frac{32}{x - 3}$$

Substituting these three computations into (3.40)

$$\frac{x^2 + 7x + 2}{x^3 - 6x^2 + 11x - 6}$$
$$= \frac{1}{2}(x + 8) + \frac{5}{x - 1} - (x + 9) - \frac{20}{x - 2} + \frac{x + 10}{2} + \frac{16}{x - 3}$$

and integrating, we get

$$\int \frac{x^2 + 7x + 2}{x^3 - 6x^2 + 11x - 6} dx = \frac{x^2}{4} + 4x + 5 \log (x - 1) - \frac{x^2}{2} - 9x$$

$$- 20 \log (x - 2) + \frac{x^2}{4} + 5x + 16 \log (x - 3)$$

$$= \log \frac{(x - 1)^5(x - 3)^{16}}{(x - 2)^{20}}$$

which is the desired answer.

Exercises

Integrate the following.

(a) $\int \dfrac{dx}{3x - 4}$

(b) $\int \dfrac{5x + 1}{2x + 3} dx$

(c) $\int \dfrac{3x + 4}{x^3 - x^2 - 2x} dx$

(d) $\int \dfrac{ax + b}{cx + d} dx$

(e) $\int \dfrac{x + a}{(x + b)(x + c)} dx$

(f) $\int \dfrac{dx}{4x^2 - 9}$

(g) $\dfrac{3x^2 + 2}{3x^2 - 25} dx$

(h) $\int \dfrac{ax^2 + bx + c}{x^2 - d^2} dx$

Repeated Differentiation; Maxima and Minima
Extremum Problems
Curve Sketching; L'Hospital's Rule
Numerical Methods
Arc Length
The Volume of a Solid of Revolution
Convexity
Contact, Curvature, and Approximation
Improper Integrals

4

Applications of the Calculus

4.1. Repeated Differentiation; Maxima and Minima

In this chapter we will discuss some applications of the analytical methods which we have derived so far. A broad area of applications arises when questions are asked about doing something in the best possible way, for instance, in such a way as to produce most profit, or least cost, or maximum efficiency, etc. The contribution of the calculus to such problems consists in giving us certain analytical machinery by the use of which we can recognize optimum courses of action. These criteria are most useful, in practice, where we have more or less complete freedom of action. If external constraints are imposed on our choices, the calculus may become less applicable.

We illustrate these remarks by a small example (see Fig. 4.1). Suppose that a certain manufacturer knows that if he retains a certain fraction x of his present labor force, his income will be x, and his costs will be x^2, so that he can expect a profit of $x - x^2$. Plotting a graph of $x - x^2$ for $0 \leqq x \leqq 1$ we notice a maximum profit of $\frac{1}{4}$, which would be reached if half the labor force were retained. In the absence of external constraints, our manufacturer would proceed to dismiss half of his workers. If, however, a layoff of more than 10% of the work force is likely to produce a general strike, then his freedom of action is limited to values of x such that $0.9 \leq x \leq 1$. In this case the domain of the function $x - x^2$ is restricted to the interval $(0.9,1)$ and the maximum of the function occurs at $x = 0.9$. The methods of the calculus are well adapted to cope with the first situation because at the optimum point the tangent

Figure 4.1

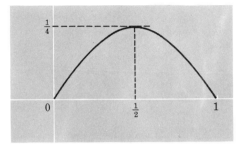

to the curve is horizontal, and, therefore, we could find the optimum by differentiating and setting the derivative equal to zero. In the second case it is the endpoint $x = 0.9$ which governs the problem and the calculus is useful only in the negative sense of telling us that there are no better choices of x interior to the interval in question.

Let us keep this example in mind and proceed to the consideration of maximum–minimum problems. We require first a notation for repeated differentiation. If $y = f(x)$ is a given function, we have denoted its derivative either by y' or f' or dy/dx or df/dx. Suppose we now take the derivative of y and differentiate it. We then have a function called the second derivative of f. This is denoted by any of the symbols

$$y''; \quad f''; \quad \frac{d^2y}{dx^2}; \quad \frac{d^2f}{dx^2}$$

Differentiating again would give the third derivative

$$y'''; \quad f'''; \quad \frac{d^3y}{dx^3}; \quad \frac{d^3f}{dx^3}$$

For example, if $y = x^{10}$, then $y' = 10x^9$, $y'' = 90x^8$, $y''' = 720x^7$, and so on. In general, if

$$y = x^n$$

then $y' = nx^{n-1}$, $y'' = n(n - 1)x^{n-2}$, $y''' = n(n - 1)(n - 2)x^{n-3}$, and

$$y^{(k)} = n(n - 1)(n - 2)(n - 3) \cdots (n - k + 1)x^{n-k}$$

For any positive integer n, the symbol $n!$ (read "n factorial") denotes the product of all of the positive integers $\leq n$. Thus

$$3! = 1 \cdot 2 \cdot 3 = 6$$
$$5! = 1 \cdot 2 \cdot 3 \cdot 4 \cdot 5 = 120$$

It is conventional to interpret the symbol $0!$ as 1. If we use this factorial notation, the kth derivative of x^n is

$$y^{(k)} = \frac{n!}{(n - k)!} x^{n-k}$$

for $k = 0, 1, \ldots, n$.

Exercises

1. Find the second and third derivatives of each of the following functions.

    (a) $\sin x$
    (b) e^{x^3}
    (c) $\cosh x$
    (d) $\tan^{-1} x$
    (e) $\log (x + 5)$
    (f) $x^{1/2}$

2. Find a general formula for the kth derivative of each of the following functions.

    (a) $\sin ax$
    (b) $\sinh x$
    (c) $\dfrac{1}{1 + x}$
    (d) a^x
    (e) $x^{1/2}$
    (f) xe^{-x}

3. Find the constant a in such a way that the function $y = \cos ax$ satisfies the equation

$$y'' + ky = 0$$

We return now to our subject of maxima and minima, and recall that if the derivative of a function f is positive, the function is increasing, while if $f' < 0$, the function is decreasing. In extremum problems we are interested in the turning points of f, that is, points to the left of which f is, say, increasing, and to the right of which f decreases. Since the derivative f' changes sign as we pass through such a turning point, it is natural to expect that $f'(x) = 0$ at the point itself. We will see that this is generally the case.

> **DEFINITION**   Let f be defined for $a \leq x \leq b$. A point $x = x_0$ is said to give a *local maximum* (respectively *minimum*) to f if there is a $\delta > 0$ such that $f(x) \leq f(x_0)$ [respectively, $f(x) \geq f(x_0)$] for all x such that $|x - x_0| < \delta$ in (a,b).

This means that, at a local maximum, f is at least as large as it is at any point near the local maximum. The function shown in Fig. 4.2 has three local maxima and the same number of local minima. The former are at the points a, x_2, x_4, and the latter are at x_1, x_3, b.

The differential calculus can be of assistance in locating local maxima and minima which lie interior to the domain of definition of the function. Extrema which occur at endpoints (as a and b in Fig. 4.2) must be found

Figure 4.2

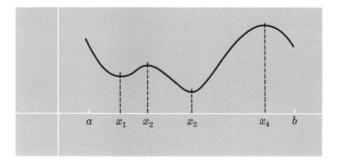

by separately examining the values of the function at those points. It is also possible for extrema to occur at points where the derivative does not exist. An example is $f(x) = |x|$ which has a minimum at $x = 0$ but no derivative there. Such points also need to be examined separately.

THEOREM 4.1. Let f be defined for $a \leqq x \leqq b$. Suppose that x_0 satisfies $a < x_0 < b$, that $f'(x_0)$ exists and that x_0 gives to f a local maximum or minimum. Then $f'(x_0) = 0$.

PROOF   Suppose, for concreteness, that x_0 is a local maximum of f. Then there is a $\delta > 0$ such that $f(x) \leqq f(x_0)$ for $|x - x_0| < \delta$. Let $0 < h < \delta$. Then the quotient

$$\frac{f(x_0 + h) - f(x_0)}{h} \tag{4.1}$$

is nonpositive because its numerator is nonpositive and its denominator is positive. On the other hand, if $-\delta < h < 0$, then the quotient (4.1) is nonnegative because its numerator is nonpositive and its denominator is negative. Hence, $f'(x_0)$, which is the limit of (4.1) as h approaches zero, and which exists, by hypothesis, is both nonnegative and nonpositive, and, therefore, must be zero, which was to be shown.

Note that this theorem must not be used in the reverse direction. That is, if $f'(x_0) = 0$, we do *not* know that x_0 gives either a local maximum or a local minimum to f, and, indeed, it may do neither. For example, if $f(x) = x^3$, then f' is zero at $x = 0$, but by graphing the function one sees easily that the origin is neither a local maximum nor a local minimum of this function, but only a resting place before f resumes its upward climb (Fig. 4.3).

Figure 4.3

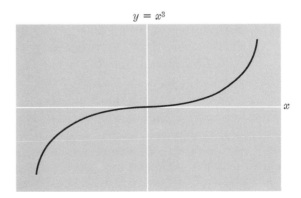

$y = x^3$

x

Example 1.

Find the maximum of xe^{-x} for $x \geq 0$.

   If $y = xe^{-x}$, we have

$$y' = (1 - x)e^{-x}$$

from which we see that if $0 < x < 1$, y' is positive so y is increasing. For $x > 1$, y' is negative, so y decreases. At $x = 1$, $y' = 0$. This is a local maximum since to the left y increases and to the right y decreases. There can be no other positive maxima or minima, since, if there were, y' would be zero again. Thus xe^{-x} is largest at $x = 1$, where it has the value e^{-1}. We have proved that

$$0 \leq xe^{-x} \leq e^{-1} \qquad (x \geq 0)$$

   We have so far seen that if it is desired to find the points at which a given function has a local maximum or minimum, the first thing to do is to differentiate the function, set its derivative equal to zero, and solve for the values of x thereby determined. By considering these values of x together with the endpoints of the domain of the function, if any, together with the points at which f has no derivative, if any, we will find such local extrema as may exist.

   If we have this list of suspicious points in hand, the next step is to sort the points into three piles: those which are local maxima, those which are local minima, and those which are neither. For this sorting operation the second derivative will be found useful. Indeed, suppose we are considering a certain point x_0 on our list, and suppose it was on our list because $f'(x_0) = 0$. Suppose $f''(x_0) > 0$. Since f'' is the first derivative of f', to say that $f'' > 0$ is to say that f' is increasing. Thus, $f''(x_0) > 0$ means that the function f' is increasing at $x = x_0$. Since $f'(x_0) = 0$, this implies that f' is negative to the left of x_0 and positive to the right of x_0. Hence, the slope of the curve is downward to the left of x_0 and upward to the right of x_0. Hence, x_0 is a local minimum of the function f. In a similar way we see that if $f''(x_0) < 0$, then x_0 is a local maximum of f.

   Instead of the picturesque argument just given, we can reach the same conclusion by use of the mean-value theorem. In fact, if $f'(x_0) = 0$ and $f''(x_0) \neq 0$, then f'' will remain $\neq 0$ in some neighborhood of x_0, and if

$x \neq x_0$ is in this neighborhood, then

$$f(x) - f(x_0) = (x - x_0)f'(\xi_1) \qquad (4.2)$$
$$= (x - x_0)(f'(\xi_1) - f'(x_0))$$
$$= (x - x_0)(\xi_1 - x_0)f''(\xi_2)$$

where ξ_1 is between x_0 and x, ξ_2 is between x_0 and ξ_1. Thus, $x - x_0$ and $\xi_1 - x_0$ have the same sign, and so by (4.2), the sign of $f(x) - f(x_0)$ is the same as the sign of $f''(\xi_2)$. Hence, $f''(x_0) > 0$ implies $f''(\xi_2) > 0$ which means that $f(x) - f(x_0) > 0$, and so x_0 is a local minimum. Similarly, if $f''(x_0) < 0$, x_0 is a local maximum.

We summarize these arguments in

THEOREM 4.2. Let f be defined for $a < x < b$, and let it be twice continuously differentiable there. Suppose that $a < x_0 < b$, that $f'(x_0) = 0$ and that $f''(x_0) > 0$. Then x_0 gives a local minimum to f. If $f'(x_0) = 0$ and $f''(x_0) < 0$, then x_0 gives a local maximum to f. If $f'(x_0) = 0$ and $f''(x_0) = 0$, no conclusion can yet be drawn.

Example 2.
Find the local maxima and minima of the function

$$f(x) = x^3 - 9x^2 + 24x - 1$$

We calculate $f'(x)$ and set it equal to zero and find

$$3x^2 - 18x + 24 = 0$$

from which $(x - 4)(x - 2) = 0$ and so $x = 2$ and $x = 4$ are the only candidates. Now at $x_0 = 2$, $f''(x_0) = f''(2) = -6 < 0$, whence $x = 2$ is a local maximum. At $x = 4$, $f''(4) = 6 > 0$, from which $x = 4$ is a local minimum. Now a graph of this function can be easily made and is shown in Fig. 4.4.

Example 3.
Show that the sum of a positive number and its reciprocal is always at least 2.

What we have to show is that if $x > 0$, then $f(x) = x + (1/x) \geq 2$, that is, we must show that the minimum of $f(x)$ for $x > 0$ is at least 2. Now

$$f'(x) = 1 - \frac{1}{x^2}$$

and so $f'(1) = 0$, $f''(1) > 0$, and, therefore, $x_0 = 1$ is a local minimum of f. Since f gets very large as x approaches zero or infinity, $x_0 = 1$ is the absolute minimum of f for $x > 0$. Since $f(1) = 2$, we have $f(x) \geq 2$ for

Figure 4.4

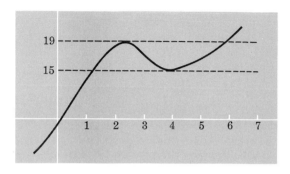

$x > 0$ as required. Actually, it is easier to prove this result without the calculus, for to show that

$$x + \frac{1}{x} \geqq 2 \qquad (x > 0)$$

it is enough to show that

$$x^2 + 1 \geqq 2x \qquad (x > 0)$$

or that

$$x^2 - 2x + 1 \geqq 0 \qquad (x > 0)$$

or finally that

$$(x - 1)^2 \geqq 0 \qquad (x > 0)$$

which is obvious.

Exercises

1. Find all local maxima and minima of the following functions, identifying each as a maximum or a minimum.

    (a) $\dfrac{\log x}{x}$ $\qquad (x > 0)$

(b) $x^2 e^{-x}$

(c) $(x^2 - 1)^{10}$

(d) $x^3 - x^2 - x - 1$

(e) $\dfrac{x+1}{x^2+2}$

(f) x^4

(g) $\cosh x$

2. Among all pairs of positive numbers whose product is K find the pair whose sum is smallest. What is the value of the smallest sum?

3. If the sum of the squares of two numbers is A, how large can the sum of their sixth powers be? How small?

4.2. Extremum Problems

In this section we apply the results of the preceding section to some "word problems." In the solution of such problems the essential steps are:

(a) Determine the variable which is to be maximized or minimized. Give it a symbol.

(b) Determine the variables on which it depends, that is, the variables whose values we are to choose in such a way as to optimize the variable in part (a).

(c) Write down the explicit functional relationship between the variable to be optimized and the variables on which it depends.

(d) Write down any additional relationships which exist among the "independent" variables.

(e) Taking account of these relationships (see examples following) differentiate the function appearing in (c), set the derivative equal to zero, and thereby find the optimal values of the independent variable.

Example 1.

Which rectangle of perimeter P has the greatest area?

Step (a). The variable to be maximized is the area A.

Step (b). The variables on which A depends are the length and width of the rectangle, call these l and w. We are to determine l and w to maximize A.

Step (c). The explicit functional relationship between A, l, and w is

$$A = lw \tag{4.3}$$

Step (d). Additional relationships which hold among the independent variables are that the perimeter must be P, which is to say that

$$2l + 2w = P \tag{4.4}$$

Step (e). At this point there are two possible approaches. Note that in (4.3) A apparently depends on two variables l and w. But, because of (4.4), only one of these is independent because as soon as the value of, say, l is fixed, the value of w is determined by (4.4). The straightforward procedure, which is surely the right one for this easy problem, is to eliminate one of the variables, say l. We call this the "explicit" method.

EXPLICIT METHOD   from (4.4),

$$l = \frac{P}{2} - w$$

and then from (4.3),

$$A = \left(\frac{P}{2} - w\right)w \tag{4.5}$$

Now the area depends on only one variable w, and we wish to find the value of w which maximizes A. If we differentiate with respect to w,

$$\frac{dA}{dw} = \frac{P}{2} - 2w$$

and if we set this equal to zero, we find that $w = P/4$. Since $d^2A/dw^2 = -2 < 0$, this is a local maximum. To see that it is an absolute maximum we need only check the endpoints $w = 0$ and $w = P/2$ of the domain of definition of A, and since both of these correspond to zero area, $w = P/4$ is indeed the desired maximum. If we use (4.4), we find $l = P/4$, and so the desired rectangle which, for given perimeter, has maximum area, is a square, the maximum possible area being $P^2/16$.

IMPLICIT METHOD   The implicit method is designed for problems in which it is difficult or impossible to eliminate one of the variables because of the difficulty of solving the equation connecting them. In this trivial problem there is, of course, no difficulty in solving (4.4) for l, thereby eliminating it. Let us pretend, though, that we are unable to solve (4.4) for either variable in terms of the other. In that case we would imagine that Eq. (4.4) determines l in terms of w, and so we think of the letter l as representing a function of w, which, alas, we are unable to write down explicitly.

We think of l as a function of w, and we differentiate (4.3), getting

$$\frac{dA}{dw} = l + w\frac{dl}{dw} \tag{4.6}$$

To find dl/dw we differentiate (4.4), as it stands, with respect to w, and get

$$2\frac{dl}{dw} + 2 = 0$$

from which

$$\frac{dl}{dw} = -1$$

If we substitute this in (4.6),

$$\frac{dA}{dw} = l - w$$

and if we set this equal to zero, we find $l = w$, that is, the best rectangle is a square, just as we discovered earlier.

We next give an example in which the implicit method is the easier, rather than the harder, choice.

Example 2.
Among all cylinders inscribed in a sphere of radius R, find the one of maximum possible volume.

Step (a). We are to maximize the volume, call it V.

Step (b). V depends upon the radius and the height of the cylinder, say r and h.

Step (c). The explicit dependence of V on r and h is

$$V = \pi r^2 h \tag{4.7}$$

Step (d). An additional relation between r and h is present because of the condition that the cylinder be inscribed in the sphere of given radius R. Referring to Fig. 4.5, we see that if the cylinder is inscribed in the sphere, then

$$R^2 = r^2 + \frac{h^2}{4} \qquad (4.8)$$

Figure 4.5

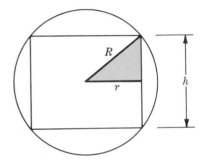

Step (e). Our problem is to maximize V in (4.7), where r and h are not independent of each other, but are connected by the condition (4.8). Instead of eliminating r explicitly by solving (4.8) for it in terms of h, let us only imagine that we have done so and think of the letter r as representing a function of h. In this state of mind we differentiate (4.7) with respect to h, getting

$$\frac{dV}{dh} = \pi r^2 + 2\pi rh \frac{dr}{dh} \qquad (4.9)$$

To find dr/dh we differentiate (4.8) with respect to h, and find

$$0 = 2r\frac{dr}{dh} + \frac{h}{2}$$

Hence,

$$\frac{dr}{dh} = -\frac{h}{4r}$$

and if we substitute this in (4.9) we get

$$\frac{dV}{dh} = \pi r^2 - \frac{\pi h^2}{2} \tag{4.10}$$

When we equate this to zero we discover that the optimum choice of r is

$$r = \frac{h}{\sqrt{2}} \tag{4.11}$$

To find r explicitly we substitute (4.11) into (4.8) and get

$$h = \frac{2R}{\sqrt{3}}$$
$$r = \sqrt{\tfrac{2}{3}} R$$

for the required dimensions. The maximum volume is

$$V_{\max} = \pi r^2 h$$
$$= \pi \frac{2}{3} R^2 \frac{2}{\sqrt{3}} R$$
$$= \frac{4}{3\sqrt{3}} \pi R^3$$

Since the volume of the sphere is $\frac{4}{3}\pi R^3$, we see that the best cylinder occupies about 58% of the available volume.

Exercises

1. Given a wire of length L. Cut it into two pieces, form one into a circle and the other into an equilateral triangle. What is the minimum possible total area? The maximum?
2. If the product of two positive numbers is K, how large can the sum of their squares be? How small?
3. How do we make a tin can of volume V using the least amount of tin?
4. Which cylinder inscribed in a sphere of radius R has maximum surface area?
5. Which circular sector of perimeter P has maximum area?
6. Determine the maximum volume of a closed box whose total surface area is 100 sq in. if the area of the bottom is 40 sq in.

7. Find the point on the curve $y = ax^2$ which is nearest to the point $(0,b)$.
8. An office manager observes that if he has 50 workers they will produce 100 units per worker of finished goods, and that the productivity drops by 1% as each new worker is added. How many workers should he have for maximum production?

4.3. *Curve Sketching; L'Hospital's Rule*

The ability to make a rapid sketch of a graph, showing all features of importance, can be most useful to a mathematician or scientist. The theory of maxima and minima, developed in the preceding sections, may be of great value in such situations. A complete sketch of a graph should display clearly all local extrema together with the values of the function at those extreme points, it should show where the function increases and where it decreases, it should display asymptotes, which are straight lines toward which the graph tends as a limit, and any other unusual or interesting characteristics of the function which seem appropriate.

Example 1.
Sketch the curve

$$y = \frac{x}{1 - x} \tag{4.12}$$

The domain of this function, in accordance with our usual convention, is the set of all real numbers $\neq 1$. By differentiation we find

$$y' = \frac{1}{(1 - x)^2}$$

which is positive where it is defined, and so our function is increasing where it is defined.

Suppose now that x is very large (say 10,000,000). Evidently, from (4.12), y is very near -1 and approaches -1 in the limit as x approaches ∞. Similarly, if $x = -10,000,000$, y is very near -1. Now suppose that x is just a bit less than 1. Then $1 - x$ is a small positive number, and so y is a large positive number. Therefore, as x approaches 1 from the left, y gets large without bound. If x is a bit larger than 1, $1 - x$ is negative and near zero, so y is a large negative number.

It is convenient to summarize this by saying that as $x \to 1$ from the left, $y \to +\infty$, while if $x \to 1$ from the right, $y \to -\infty$. We now have all the information required to sketch the graph, which is Fig. 4.6.

Figure 4.6

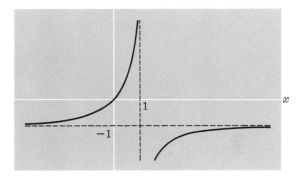

Example 2.
Sketch the curve

$$y = \frac{x + 2}{(x + 1)(x - 2)} \qquad (4.13)$$

By differentiation, we get

$$y' = -\frac{x(x + 4)}{(x + 1)^2(x + 2)^2} \qquad (4.14)$$

Thus $y' = 0$ when $x = 0$ and when $x = -4$. To discover which of these is a local minimum and which a local maximum we could differentiate again and use Theorem 4.2. A simpler approach is to note from (4.14) that if x is just a bit negative, then $y' > 0$, while if x is a bit positive, $y' < 0$, hence, $x = 0$ is a local maximum. Similarly, if x is slightly to the left of -4, $y' < 0$, and if x is just to the right of -4, $y' > 0$, so $x = -4$ is a local minimum. We also see from (4.13) that the lines $x = -1$, $x = 2$ will be vertical asymptotes since y gets very large in the neighborhood of these two points. So far, our graph looks like Fig. 4.7.

Concerning the asymptote at $x = -1$, if x is a shade less than -1

$$y = \frac{\text{(something positive)}}{\text{(something small and negative)(something negative)}}$$

$$= \text{something large and positive}$$

Figure 4.7

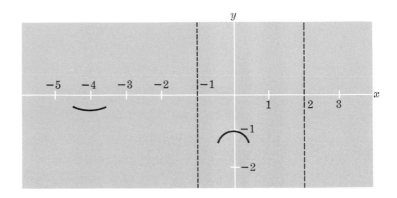

hence, $y \to +\infty$ as $x \to -1$ from the left. Similarly, $y \to -\infty$ as $x \to -1$ from the right, $y \to -\infty$ as $x \to 2$ from the left, and $y \to +\infty$ as $x \to 2$ from the right. Finally, when x is very large y is very near $1/x$, and so $y \to 0$ through positive values as $x \to +\infty$. Similarly, $y \to 0$ through negative values as $x \to -\infty$. The complete graph is Fig. 4.8.

Figure 4.8

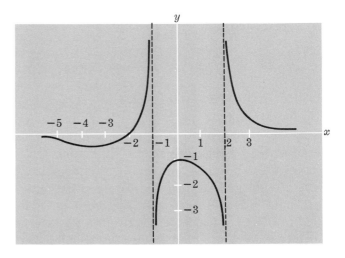

Exercises

Sketch the graphs of the following functions.

1. $x^2(1 + x^2)^{-1}$
2. $x(1 + x^2)^{-1}$
3. $\sqrt{1 + x^2}$
4. $x^3 - 6x^2 + 2x - 1$
5. $(x^3 - 1)^{16}$

6. $\dfrac{x}{x^2 - 4}$

7. $\sqrt{\dfrac{1 + x^2}{2 + x^2}}$

We would now like to be able to sketch graphs which involve tran-scendental (nonalgebraic) functions, such as

$$y = \frac{\log x}{x} \qquad (x > 0) \tag{4.15}$$

For the most part this is a simple matter, the only difficulty being our inability to see how y behaves when x is very large. By differentiating we would find that

$$y' = \frac{1 - \log x}{x^2}$$

so that y increases when $x < e$ and decreases when $x > e$. Thus, when x is very large, y decreases and is always positive. But what is

$$\lim_{x \to \infty} \frac{\log x}{x}?$$

We need the value of this limit in order to be able to draw the proper horizontal asymptote on our sketch of the graph. Fortunately, there is available a generally applicable method for evaluating troublesome limits like this one.

The method in question, known as L'Hospital's rule (lō-pē-tal) is useful in precisely those limits where obvious methods do not work. By "obvious methods" we mean that in a limit such as

$$\lim_{x \to 2} (x^2 + 8)$$

we can simply replace x by 2 and find the correct value, 12, of the limit. In a more difficult case, such as

$$\lim_{x \to 0} \frac{e^x - 1}{x} \tag{4.16}$$

if we replace x by zero, we are confronted by $0/0$, and, therefore, have learned nothing about the limit. In just such a case L'Hospital's rule can help. Roughly, what it says is that if when we try to evaluate

$$\lim_{x \to a} \frac{f(x)}{g(x)} \tag{4.17}$$

we replace x by a and see $0/0$, then the limit (4.17) is the same as

$$\lim_{x \to a} \frac{f'(x)}{g'(x)} \tag{4.18}$$

which may be easier to handle.

For instance, the use of (4.18) would tell us that

$$\lim_{x \to 0} \frac{\sin x}{x} = \lim_{x \to 0} \frac{\cos x}{1}$$

which is obviously equal to 1. We state this rule as

THEOREM 4.3 *(L'Hospital's Rule).*   Let it be required to find the limit (4.17). Suppose $f(a) = 0$ and $g(a) = 0$ and that f, g have continuous derivatives in a neighborhood of $x = a$. Then the limits (4.17) and (4.18) are equal, in the sense that if either of them exists then so does the other and they are equal.

In order to prove this theorem it is necessary to use the following result, which is a slight generalization of the mean-value theorem.

LEMMA   Let f and g be two functions which are defined and differentiable for $a < x < b$ and continuous in $a \leq x \leq b$. Suppose further that $g'(x) \neq 0$ for $a < x < b$. Then there is a number

ξ, $a < \xi < b$, such that

$$\frac{f(b) - f(a)}{g(b) - g(a)} = \frac{f'(\xi)}{g'(\xi)} \tag{4.19}$$

PROOF OF LEMMA   Just as in the proof of the mean-value theorem we define a new function

$$\varphi(x) = [f(x) - f(a)][g(b) - g(a)] - [g(x) - g(a)][f(b) - f(a)]$$

We observe that $\varphi(a) = \varphi(b) = 0$, so we see that $\varphi(x)$ satisfies the conditions of Rolle's theorem; hence, there is an interior point ξ at which $\varphi'(\xi) = 0$, which is to say that

$$\varphi'(\xi) = f'(\xi)[g(b) - g(a)] - g'(\xi)[f(b) - f(a)] \tag{4.20}$$
$$= 0$$

Now $g(a) \neq g(b)$, for, if it were, then by Rolle's theorem g' would vanish somewhere, contradicting the hypothesis. Hence, we can divide through in (4.20) by $g'(\xi)[g(b) - g(a)]$ and obtain the desired result (4.19).

We now use the lemma to prove L'Hospital's rule. Under the hypotheses of Theorem 4.3, $f(a) = g(a) = 0$. Consequently, (4.19) takes the form

$$\frac{f(x)}{g(x)} = \frac{f'(\xi)}{g'(\xi)} \tag{4.21}$$

where, in (4.19), we have replaced the letter b by x, and the point ξ lies between a and x. Now, as x approaches a the point ξ is caught between a and x, and so also approaches a. Therefore, by (4.21), if either of the limits (4.17) or (4.18) exists, so does the other, and they are equal.

By small modifications of these arguments, which we shall not enter into here, one can show that the limits

$$\lim_{x \to a} \frac{f(x)}{g(x)} \quad \text{and} \quad \lim_{x \to a} \frac{f'(x)}{g'(x)}$$

are equal whenever a is either finite or infinite and when the substitution of a for x in $f(x)/g(x)$ results in either $0/0$ or ∞/∞. Aside from these last two possibilities there are several other forms which can be assumed by

f/g when x is replaced by a and with which L'Hospital's rule can be of assistance. For example, in

$$\lim_{x\to\infty}\left(1 + \frac{a}{x}\right)^x \tag{4.22}$$

if we formally replace x by ∞, we would be looking at 1^∞ and would know nothing about the existence of or value of the limit.

In

$$\lim_{x\to 0} x \log x \tag{4.23}$$

we would be confronted by $0(-\infty)$, even though the limit is a perfectly reasonable number. In

$$\lim_{x\to 0}\left\{\frac{1}{\sin x} - \frac{1}{x}\right\} \tag{4.24}$$

replacing x by 0 results in $\infty - \infty$, equally uninformatively. In each of these cases L'Hospital's rule can be employed to find the correct value of the limit, sometimes after a preliminary transformation.

Examples
1.   Evaluate

$$\lim_{x\to 0}\frac{e^x - 1}{x}$$

Here we have a "0/0" type which is handled by direct application of the rule. We find

$$\lim_{x\to 0}\frac{e^x - 1}{x} = \lim_{x\to 0}\frac{e^x}{1} = 1$$

2.   Find

$$\lim_{x\to\infty}\frac{\log x}{x}$$

This one assumes the form ∞/∞. Applying L'Hospital's rule,

$$\lim_{x\to\infty}\frac{\log x}{x} = \lim_{x\to\infty}\frac{1/x}{1}$$

$$= \lim_{x\to\infty}\frac{1}{x}$$

$$= 0$$

3. Find

$$\lim_{x \to 0} \frac{1 - \cos x}{x^2}$$

This is a case where two applications of the rule are needed since the first one converts the given limit to another $0/0$ form

$$\lim_{x \to 0} \frac{1 - \cos x}{x^2} = \lim_{x \to 0} \frac{\sin x}{2x}$$

$$= \lim_{x \to 0} \frac{\cos x}{2}$$

$$= \frac{1}{2}.$$

4. Find the limit (4.22).

Denote the value of this limit by L. We cannot make a direct application of L'Hospital's rule here because the function whose limit is being taken does not assume the form $0/0$ or the form ∞/∞. However, if we take logarithms,

$$\log L = \lim_{x \to \infty} x \log \left(1 + \frac{a}{x}\right)$$

$$= \lim_{x \to \infty} \frac{\log (1 + a/x)}{1/x} \qquad \text{(now of } 0/0 \text{ type)}$$

$$= \lim_{x \to \infty} \frac{(1 + a/x)^{-1}(-a/x^2)}{-1/x^2} \qquad \text{(using the rule)}$$

$$= \lim_{x \to \infty} \frac{a}{1 + a/x} \qquad \text{(just algebra)}$$

$$= a \qquad \text{(obviously)}$$

Since $\log L = a$, the desired limit (4.22) is $L = e^a$.

Exercises

1. Find the following limits.

   (a) The limit in (4.23)
   (b) The limit in (4.24)

   (c) $\lim\limits_{x \to 0} \dfrac{\sin x - x}{x^3}$

(d) $\displaystyle\lim_{x \to 0} \left(1 + \frac{1}{x^2}\right)^x$

(e) $\displaystyle\lim_{x \to 0} \left(\frac{a^x + b^x}{2}\right)^{1/x}$ $(a > 0, b > 0)$

(f) $\displaystyle\lim_{x \to 0} \frac{\cos x - 1 + (x^2/2)}{x^4}$

(g) $\displaystyle\lim_{x \to \infty} x^4 e^{-x}$

(h) $\displaystyle\lim_{x \to \infty} x^{1/x}$

2. Sketch the graph of $y = (\log x)/x$ for $x > 0$, showing extrema and asymptotes.
3. For a fixed positive integer k, sketch the graph of $x^k e^{-x}$ for $x \geq 0$.
4. If a and b are fixed positive numbers, sketch the graph of the function

$$y = \left(\frac{a^x + b^x}{2}\right)^{1/x}$$

(This one is difficult. Try first to understand the behavior of y as x approaches $+\infty$ and $-\infty$.)

4.4.   Numerical Methods

It seems desirable at this point to remind ourselves that not all integrals can be performed in terms of well-known functions, not all equations can be solved by means of simple formulas, and, generally, analytical methods often are insufficient for problems which require numerical answers. To fill this gap mathematicians have devised large families of numerical methods to cope with a great variety of problems which are not amenable to exact solution. The influence of electronic computing equipment has accelerated these developments. In this section we pause briefly to examine two specific numerical problems which involve the calculus: the solution of equations and the evaluation of integrals.

Suppose then that we require the numerical solution of the equation

$$f(x) = 0 \tag{4.25}$$

for x. One widely used method, first suggested by Newton, proceeds by iteration. In general, we can say a process is iterative if, in order to solve certain equations, we first guess at the solution and then, somehow, repetitively refine our guess so that we get arbitrarily good approximations to the solution.

In Fig. 4.9, x^* represents the correct solution to (4.25), x_0 is our first

Figure 4.9

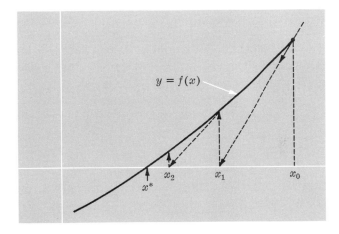

guess to that solution, x_1 is the next guess obtained from Newton's method, x_2 the next guess, and so on.

We start at x_0, then go up to the curve $y = f(x)$, meeting it at the point $(x_0, f(x_0))$. We then slide down the tangent line to the curve at that point until we meet the x axis. This intersection point is x_1. By treating x_1 just as we did x_0, we arrive at x_2, etc. If our initial guess was not too far away from x^*, we could expect the successive approximations x_0, x_1, x_2, ... to get nearer and nearer to x^*, and to approach x^* as a limit.

To analyze Newton's method let us try to write the explicit relationship between one approximation and its successor. We start from x_0 and need first to know the equation of the tangent line to the curve at the point $(x_0, f(x_0))$. This is

$$y = mx + b$$

where m, the slope of the curve, is $f'(x_0)$ and b is determined from

$$f(x_0) = mx_0 + b$$
$$= x_0 f'(x_0) + b$$

Thus the tangent line in question is

$$y = f'(x_0) x + f(x_0) - x_0 f'(x_0)$$

To find out where this line crosses the x axis we set $y = 0$ and solve for x, getting

$$x = x_0 - \frac{f(x_0)}{f'(x_0)}$$

But this value of x is just x_1, our next approximation. To summarize Newton's method we would say, then, start with a guess x_0, and compute successively

$$x_1 = x_0 - \frac{f(x_0)}{f'(x_0)}$$

$$x_2 = x_1 - \frac{f(x_1)}{f'(x_1)}$$

$$\ldots$$

and, in general,

$$x_{n+1} = x_n - \frac{f(x_n)}{f'(x_n)} \qquad (n = 0, 1, 2, \ldots) \tag{4.26}$$

Example
Solve the equation

$$x^2 - A = 0$$

A solution is clearly $x = \sqrt{A}$, so whatever Newton's method tells us about this equation will be a numerical method for calculating square roots. In fact, for $f(x) = x^2 - A$, Eq. (4.26) becomes

$$x_{n+1} = x_n - \frac{x_n^2 - A}{2x_n}$$

$$= \left(\frac{1}{2}\right)\left(x_n + \frac{A}{x_n}\right)$$

For instance, to find $\sqrt{2}$, take $x_0 = 1$. Then

$$x_1 = \left(\frac{1}{2}\right)\left(1 + \frac{2}{1}\right) = \frac{3}{2} = 1.5$$

$$x_2 = \left(\frac{1}{2}\right)\left(\frac{3}{2} + \frac{2}{\frac{3}{2}}\right) = \frac{17}{12} = 1.4166\ldots$$

$$x_3 = \left(\frac{1}{2}\right)\left(\frac{17}{12} + \frac{2}{\frac{17}{12}}\right) = \frac{577}{408}$$

$$= 1.4142156\ldots$$

The rate of approach to the true value of $\sqrt{2} = 1.414214\ldots$ is obviously excellent.

Exercises

1. Using Newton's method, what procedure do you find for calculating the kth root of a positive number?
2. Calculate $7^{1/5}$ by Newton's method, correct to three figures, using a first guess of 1.
3. Prove that the equation $xe^x = 1$ has exactly one positive root. Find it to three-figure accuracy.
4. Use the result of Exercise 2 at the end of Section 4.1 to prove that if we calculate the square root of a positive number by Newton's method, then, except possibly for the initial guess, each approximation is not smaller than the correct square root.
5. Find the real root of the equation $x^3 - 2x + 5 = 0$ to three decimal place accuracy.
6. Find the smallest positive root of the equation $\sin x = \frac{1}{2}x$ with two-digit accuracy.

The other numerical problem we consider is the question of numerical evaluation of definite integrals. If we are given an integral such as

$$\int_0^1 e^{\sqrt{\sin x}}\, dx$$

which is difficult or impossible to evaluate by analytical methods, one course of action which is always open to us is to choose a partition of the interval of integration and compute the value of a Riemann sum. In this way we can be sure that by choosing a partition whose norm is small enough we will be able to approximate the correct value of the integral as closely as we wish.

Numerical methods which are, in fact, used to perform integrations are closely related to this Riemann sum approach, but are a bit more systematic. It is highly desirable in such problems to be able to estimate how much error is made by calculating the integral by the approximate method used. For this reason approximations have been developed which permit relatively easy estimates of the error to be made.

Consider the integral

$$\int_a^{a+h} f(t)\, dt \qquad\qquad (4.27)$$

To find an approximate value for this integral, let us replace the true function f by a straight line which agrees with f at the endpoints $x = a$ and $x = a + h$ (Fig. 4.10). This straight line is

$$y = \frac{x - a}{h}\, \{f(a + h) - f(a)\} + f(a) \qquad\qquad (4.28)$$

Figure 4.10

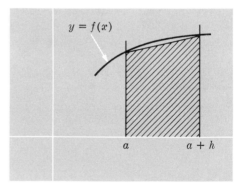

If now we integrate (4.28), we shall be calculating the area of the shaded trapezoid in Fig. 4.10 instead of the true area under the curve. The area of this trapezoid is

$$\frac{h}{2}(f(a) + f(a + h))$$

and we may use this as an approximation to the desired integral (4.27). This method of calculating approximate integrals is called the trapezoidal rule. We can do somewhat better by further subdivision of the interval of integration. To calculate

$$\int_a^b f(x)\, dx$$

we divide the interval (a,b) into n pieces, each of size $(b - a)/n$. Then

$$\int_a^b f(x)\, dx =$$

$$\int_a^{a+h} f(x)\, dx + \int_{a+h}^{a+2h} f(x)\, dx + \int_{a+2h}^{a+3h} f(x)\, dx + \cdots + \int_{a+(n-1)h}^{b} f(x)\, dx$$

where we have written

$$h = \frac{b - a}{n}$$

If we now do each one of these integrals above by the trapezoidal rule, we will get

$$\frac{h}{2}(f(a) + f(a + h)) + \frac{h}{2}(f(a + h) + f(a + 2h)) + \cdots$$

$$+ \frac{h}{2}(f(a + (n - 1)h) + f(a + nh))$$

$$= \frac{h}{2}\{f(a) + 2f(a + h) + 2f(a + 2h) + 2f(a + 3h) + \cdots$$

$$+ 2f(a + (n - 1)h) + f(b)\} \quad (4.29)$$

Example

Calculate

$$\int_0^1 \frac{dx}{1 + x}$$

by the trapezoidal rule using five subintervals.
   Here

$$h = \frac{b - a}{n} = \frac{1 - 0}{5} = \frac{1}{5}$$

and from (4.29) the approximate value of the integral is

$\frac{1}{10}(f(0) + 2f(\frac{1}{5}) + 2f(\frac{2}{5}) + 2f(\frac{3}{5}) + 2f(\frac{4}{5}) + f(1))$
$$= \tfrac{1}{10}(1 + \tfrac{10}{6} + \tfrac{10}{7} + \tfrac{10}{8} + \tfrac{10}{9} + \tfrac{1}{2})$$
$$= 0.695\dots$$

This answer should be compared with the true value of the integral which is $\log 2 = 0.693\dots$, which gives an error, in this case, of about two units in the third decimal place.

Exercises

Evaluate each of the following integrals both exactly and approximately by the trapezoidal rule with three subintervals.

(a) $\displaystyle\int_0^1 \frac{dx}{1 + x^2}$

(b) $\displaystyle\int_0^1 x\, dx$

(c) $\displaystyle\int_0^\pi \sin x\, dx$

(d) $\displaystyle\int_0^{3/2} 2^x\, dx$

(e) $\displaystyle\int_0^3 \sqrt{x}\, dx$

(f) $\displaystyle\int_0^1 x^3\, dx$

4.5. Arc Length

As an application of the integral we now discuss the question of defining and calculating the length of arc of a given curve. Intuitively what we mean by arc length is that if we think of the curve as a piece of string, then its length is the length of the straight piece of string obtained by pulling taut the original one. A precise definition requires the idea of a partition of an interval and the norm of a partition, both of which we have already met in connection with the definition of an integral.

Let $y = f(x)$ be defined for $a \leq x \leq b$, and have a continuous deriva-tive in $a < x < b$. To define the length of the curve from a to b let us choose a partition

$$a = x_1 < x_2 < x_3 \cdots < x_n = b$$

of the interval (a,b). In the subinterval between any two consecutive x's, say x_i and x_{i+1}, consider the length of the *chord* joining the points $(x_i, f(x_i))$ and $(x_{i+1}, f(x_{i+1}))$. This length is evidently (Fig. 4.11)

$$\sqrt{(x_{i+1} - x_i)^2 + (f(x_{i+1}) - f(x_i))^2}$$

Figure 4.11

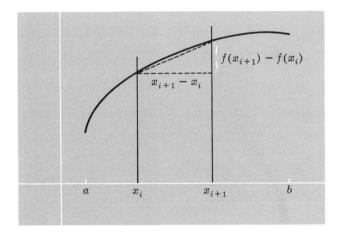

Consequently, the total length of all such chords (i.e., between every pair of consecutive points of the partition) is

$$\sqrt{(x_2 - x_1)^2 + (f(x_2) - f(x_1))^2} + \cdots$$

$$+ \sqrt{(x_n - x_{n-1})^2 + (f(x_n) - f(x_{n-1}))^2} \quad (4.30)$$

The arc length of the curve is defined as the limit of the sums (4.30) as the norm of the partition approaches zero, if that limit exists. More precisely, we shall say that the length of the arc is L if, given any $\epsilon > 0$, there is a $\delta > 0$ such that for all partitions of norm $< \delta$ the difference between L and the number in (4.30) is, in absolute value, $< \epsilon$. We will now show that under our present hypotheses on the function f the limit always exists and can be expressed rather simply as an integral.

Consider, for instance, the first term in (4.30). By the mean-value theorem,

$$f(x_2) - f(x_1) = (x_2 - x_1)f'(\xi_1) \qquad (x_1 < \xi_1 < x_2)$$

and so

$$\sqrt{(x_2 - x_1)^2 + (f(x_2) - f(x_1))^2} = (x_2 - x_1)\sqrt{1 + f'(\xi_1)^2}$$

In the same way, for every term in (4.30), we find

$$\sqrt{(x_{i+1} - x_i)^2 + (f(x_{i+1}) - f(x_i))^2} = (x_{i+1} - x_i)\sqrt{1 + f'(\xi_i)^2}$$

$$(x_i < \xi_i < x_{i+1})$$

Thus, for a given partition the total chord length is just

$$\sqrt{1 + f'(\xi_1)^2}\,(x_2 - x_1) + \sqrt{1 + f'(\xi_2)^2}\,(x_3 - x_2) + \cdots$$

$$+ \sqrt{1 + f'(\xi_{n-1})^2}\,(x_n - x_{n-1}) \quad (4.31)$$

If we define $g(x) = \sqrt{1 + f'(x)^2}$, then (4.31) becomes

$$g(\xi_1)(x_2 - x_1) + g(\xi_2)(x_3 - x_2) + \cdots + g(\xi_{n-1})(x_n - x_{n-1}) \quad (4.32)$$

where each of the ξ's lies between the pair of x's appearing to its right. The expression (4.32) should immediately be recognized as a Riemann sum for the integral

$$\int_a^b g(x)\,dx = \int_a^b \sqrt{1 + f'(x)^2}\,dx$$

But this last integral exists because we assumed that $f'(x)$ exists and is continuous throughout the interval (a,b). Consequently, the approximating sums (4.32) will approach this integral as the norm of the partition shrinks to zero. We have proved

THEOREM 4.4.   Let $f(x)$ be defined for $a \le x \le b$ and have a continuous derivative for $a < x < b$. Then the length of the curve $y = f(x)$ for $a \le x \le b$ is given by

$$L = \int_a^b \sqrt{1 + f'(x)^2}\,dx \qquad (4.33)$$

Example 1.

Calculate the length of the curve $y = \cosh x$ between $x = 0$ and $x = 1$.

Here $f(x) = \cosh x$, $f'(x) = \sinh x$, $\sqrt{1 + f'(x)^2} = \cosh x$ and so the required length is

$$L = \int_0^1 \sqrt{1 + f'(x)^2}\, dx$$

$$= \int_0^1 \cosh x\, dx$$

$$= \sinh x \Big]_0^1$$

$$= \sinh 1$$

$$= \frac{1}{2}\left(e - \frac{1}{e}\right)$$

Example 2.

Calculate the length of the portion of the circle

$$x^2 + y^2 = R^2$$

which lies in the first quadrant.

Here

$$f(x) = \sqrt{R^2 - x^2}$$

$$f'(x) = -\frac{x}{\sqrt{R^2 - x^2}}$$

and the arc length is

$$L = \int_0^R \sqrt{1 + \frac{x^2}{R^2 - x^2}}\, dx$$

$$= R\int_0^R \frac{dx}{\sqrt{R^2 - x^2}}$$

If we make the substitution $x = R\cos\theta$, $dx = -R\sin\theta\, d\theta$, we find

$$L = R\int_{\pi/2}^0 \frac{-R\sin\theta\, d\theta}{R\sin\theta}$$

$$= R\int_0^{\pi/2} d\theta$$

$$= \frac{\pi R}{2}$$

Exercises

Find the arc lengths of the following curves between the endpoints given.

1. $y = x^2$ $a = 0, b = 1$
2. $y = ax$ $a = 0, b = 1$
3. $y = \log \cos x$ $a = 0, b = \pi/3$
4. $y = \log x$ $a = 1, b = 2$

The equation of the curve need not be given in the form $y = f(x)$. Another way to describe the curve is in *parametric form*. This means that instead of giving y in terms of x, we give both y and x in terms of some third variable (the "parameter"), say t.

For example, if the curve is given by the pair of formulas

$$\begin{cases} x = 2t \\ y = 3t^2 \end{cases} \tag{4.34}$$

we could plot the curve by making a table with three columns headed t, x, y, then ignoring the first column, and plotting the corresponding values of x and y in the usual way. Table II might be appropriate for the

Table II

t	x	y
0	0	0
1	2	3
2	4	12
3	6	27
	etc.	

curve (4.34). We would then plot the points (0,0), (2,3), (4,12), (6,27), and so on, to sketch the curve. Actually, in the case (4.34) we can solve the first equation for t

$$t = \frac{x}{2}$$

and substitute in the second equation getting

$$y = \tfrac{3}{4}x^2$$

which is the equation of our curve in the usual, nonparametric, form. We therefore recognize that (4.34) represents a parabola.

As another example, consider the curve

$$\begin{cases} x = R \cos t \\ y = R \sin t \end{cases} \tag{4.35}$$

where R is a constant and t ranges over the interval $0 \leqq t < 2\pi$. We see, by squaring and adding, that

$$\begin{aligned} x^2 + y^2 &= R^2 \cos^2 t + R^2 \sin^2 t \\ &= R^2(\cos^2 t + \sin^2 t) \\ &= R^2 \end{aligned}$$

Thus as t runs from 0 to 2π, Eqs. (4.35) describe a circle centered at the origin of radius R.

One must not expect always to be able to carry out such an elimination and bring the equations into nonparametric form. For instance, any attempt to eliminate t from the equations

$$x = te^t$$
$$y = t + e^{t^2}$$

would be most difficult to carry out and probably would not be worth the trouble since the parametric equations would be easiest to handle for most purposes.

It is possible to calculate arc length directly from the parametric representation of the curve. One can show, by an argument very similar to that which proved (4.33), that if a curve is given by the equations

$$x = x(t)$$
$$y = y(t)$$

where t is the parameter, then the length of the arc of the curve between the points corresponding to the parameter values $t = a$ and $t = b$ is

$$L = \int_a^b \sqrt{\left(\frac{dx}{dt}\right)^2 + \left(\frac{dy}{dt}\right)^2}\, dt \tag{4.36}$$

Example 3.

Calculate the arc length of the curve

$$\begin{cases} x = \cos\theta \\ y = \sin\theta \end{cases} \tag{4.37}$$

for $0 \leqq \theta \leqq \pi/2$.

If we refer to (4.35), we note that we are again dealing with that portion of a circle of radius 1, centered at the origin, which lies in the first quadrant, though it is not necessary to realize this in order to get the right answer (Fig. 4.12).

Figure 4.12

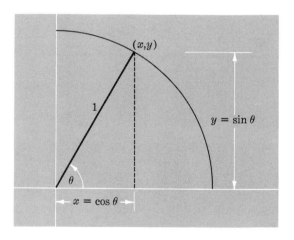

If we differentiate (4.37), we find

$$\frac{dx}{d\theta} = -\sin\theta$$

$$\frac{dy}{d\theta} = \cos\theta$$

and from (4.36) the required arc length is then

$$\int_0^{\pi/2} \sqrt{\left(\frac{dx}{d\theta}\right)^2 + \left(\frac{dy}{d\theta}\right)^2}\, d\theta = \int_0^{\pi/2} \sqrt{\sin^2\theta + \cos^2\theta}\, d\theta$$

$$= \int_0^{\pi/2} d\theta$$

$$= \frac{\pi}{2}$$

Exercises

1. Calculate the lengths of the following curves without eliminating the parameter.

   (a) $\begin{cases} x = t \\ y = t^2 \end{cases}$ $(0 \le t \le 1)$

   (b) $\begin{cases} x = t \\ y = at \end{cases}$ $(0 \le t \le 1)$

   (c) $\begin{cases} x = e^t \\ y = t \end{cases}$ $(0 \le t \le 1)$

2. Sketch graphs of the following curves.

   (a) The curves in Exercise 1 above.

   (b) $\begin{cases} x = t \cos t \\ y = t \sin t \end{cases}$ $(0 \le t \le \pi/2)$

   (c) $\begin{cases} x = \cosh t \\ y = \sinh t \end{cases}$

   (d) $\begin{cases} x = a \cos t \\ y = b \sin t \end{cases}$ $(0 \le t \le 2)$

3. For each of the curves in Exercise 2 above, eliminate the parameter, thereby obtaining the equation of the curve in a form which involves x and y only.

4.6. The Volume of a Solid of Revolution

Let f be defined, positive and continuous for $a \le x \le b$. Consider the curve $y = f(x)$, and imagine this curve and the area between it and the x axis to be rotated around the x axis, thereby sweeping out a solid of revolution. For instance, if the curve is a portion of a circle centered at the origin, the part above the x axis, then the solid generated is a sphere (Fig. 4.13). In this section we derive a general formula for the volume of such a solid explicitly in terms of the function f which defines the rotating curve.

We will derive this formula by the following device. We will first find a solid whose volume is easy to compute which surely has *less* volume than

Figure 4.13

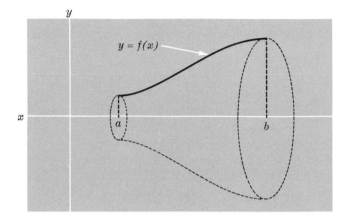

the solid of revolution whose volume we seek. Next we find another solid whose volume is also easy to compute which surely has *greater* volume than the solid in question. Thus we will have

$$\text{(something known)} \leqq \text{(desired volume)} \leqq \text{(something known)} \quad (4.38)$$

By suitably refining these upper and lower bounds we will be able to make both of the quantities labeled "something known" approach the same limit, which we will then take as the definition of the volume of our given solid of revolution.

Suppose then that $y = f(x)$, $a \leqq x \leqq b$ is a given curve, where $f(x) \geqq 0$, and f is continuous. Take a partition

$$a = x_0 < x_1 < x_2 \cdots < x_n = b$$

of the interval (a,b). Within each subinterval determined by the partition find a point at which $f(x)$ takes its minimum value on that subinterval. To give a name to this, suppose $f(\xi_i)$ is the smallest value f takes anywhere between x_i and x_{i+1}.

Now construct a new function, call it f_L, which has a constant value in each subinterval determined by the partition, namely, if x lies between x_i and x_{i+1}, then $f_L(x) = f(\xi_i)$. Thus, the graph of $f_L(x)$ is a series of horizontal straight lines (see Fig. 4.14). It is obvious that the solid obtained by rotating the area under the graph of $y = f_L(x)$ around the x axis

Figure 4.14

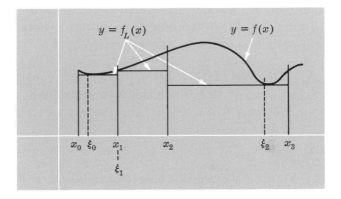

is entirely contained within the solid generated by our original given function f. But rotating the graph of $y = f_L(x)$ about the x axis produces a stack of cylinders whose total volume is evidently

$$\pi f(\xi_0)^2(x_1 - x_0) + \cdots + \pi f(\xi_{n-1})^2(x_n - x_{n-1}) \qquad (4.39)$$

We have now found the "something known" on the left-hand side of (4.38).

To find an upper bound for the desired volume we repeat the whole process, except that this time we use the *maximum,* instead of the minimum, value of f in each subinterval. More precisely, suppose that the largest value taken by f between x_i and x_{i+1} is $f(\eta_i)$. Define a new function f_U by saying that for all x between x_i and x_{i+1}, $f_U(x)$ has the constant value $f(\eta_i)$ (for each $i = 0, 1, 2, \ldots, n - 1$). This gives rise to a graph similar to the preceding one except that the broken line graph of f_U lies above the graph of f, rather than below it.

Hence, the solid obtained by rotating the area under the graph of $f_U(x)$ about the x axis surely contains the solid generated by the given function f. On the other hand, the volume generated by this rotation is

$$\pi f(\eta_0)^2(x_1 - x_0) + \cdots + \pi f(\eta_{n-1})^2(x_n - x_{n-1}) \qquad (4.40)$$

Since our given function was continuous, it follows that as the norm of the original partition goes to zero, both of the sums (4.39) and (4.40) approach the same limit, namely, the integral

$$\int_a^b \pi f(x)^2 \, dx \tag{4.41}$$

Thus the solid generated by $f(x)$ is contained in a solid of volume (4.40) and contains a solid of volume (4.39), and both of these latter volumes approach (4.41) in the limit. Accordingly, we take the integral (4.41) as our definition of the volume generated by f.

> **DEFINITION**   Let f be defined, continuous and nonnegative for $a \le x \le b$. The volume of the solid of revolution generated by rotating about the x axis the area between the x axis and the curve $y = f(x)$ is given by the integral (4.41).

Examples
1.   Find the volume of a sphere of radius R.

       This sphere is the result of rotating about the x axis the semicircle

$$y = \sqrt{R^2 - x^2} \qquad (-R \le x \le R)$$

Hence the volume is

$$\int_{-R}^{R} \pi y^2 \, dx = \int_{-R}^{R} \pi(R^2 - x^2) \, dx$$

$$= \pi R^2 x \Big]_{-R}^{R} - \frac{\pi x^3}{3} \Big]_{-R}^{R}$$

$$= 2\pi R^3 - \tfrac{2}{3}\pi R^3$$

$$= \tfrac{4}{3}\pi R^3$$

2.   Find the volume of the ellipsoid of revolution formed by rotating the upper half of the ellipse

$$\frac{x^2}{a^2} + \frac{y^2}{b^2} = 1$$

about the x axis.

       Here the upper half of the ellipse is described by

$$y = +b \sqrt{1 - \frac{x^2}{a^2}} \qquad (-a \le x \le a)$$

The volume is then

$$V = \int_{-a}^{a} \pi y^2 \, dx = \int_{-a}^{a} \pi b^2 \left(1 - \frac{x^2}{a^2}\right) dx$$

$$= \pi b^2 x \Big]_{-a}^{a} - \frac{\pi b^2}{a^2} \frac{x^3}{3} \Big]_{-a}^{a}$$

$$= 2\pi a b^2 - \frac{2\pi b^2 a}{3}$$

$$= \tfrac{4}{3}\pi a b^2$$

Exercises

1. Find the volumes of the solids of revolution obtained by rotating about the x axis the area under the graph of each of the following curves.

   (a) The parabolic arc $y = ax^2$, $0 \leq x \leq 1$.
   (b) The first arch of the sine function, $y = \sin x$, $0 \leq x \leq \pi$. (Hint: Use the double-angle identities of trigonometry.)
   (c) The arc of the curve $y = \log x$ between $x = 1$ and $x = 2$.
   (d) The polynomial curve $y = a_0 + a_1 x + a_2 x^2 + \cdots + a_n x^n$ for $0 \leq x \leq 1$.
   (e) The curve $y = x^a$, $0 \leq x \leq A$.

2. By rotating a suitable straight line about the x axis, find the formula for the volume of a cone of altitude H and radius of base R.

3. A cone of radius R ft and altitude H ft is standing on its vertex, and is initially full of water. If water runs out of the vertex at the rate of r cu ft per sec, express the height of water in the cone as a function of time. How fast is the water level dropping after t_0 sec? How long does it take for the cone to empty?

4.7. *Convexity*

The second derivative can be used to give information about the convexity of a function. The left-hand graph in Fig. 4.15 shows a function which is convex downward; the right-hand graph is convex upward. Even without having given a precise definition of what convexity is, one sees intuitively that the function on the left has a derivative (slope) which steadily increases, while that on the right has a steadily decreasing derivative. Note that it is not the function itself which is increasing or decreasing, but the derivative. We should not be surprised, therefore, to find that in order to test for convexity we have to calculate a second derivative and check its sign.

Figure 4.15

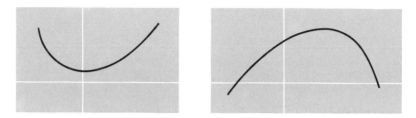

There are numerous ways of formulating the definition of a convex function. We choose to say that f is convex downward (or just "convex" if we adopt the convention that "convex" with no qualification means convex downward) if the midpoint of every chord lies above the curve.

In Fig. 4.16, x_1 and x_2 are two fixed points and $\frac{1}{2}(x_1 + x_2)$ is their mid-

Figure 4.16

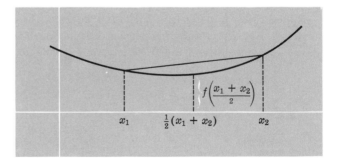

point. At the midpoint the height of the graph is $f((x_1 + x_2)/2)$, while the height of the chord joining $(x_1, f(x_1))$ to $(x_2, f(x_2))$ is

$$\tfrac{1}{2}(f(x_1) + f(x_2))$$

For the function f to be convex, then, we shall ask that

$$f\left(\frac{x_1 + x_2}{2}\right) \leqq \frac{1}{2}f(x_1) + \frac{1}{2}f(x_2) \tag{4.42}$$

DEFINITION Let f be defined for $a \leqq x \leqq b$. We say that f is convex in (a,b) if for every pair of points x_1, x_2 in the interval, we have the inequality (4.42).

This definition is basically a geometric one, and it may be difficult to work with analytically. Hence, we wish to show that one can test for convexity by calculating $f''(x)$ and examining its sign. To do this we first need a certain limit, analogous to

$$f'(x) = \lim_{h \to 0} \frac{f(x + h) - f(x)}{h}$$

which will permit us to calculate the second derivative of a function directly in terms of the function, without going through the first derivative.

If x is fixed, consider the difference quotient

$$\frac{f(x + h) - 2f(x) + f(x - h)}{h^2}$$

$$= \frac{(f(x + h) - f(x)) - (f(x) - f(x - h))}{h^2} \tag{4.43}$$

where h is small, either positive or negative. If we temporarily define

$$G(x) = f(x) - f(x - h)$$

then the right-hand side of (4.43) becomes

$$\frac{G(x + h) - G(x)}{h^2} = \frac{hG'(\xi)}{h^2}$$

$$= \frac{G'(\xi)}{h}$$

where ξ lies between x and $x + h$, and the mean-value theorem has been used. Since $G'(x) = f'(x) - f'(x - h)$, we find

$$\frac{G(x + h) - G(x)}{h^2} = \frac{1}{h}(f'(\xi) - f'(\xi - h))$$

$$= \frac{1}{h} \cdot h \cdot f''(\eta)$$

$$= f''(\eta)$$

where η lies between $\xi - h$ and ξ, and the mean-value theorem has again been applied. Now, as h approaches zero, the point η lies between $\xi - h$ and ξ and so also between $x - h$ and $x + h$. Hence, η approaches x as h approaches zero, so $f''(\eta) \to f''(x)$, if f'' is continuous at x. Summarizing, we have proved

THEOREM 4.5.   Let f be twice continuously differentiable in a neighborhood of x. Then

$$f''(x) = \lim_{h \to 0} \frac{f(x + h) - 2f(x) + f(x - h)}{h^2} \tag{4.44}$$

Returning to the question of convexity, notice that the numerator on the right of (4.44) is

$$2\left(\frac{f(x + h) + f(x - h)}{2} - f(x)\right)$$

If we compare this with (4.42), we notice that x is the midpoint of the interval from $x - h$ to $x + h$ and so if f is convex, the numerator in (4.44) is nonnegative. Since the limit of a nonnegative quantity is nonnegative we conclude that if f is convex and twice continuously differentiable around x, then $f''(x) \geq 0$.

Conversely, suppose $f''(x) \geq 0$. Then we claim that f is convex. Indeed, the difference between the right and left sides of (4.42) is

$$\frac{1}{2}f(x_1) + \frac{1}{2}f(x_2) - f\left(\frac{x_1 + x_2}{2}\right)$$

$$= \frac{1}{2}\left\{f(x_2) - f\left(\frac{x_1 + x_2}{2}\right)\right\} + \frac{1}{2}\left\{f(x_1) - f\left(\frac{x_1 + x_2}{2}\right)\right\}$$

$$= \frac{1}{2}\frac{x_2 - x_1}{2}f'(\xi) + \frac{1}{2}\frac{x_1 - x_2}{2}f'(\eta)$$

$$= \frac{x_2 - x_1}{4}(f'(\xi) - f'(\eta))$$

$$= \tfrac{1}{4}(x_2 - x_1)(\xi - \eta)f''(\xi_1)$$

From the mean-value theorem one sees at once that if $x_2 > x_1$ then $\xi > \eta$, while if $x_2 < x_1$ then $\xi < \eta$. In either case, $(x_2 - x_1)(\xi - \eta) > 0$, and so we have proved that if $f''(x) \geq 0$ then (4.42) holds for all x_1 and x_2 whence f is convex.

> **THEOREM 4.6.**   Let f be defined on the interval (a,b), and let it be twice continuously differentiable there. For f to be convex on (a,b), it is necessary and sufficient that $f''(x) \geq 0$, for all x in the interval.

A point $x = x_0$ is a *point of inflection* of a function f if the function is convex in one direction, say upward, to the left of x_0 and in the other direction, say downward, to the right of x_0. Clearly, at a point of inflection $f''(x_0) = 0$, though not every point at which f'' is zero need be a point of inflection.

Example
Discuss the convexity of the function $f(x) = x^3 - 2x^2 + 1$.
    We find that

$$f''(x) = 6x - 4.$$

Thus $f'' \geq 0$ if $x \geq \tfrac{2}{3}$, while $f'' \leq 0$ if $x \leq \tfrac{2}{3}$. Hence, f is convex downward for all $x \geq \tfrac{2}{3}$ and upward for $x \leq \tfrac{2}{3}$. The point $x_0 = \tfrac{2}{3}$ is a point of inflection. A graph of f is shown in Fig. 4.17.

Figure 4.17

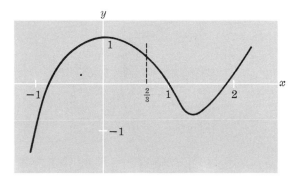

Exercises

1. (a) Show that $f(x) = -\log x$ is convex on every interval of the positive real axis.
    (b) Using the result of (a), show that the geometric mean of two positive numbers cannot exceed their arithmetic mean, i.e., that

$$\sqrt{x_1 x_2} \leqq \frac{x_1 + x_2}{2} \qquad (x_1 > 0, x_2 > 0)$$

    (c) Give an entirely elementary (calculus-free) proof of the result of (b).

2. Find a polynomial of degree 3 which is convex downward if $x > 5$ and upward if $x < 5$. Find all such polynomials.
3. The second derivative of $y = x^4$ is zero at the origin, which nevertheless is not a point of inflection. Sketch the curve and explain.
4. (a) Suppose we have a function f whose domain is the set of integers. Formulate a reasonable definition of convexity for such a function.
    (b) Is the function f which assigns to every integer n its square convex according to your definition?
    (c) Is the function

$$f(n) = \begin{cases} 1 & n \text{ odd} \\ 0 & n \text{ even} \end{cases}$$

    convex according to your definition?

5. Sketch each of the following curves, labeling points of inflection and regions of convexity.

    (a) $y = xe^{-x}$

    (b) $y = \int_0^x e^{t^2}\, dt$ (do not try to evaluate the integral!)

4.8.   *Contact, Curvature, and Approximation*

In this section we discuss the idea of *contact* of two curves and develop some of its applications. This idea can be thought of from the point of view of an ant crawling along a curve (Fig. 4.18). If another curve touches the first one at a certain point, the ant may pause for a moment, before deciding which path to pursue, and then proceed along the path which represents the least radical departure from the characteristics of the curve whence it came. The second curve can, however, make this decision more difficult for the ant if, in addition to merely touching the first curve at the point in question, it also has the same slope as the first curve

Figure 4.18

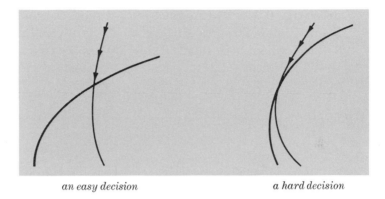

an easy decision　　　　　　　*a hard decision*

at that point. The second curve can be made to fit still more snugly into the first one at the point in question by making not only the function values and the first derivatives agree, but also several higher derivatives. In such a case the first curve would be very well approximated by the second in a neighborhood of the point of contact, and the ant would be thoroughly confused.

> **DEFINITION** The two curves $y = f(x)$ and $y = g(x)$ are said to have contact of order k at the point P if $f(P) = g(P)$, $f'(P) = g'(P)$, $f''(P) = g''(P), \ldots, f^{(k)}(P) = g^{(k)}(P)$.

Thus contact of order 0 means only that the two curves pass through the same point P, while contact of order 2, for instance, means that not only do the curves pass through the same point P, but at the point P the two curves have the same first and second derivatives.

Examples
1.   The two curves

$$y = e^x \quad \text{and} \quad y = 1 + x$$

have contact of order 1 at the point (0,1) because both curves pass through that point and their derivatives are each equal to 1 there.

2. The two curves

$$y = \sin x \qquad \text{and} \qquad y = x - \tfrac{1}{6}x^3$$

have contact of order 4 at the origin because in both cases the function has the value 0 at the origin, the first derivative 1, the second derivative 0, the third derivative -1, and the fourth derivative 0. We may, therefore, expect that sin x is quite well approximated by $x - \tfrac{1}{6}x^3$ when x is small. Table III shows that this expectation is well justified.

Table III

x	$\sin x$	$x - \tfrac{1}{6}x^3$
0.05	0.0500	0.0500
0.1	0.0998	0.0998
0.15	0.1494	0.1494
0.20	0.1987	0.1987
0.25	0.2474	0.2474
0.50	0.4794	0.4792

As our first application of the theory of contact we discuss the *curvature* of a given curve at a point. Intuitively speaking, we would like the curvature of a given curve at a particular point to be a small number if the curve is only very gently curving (i.e., is nearly a straight line), and a large number if there is a sharp curve at that point. To formulate this concept in a quantitative way we choose, at the given point on the curve, that circle which fits most snugly into the curve in the sense of contact, and we call the radius of that circle the *radius of curvature* of the given curve at that point. If the curve is turning sharply at the point in question, this circle will be small, while if the curve is nearly a straight line, the circle will be large. The *curvature* of the given curve at this point is defined to be the reciprocal of the radius of curvature. If we imagine that the given curve is a railroad track and that we are in a train passing by the given point, we will, of course, be subject to a certain centrifugal force. The radius of curvature is the radius of a *circular* track which would produce the same centrifugal force if the speed of motion were the same.

If the curve is the graph of $y = f(x)$, we now derive a formula for the radius of curvature at a given point on the curve, in terms of the function f. Suppose first that the curve passes through the origin, and that we wish to calculate the radius of curvature at the origin. The most general equation of a circle is

$$(x - a)^2 + (y - b)^2 = R^2 \tag{4.45}$$

and we will now find the values of a, b, and R in such a way that the circle will have contact with the given curve $y = f(x)$ of as high order as possible at the origin (Fig. 4.19). First we differentiate (4.45) with respect

Figure 4.19

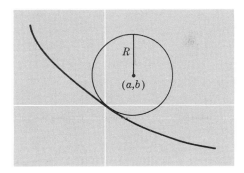

to x, getting

$$x - a + (y - b)y' = 0 \tag{4.46}$$

and then we differentiate (4.46) with respect to x and obtain

$$1 + (y')^2 + yy'' - by'' = 0 \tag{4.47}$$

The first condition on the circle (4.45) is that it should pass through the origin. If we substitute $x = y = 0$ in (4.45), we find that

$$R^2 = a^2 + b^2 \tag{4.48}$$

Next, the slope of the circle at the origin should be the same as the slope of the given curve at the origin, namely, $f'(0)$. When we put $x = y = 0$ and $y' = f'(0)$ in (4.46), there results

$$a + bf'(0) = 0 \tag{4.49}$$

Finally (because there are three free constants a, b, R we can expect to impose only three conditions), the second derivative of the circle at the origin should be the same as the second derivative of our given function at the origin, namely, $f''(0)$. Putting $x = y = 0$, $y' = f'(0)$, $y'' = f''(0)$ in (4.47), we obtain

$$1 + (f'(0))^2 - bf''(0) = 0 \qquad (4.50)$$

We can now solve (4.50) for b, substitute the result in (4.49), solve for a, and substitute both of these in (4.48) to obtain, finally, the formula

$$R = \frac{\{1 + f'(0)^2\}^{3/2}}{|f''(0)|} \qquad (4.51)$$

Clearly, if we want the radius of curvature at any point x instead of the origin, the result will be identical in form with (4.51) except that the functions f, f', f'' will be evaluated at x instead of at the origin. Therefore, the radius of curvature R of an arbitrary curve $y = f(x)$ at the point x on the curve is

$$R = \frac{\{1 + f'(x)^2\}^{3/2}}{|f''(x)|} \qquad (4.52)$$

where, of course, the positive square root is to be taken. The circle, whose equation we found in the derivation of (4.52), which fits the curve best at the point x (has second-order contact with it), we call the *circle of curvature* at the point x.

Exercises

For each of the curves below, at the point x shown, find the equation of the circle of curvature, the radius of curvature, and the curvature at that point. Plot on the same graph the function given and its circle of curvature at the point shown.

1. $y = x^2$ $x = 0$
2. $y = e^x$ $x = 0$
3. $y = \log x$ $x = 1$
4. $y = \dfrac{1}{x}$ $x = 1$

As another application of contact we consider the question of approximating a given function by another function which is determined in such a way as to have a contact of high order with the given one at a certain point. We have already seen an example of this in the remarkable approximation to $\sin x$ which is afforded by the polynomial of third degree $x - \frac{1}{6}x^3$ near the origin.

Let us take this time the function e^x and find a polynomial which has contact of high order with it at the origin. To do this we compute first all of the derivatives of e^x at the origin and then find a polynomial which has as many as possible of the same derivatives there. The first part is very easy since every derivative of e^x has the value 1 at $x = 0$. For the second part, consider the following polynomial of degree n

$$f(x) = a_0 + a_1 x + a_2 x^2 + \cdots + a_n x^n \tag{4.53}$$

We wish to determine the coefficients in such a way that each derivative of f up to the nth will have the value 1 at the origin. Now the kth derivative of f is

$$f^{(k)}(x) = k! a_k + \text{terms involving } x \tag{4.54}$$

and, therefore, the value of the kth derivative at the origin is just $k! a_k$. To make this equal to 1, then, we choose $a_k = 1/k!$ for each $k = 0, 1, \ldots, n$. With these values of the coefficients, the polynomial (4.53) takes the form

$$f(x) = 1 + x + \frac{1}{2}x^2 + \frac{1}{3!}x^3 + \frac{1}{4!}x^4 + \cdots + \frac{1}{n!}x^n \tag{4.55}$$

Hence, among all polynomials of degree n, the polynomial in (4.55) gives the best possible approximation to e^x in the sense that it has contact with e^x at the origin of highest possible order n. The reader may wish to compute values of the polynomial (4.55) for small values of x to see how well they agree with tabulated values of e^x.

Next we attempt to carry out this calculation in general, using an arbitrary function f instead of e^x and an arbitrary point a instead of the origin. Hence, if f is a given function, let us determine the polynomial of degree n which is the best approximation to f in the sense that the polynomial has contact with f of order n at the point $x = a$. Our work is greatly simplified if we take the equation of the polynomial in the form

$$a_0 + a_1(x - a) + a_2(x - a)^2 + \cdots + a_n(x - a)^n \tag{4.56}$$

The kth derivative of this polynomial is

$$k!a_k + \text{terms involving } (x - a) \tag{4.57}$$

and so the value of the kth derivative of this polynomial at the point $x = a$ is $k!a_k$. To make the polynomial and the given function have the same kth derivative at the point $x = a$ we would choose, therefore,

$$a_k = \frac{f^{(k)}(a)}{k!} \tag{4.58}$$

for each $k = 0, 1, 2, \ldots, n$. With the coefficients so selected, our polynomial (4.56) becomes

$$f(a) + (x - a)f'(a) + \frac{(x - a)^2}{2!}f''(a) + \frac{(x - a)^3}{3!}f'''(a) + \cdots$$

$$+ \frac{(x - a)^n}{n!}f^{(n)}(a) \tag{4.59}$$

We have proved

THEOREM 4.7.   Let f be a given function which is n times differentiable at the point $x = a$, n being a given integer. Among all polynomials of degree n, the polynomial (4.59) is the best approximation to the function f in the neighborhood of a in the sense that it is the only polynomial of that degree which has contact of order n with f at $x = a$.

Exercises

1.   If $f(x) = \sin x$, find the best fourth-degree approximation to f; the best nth degree approximation (take $a = 0$).
2.   With $f(x) = e^x$, what is the best approximation of degree n at $x = a$?
3.   Find the best approximation to $\log (1 + x)$ of degree n, at $x = 0$. Using $n = 4$, compute approximate values of $\log 1.2$, $\log 1.5$, $\log 1.7$, and $\log 2$; compare with the exact values.
4.   For the function $f(x) = \cos x$ find the best approximation by a polynomial of degree 4 in each of the cases $a = 0$, $a = \pi/2$.
5.   (a) Calculate the derivatives of $\sqrt{x}$ up to fourth order at $x = 1$.
     (b) Write out the polynomial of degree 4 which has fourth-order contact with $\sqrt{x}$ at $x = 1$.

(c) Using the above polynomial make a table of approximate values of $\sqrt{x}$ at $x = 1$, 1.1, 1.2, 1.3, 1.4, 1.5, 1.6, 2.0, and compare with the exact values.

6. Make a table of approximate values of e^x for $x = 0$, 0.2, 0.4, 0.6, 1.0 by using the polynomial of degree 4 from Exercise 2, with $a = 0$. Compare with the true values.

7. Find the polynomial of degree n with contact of order n with $\sinh x$ at $x = 0$; with $\cosh x$ at $x = 0$; show that the sum of these two polynomials is the answer to Exercise 2 with $a = 0$.

4.9. *Improper Integrals*

We now wish to define an integral whose limits may include ∞ or $-\infty$. Such an integral is called "improper." Examples of such integrals are

$$\int_1^\infty \frac{dx}{x^2}; \qquad \int_{-\infty}^2 \frac{dx}{3 + x^4}$$

$$\int_0^\infty xe^{-x^2}\, dx; \qquad \int_2^\infty \frac{\sin x}{x^2}\, dx$$

DEFINITION   Let a be a fixed real number. Suppose

$$\lim_{x \to \infty} \int_a^x f(t)\, dt$$

exists. Then the value of the limit is denoted by the symbol

$$\int_a^\infty f(t)\, dt$$

Similarly,

$$\lim_{x \to -\infty} \int_x^a f(t)\, dt = \int_{-\infty}^a f(t)\, dt$$

if the limit exists.

Examples
1. Find

$$\int_0^\infty e^{-t}\, dt$$

Here

$$\int_0^x e^{-t}\, dt = -e^{-t}\Big]_0^x$$

$$= 1 - e^{-x}$$

Therefore

$$\lim_{x\to\infty} \int_0^x e^{-t}\, dt = \lim_{x\to\infty} (1 - e^{-x})$$

$$= 1$$

Hence

$$\int_0^\infty e^{-t}\, dt = 1$$

2. Calculate

$$\int_1^\infty \frac{dt}{t^2}$$

In this case

$$\int_1^x \frac{dt}{t^2} = -\frac{1}{t}\Big]_1^x$$

$$= 1 - \frac{1}{x}$$

Thus

$$\lim_{x\to\infty} \int_1^x \frac{dt}{t^2} = \lim_{x\to\infty}\left(1 - \frac{1}{x}\right)$$

$$= 1$$

and so

$$\int_1^\infty \frac{dt}{t^2} = 1$$

3. Find

$$\int_0^\infty \sin t\, dt$$

Now

$$\int_0^x \sin t\, dt = -\cos t\Big]_0^x$$

$$= 1 - \cos x$$

Hence

$$\lim_{x \to \infty} \int_0^x \sin t \, dt$$

does not exist, and the symbol

$$\int_0^\infty \sin t \, dt$$

is meaningless.

There are a few rules of thumb which can be useful in recognizing improper integrals which exist and in distinguishing them from integrals which do not exist. If the values $f(t)$ of the function which is being integrated drop off to zero rapidly enough when t is large, the improper integral may exist. Otherwise, it will not.

Thus e^{-t} goes to zero very rapidly for large t, $1/t^2$ goes to zero for large t, but $\sin t$ does not, which, roughly speaking, accounts for the results in the three examples above. On the other hand, $1/\sqrt{t}$ approaches zero as $t \to \infty$ but not fast enough. Indeed,

$$\int_1^x \frac{1}{\sqrt{t}} \, dt = 2\sqrt{t} \, \Big]_1^x$$
$$= 2\sqrt{x} - 2$$

and so

$$\lim_{x \to \infty} \frac{1}{\sqrt{t}} \, dt$$

does not exist.

If the integrand goes to zero faster than $1/t^{1+\delta}$ $(\delta > 0)$, the improper integral will exist. If the integrand is nonnegative and goes to zero slower than $1/t$, the improper integral will not exist.

For instance, in

$$\int_1^\infty \frac{\sin^3 x + 3}{x^{3/2}} \, dx$$

the numerator of the integrand is ≤ 4, so the whole integrand is

$$\leq \frac{4}{x^{3/2}}$$

Since $4x^{-3/2}$ goes to zero faster than $1/x^{1+\delta}$, the given improper integral exists.

Exercises

1. Which of the following integrals exist? (Do not evaluate.)

(a) $\int_1^\infty \dfrac{x^2 + x + 1}{(x^2 + 1)^3} dx$

(b) $\int_0^\infty \dfrac{\sin x + 3}{x^2 + 2} dx$

(c) $\int_0^\infty \dfrac{dx}{1 + \sqrt{x}}$

(d) $\int_0^\infty \dfrac{(3x + 2)^2}{3x^2 + 2} dx$

(e) $\int_{-\infty}^0 \dfrac{(x + 1)^4}{(x^4 + 1)^2} dx$

(f) $\int_1^\infty \dfrac{\cos x \, dx}{(x + 1)^{3/2}}$

2. Evaluate, or prove the nonexistence, of each of the following:

(a) $\int_1^\infty \dfrac{dx}{(x + 3)^2}$

(b) $\int_0^\infty xe^{-x^2} dx$

(c) $\int_2^\infty \dfrac{dx}{x \log x}$

(d) $\int_2^\infty \dfrac{dx}{x(\log x)^2}$

(e) $\int_2^\infty \dfrac{dx}{x(\log x)(\log \log x)}$

(f) $\int_{-\infty}^{-1} e^x \, dx$

(g) $\int_0^\infty \dfrac{dx}{x^2 + 1}$

(h) $\int_0^\infty xe^{-x} dx$

(i) $\int_0^\infty x^2 e^{-x} dx$

3.   For each $n = 0, 1, 2, \ldots$, define

$$\lambda_n = \int_0^\infty x^n e^{-x}\, dx$$

Integrate by parts to show that

$$\lambda_n = n\lambda_{n-1} \qquad (n = 1, 2, \ldots)$$

Evaluate λ_n for $n = 0, 1, 2, 3, 4, 5, 6$.

Sequences of Real Numbers
The Cauchy Convergence Criterion
Infinite Series of Real Numbers
Tests for Convergence: The Comparison Test
Tests for Convergence: The Integral Test
Tests for Convergence: Order of Magnitude
Alternating Series
Absolute Convergence
Sequences and Series of Functions
The Radius of Convergence
Taylor's Theorem

5

Sequences and Series

5.1. Sequences of Real Numbers

A sequence is a function whose domain is a set of integers. The set of integers may be finite or infinite in which case we speak of a finite sequence or an infinite sequence, respectively. An example of a finite sequence is the function f which is defined on the integers 1, 2, 3, 4, 5 and which takes the values $f(1) = 3$, $f(2) = 15$, $f(3) = -7$, $f(4) = 0$, $f(5) = 2^{1/2}$. An example of an infinite sequence is the function whose values are

$$f(n) = n^2 \qquad (n = 0, 1, 2, 3, \ldots) \tag{5.1}$$

The parenthetical remark in (5.1) serves to identify the set of integers for which the function is defined.

The conventional way to describe a sequence is just to write out the set of values of the function in question separated by commas. Thus the finite sequence above would be written

$$3, \ 15, \ -7, \ 0, \ 2^{1/2}$$

and the infinite sequence (5.1) would be written

$$0, \ 1, \ 4, \ 9, \ 16, \ 25, \ 36, \ldots$$

Another convention which is often adopted is that instead of using the

185

usual functional notation $f(n)$ for the value of the function at the integer n, the letter n is used as a subscript, and we use f_n to denote the nth member of the sequence.

Thus, the letter p_n may be used to denote the nth member of the sequence of prime numbers

$$2, 3, 5, 7, 11, 13, 17, 19, 23, \ldots$$

and the sequence $x_q = 1/q$ $(q = 1, 2, 3, \ldots)$ can be written out in the form

$$1, \tfrac{1}{2}, \tfrac{1}{3}, \tfrac{1}{4}, \tfrac{1}{5}, \tfrac{1}{6}, \ldots$$

Evidently, the choice of the letter of the alphabet to be used for the subscript is quite immaterial. A final bit of notation is that while we use a symbol such as x_n to denote the nth member of a certain sequence, if we wish to refer to the entire sequence, a curly brace { } is used, enclosing the symbol representing the nth member. The sequence of reciprocals of positive integers, for example, could be referred to as

$$\left\{ \frac{1}{n} \right\} \qquad (n = 1, 2, 3, 4, \ldots) \tag{5.2}$$

We restrict attention, for the time being, to sequences of real numbers, that is to say, to functions whose values are real numbers, though later we will broaden, somewhat, the class of sequences considered.

The first idea we need is that of *convergence* of a sequence. This concept is defined only for infinite sequences, and, roughly speaking, we say that a sequence is convergent if there is a fixed number toward which the members of the sequence approach as a limit. The sequence of (5.2), for example, converges to the limit zero because, if we go far out in the sequence (i.e., to large values of n), the members of the sequence are close to zero, and can be made to stay as close to zero as we wish by going out far enough.

DEFINITION   The sequence $\{x_n\}$ $(n = 1, 2, 3, \ldots)$ is said to converge to the number x if given any $\epsilon > 0$ we can find an integer N such that

$$|x_n - x| < \epsilon$$

for all $n > N$. In this case we write either $x_n \to x$ or

$$\lim_{n \to \infty} x_n = x$$

A sequence which is not convergent is said to *diverge* or to be divergent.

Examples

1. The sequence (5.2) converges to zero, for if $\epsilon > 0$ is given, we have

$$\left| \frac{1}{n} - 0 \right| < \epsilon$$

for all $n > 1/\epsilon$. In other words, for the given ϵ we can take $N = 1/\epsilon$.

2. The sequence $\{(-1)^n\}$ $(n = 0, 1, 2, 3, \ldots)$, that is,

$$1, -1, 1, -1, 1, -1, \ldots$$

diverges because if a small ϵ is given, then no matter how far out in the sequence we go there will be some 1's and some -1's still further out. Therefore, it is false to say that all members of the sequence from that point on stay close to some fixed number.

3. The sequence

$$0, \tfrac{1}{2}, 0, \tfrac{1}{3}, 0, \tfrac{1}{4}, 0, \tfrac{1}{5}, 0, \ldots$$

converges to the limit zero, for if $\epsilon > 0$ is given the difference between the nth member of this sequence and zero is, in absolute value, less than ϵ for all $n > 2/\epsilon$, i.e., we can take the N appearing in the definition of convergence to be $2/\epsilon$.

4. The sequence $x_n = n/(n + 1)$ $(n = 1, 2, 3, \ldots)$ converges to 1, for suppose $\epsilon > 0$ is given. Then we must find an N such that

$$\left| \frac{n}{n + 1} - 1 \right| < \epsilon$$

for all $n > N$. But

$$\left| \frac{n}{n + 1} - 1 \right| = \frac{1}{n + 1}$$

which will become and remain $< \epsilon$ for all $n > 1/\epsilon = N$.

Theorem 5.1 summarizes certain properties of convergent sequences. The proof of the theorem is in all respects parallel to the corresponding proofs for functions given in the section on limits, Section 1.4, and is, therefore, omitted here.

THEOREM 5.1.

(a) A sequence can have only one limit. That is, if

$$\lim_{n \to \infty} x_n = x \qquad \text{and} \qquad \lim_{n \to \infty} x_n = y$$

then $x = y$.

(b) The limit of the sum of two sequences which converge is equal to the sum of their limits; if

$$\lim_{n \to \infty} x_n = x \qquad \text{and} \qquad \lim_{n \to \infty} y_n = y$$

then $\lim_{n \to \infty} (x_n + y_n) = x + y$.

(c) The limit of the product of two convergent sequences is the product of their limits.

(d) If the sequence $\{x_n\}$ $(n = 1, 2, 3, \ldots)$ converges to x, and if a is any real number, then the sequence $\{ax_n\}$ $(n = 1, 2, 3, \ldots)$ converges to ax.

(e) If $\{s_n\}$ converges to s, if no s_n is zero and if $s \neq 0$, then

$$\lim_{n \to \infty} \frac{1}{s_n} = \frac{1}{s}$$

Exercises

1.   Prove that each of the following sequences converges to zero.

(a) $1, \dfrac{1}{2^p}, \dfrac{1}{3^p}, \dfrac{1}{4^p}, \ldots$ $(p > 0)$

(b) $1, -1, \frac{1}{2}, -\frac{1}{2}, \frac{1}{3}, -\frac{1}{3}, \ldots$

(c) $e - 1, e^{1/2} - 1, e^{1/3} - 1, \ldots$ (use the mean-value theorem)

(d) $\sin x, \dfrac{\sin x}{2}, \dfrac{\sin x}{3}, \dfrac{\sin x}{4}, \ldots$

2. Determine which of the following sequences converge and which diverge.

   (a) $1, x, x^2, x^3, \ldots$ $(|x| < 1)$
   (b) $1, -\frac{1}{2}, \frac{1}{3}, -\frac{1}{4}, \frac{1}{5}, \ldots$

   (c) $\dfrac{3n^2 + 1}{2n^2 + 3}$ $(n = 1, 2, 3, \ldots)$

   (d) $1 - a, 1 + 2a, 1 - 3a, 1 + 4a, \ldots$ $(a \neq 0)$

3. For which values of x does each of the following sequences converge?

   (a) $\sin x, \sin^2 x, \sin^3 x, \ldots$
   (b) $e^x, e^{2x}, e^{3x}, \ldots$

4. Construct two divergent sequences whose sum converges to 7.
5. Prove part (b) of Theorem 5.1.
6. A certain sequence (called the Fibonacci sequence) is defined as follows: $x_0 = 1$, $x_1 = 1$, and $x_{n+1} = x_n + x_{n-1}$ for $n = 1, 2, 3, 4, \ldots$. Write out the first ten members of this sequence. Does the sequence converge?

5.2. *The Cauchy Convergence Criterion*

Our definition of a convergent sequence states that if, as we go far out in the sequence, all the members of the sequence are close to some fixed number, then the sequence converges. This definition can sometimes be very difficult to apply in practice because one needs to know the fixed number in question, i.e., the limit, before one is able to use it. In many cases it is quite hard to identify the limit, and yet, if the exact value of the limit is not of much importance, we might still like to be able to prove convergence. This can often be done by using the convergence criterion of Cauchy, which we discuss in this section. The philosophy of this criterion is that in order to show convergence it is not necessary to show that the members of the sequence get close to some fixed number but only that they get close to *each other*. This provides, then, a purely internal test for convergence in which it is not necessary to know or find the limit in advance. As an example, consider the sequence whose nth member is the sum of the reciprocals of the squares of the first n positive integers

$$x_n = 1 + \frac{1}{4} + \frac{1}{9} + \frac{1}{16} + \cdots + \frac{1}{n^2} \tag{5.3}$$

In this case it is quite a formidable problem to find the limit of the sequence, which turns out, in fact, to be $\pi^2/6$. By using the Cauchy criterion, however, it is quite easy to prove that the sequence converges, and, therefore, *has* a limit, because in order to do this we will need only to show that the members of the sequence get very close to each other.

> **THEOREM 5.2** (*The Cauchy Convergence Criterion*). A sequence $s_1, s_2, \ldots$ converges if and only if for every $\epsilon > 0$ there is a N such that we have
>
> $$|s_m - s_n| < \epsilon$$
>
> for all $m > N$ and $n > N$.

The proof of the Cauchy criterion is not given here because it requires a full, rigorous development of the theory of the real numbers themselves in order to be made meaningful. Indeed, there are developments of the real number system in which the Cauchy criterion is an essential part of the *definition* of a real number and, therefore, is not to be proven at all. We avoid these questions here and instead turn immediately to applications.

By a *nondecreasing* sequence we mean a sequence $s_1, s_2, \ldots$ which satisfies

$$s_1 \leqq s_2 \leqq s_3 \leqq s_4 \leqq \ldots$$

To say that a sequence $\{s_n\}$ is *bounded* is to say that all of the numbers $s_1, s_2, \ldots$ are contained in some finite interval of the real axis. We define in the obvious way the terms *increasing, decreasing, nonincreasing, unbounded*. The sequence

$$\tfrac{1}{2}, \tfrac{2}{3}, \tfrac{3}{4}, \tfrac{4}{5}, \ldots$$

is increasing and bounded. The sequence

$$1, 2, 3, 4, \ldots$$

is increasing and unbounded. The sequence

$$1, 0, 1, 0, 1, 0, \ldots$$

is bounded but not monotonic (i.e., not increasing or decreasing, etc.).

Suppose we have a sequence which is increasing and bounded. Then the terms of the sequence get steadily larger, yet there is a roof over all of them. Clearly, they have no alternative but to get very close together and so to converge. The precise result is

THEOREM 5.3. A sequence which is bounded and monotonic must converge.

PROOF We suppose, for concreteness, that the sequence is nondecreasing; the other three cases are handled similarly. Thus we have a sequence

$$s_1 \leqq s_2 \leqq s_3 \leqq s_4 \leqq \dots$$

and which satisfies

$$|s_j| \leqq A \qquad (j = 1, 2, 3, \dots).$$

We must show that the sequence has a limit. Now, all of the members of the sequence are contained in the interval $s_1 \leqq x \leqq A$. Split this interval into two equal subintervals. One of these must contain all members of the sequence from some point on. That is, there is an N_1 such that if $n > N_1$ each term of the sequence lies in the subinterval in question. Since the length of that subinterval is

$$\frac{A - s_1}{2}$$

it follows that for all $n > N_1$ and $m > N_1$ we have

$$|s_m - s_n| \leqq \frac{A - s_1}{2}$$

Next, split this subinterval into two equal pieces. Then one of these pieces must contain all members of the sequence from some point on. Thus, there is an N_2 such that when $n > N_2$ each term of the sequence lies in this new subinterval whose length is

$$\frac{A - s_1}{4}$$

and so if $m > N_2$ and $n > N_2$ we have

$$|s_m - s_n| \leqq \frac{A - s_1}{4}$$

Continuing in this way, at the kth stage we will have an interval whose length is

$$\frac{A - s_1}{2^k}$$

which will contain all of the terms of the sequence whose subscript exceeds a certain integer N_k. Hence, if $m > N_k$ and $n > N_k$, we will have

$$|s_m - s_n| \leqq \frac{A - s_1}{2^k}$$

Since the quantity on the right of this last inequality can be made as small as we wish by taking k large enough, it follows that if $\epsilon > 0$ is given, we can find an integer N (namely, the N_k for k large enough) such that for all $m > N$, $n > N$ we have

$$|s_m - s_n| < \epsilon$$

The conditions of the Cauchy criterion are satisfied, and it follows that the sequence converges.

Example
Prove that the sequence $\{x_n\}$ whose nth member is

$$x_n = \frac{1(3)(5)(7) \ldots (2n - 1)}{2(4)(6)(8) \ldots (2n)}$$

converges.

   This sequence is monotonic, though this is not obvious from looking at it. To prove that a given sequence is monotonic when the sequence is given by some such formula as the above, one can consider the ratio x_n/x_{n-1} and try to show that it is either always less than 1 (a decreasing sequence) or greater than 1 (an increasing sequence), or else one can consider the difference $x_n - x_{n-1}$ and try to show that it is always positive (increasing sequence) or always negative (decreasing sequence). In the present case either approach will work. We use the difference, and so write

$$x_n - x_{n-1} = \frac{1(3)(5) \ldots (2n - 1)}{2(4)(6) \ldots (2n)} - \frac{1(3)(5) \ldots (2n - 3)}{2(4)(6) \ldots (2n - 2)}$$

$$= \frac{1(3)(5) \ldots (2n - 3)}{2(4)(6) \ldots (2n - 2)} \left(\frac{2n - 1}{2n} - 1 \right)$$

The last quantity is obviously negative, and so $x_n - x_{n-1} < 0$, which is to say that the sequence is decreasing. It is now clear that the sequence is bounded also, for every member of the sequence is not greater than the first member (since the sequence decreases) nor less than zero (obvious). Hence, the sequence satisfies the conditions of Theorem 5.3, and, therefore, it converges. This argument sheds no light whatever on the value of the limit of the sequence, which happens to be zero.

Exercises

Show that each of the following sequences converges.

1. $\frac{1}{2}, \frac{2}{3}, \frac{3}{4}, \frac{4}{5}, \ldots$
2. $2^{1/2}, 3^{1/3}, 4^{1/4}, 5^{1/5}, \ldots$ (Hint: Take logarithms and use the calculus.)
3. $1, 1 + \frac{1}{2}, 1 + \frac{1}{2} + \frac{1}{4}, 1 + \frac{1}{2} + \frac{1}{4} + \frac{1}{8}, \ldots$ (Hint: Plot the members of this sequence on the x axis.)
4. $x_n = 1 - \dfrac{a^n}{n!}$ $\quad (n = 1, 2, 3, \ldots)$
5. Prove that, if a finite number of terms of a convergent sequence are changed in any way, the sequence still converges.
6. Prove that, if the sequence $\{x_n\}$ converges, then so does the sequence $\{|x_n|\}$. Show by an example that the converse is false.
7. Prove that every convergent sequence is bounded.

5.3. *Infinite Series of Real Numbers*

Let x_1, x_2, x_3, be a given sequence of real numbers. From this sequence we form a new sequence by addition, as follows:

$$s_1 = x_1$$
$$s_2 = x_1 + x_2$$
$$s_3 = x_1 + x_2 + x_3$$
$$\cdots$$
$$s_n = x_1 + x_2 + x_3 + \cdots + x_n$$

It may be that the sequence $s_1, s_2, s_3, \ldots$ has a limit s. If it does, we then write

$$s = x_1 + x_2 + x_3 + \cdots \tag{5.4}$$

Equation (5.4) has the appearance of an assertion that the number s is the sum of infinitely many numbers, and so the right-hand side of (5.4) is called an infinite series. In fact, Eq. (5.4) is merely a convenient way of abbreviating the statement that the sequence $\{s_n\}$ converges.

Before we proceed further it is useful to introduce some notation. The symbol

$$\sum_{j=m}^{n} a_j$$

means

$$a_m + a_{m+1} + a_{m+2} + \cdots + a_n$$

and its use will considerably shorten the amount of writing required to discuss various sums. For instance,

$$\sum_{j=3}^{15} \frac{1}{j} = \frac{1}{3} + \frac{1}{4} + \frac{1}{5} + \cdots + \frac{1}{15}$$

and

$$\sum_{k=4}^{49} (k + 1)^2 = 25 + 36 + 49 + \cdots + 2500$$

while

$$\sum_{r=1}^{12} b_r^3 = b_1^3 + b_2^3 + \cdots + b_{12}^3.$$

Using this summation sign, we can rephrase the definition of an infinite series by saying that if a sequence $a_1, a_2, a_3, \ldots$ is given, we form a new sequence according to the rule

$$s_k = \sum_{j=1}^{k} a_j \qquad (k = 1, 2, 3, 4, \ldots) \tag{5.5}$$

and if the resulting sequence $\{s_k\}$ converges, then its limit is denoted by

$$\sum_{j=1}^{\infty} a_j \tag{5.6}$$

As an example, consider the sequence whose nth member is

$$b_n = \frac{1}{n} - \frac{1}{n+1} = \frac{1}{n(n+1)} \qquad (n = 1, 2, 3, \ldots) \qquad (5.7)$$

In this case the sequence $\{s_k\}$ of (5.5) becomes

$$s_k = \left(1 - \frac{1}{2}\right) + \left(\frac{1}{2} - \frac{1}{3}\right) + \left(\frac{1}{3} - \frac{1}{4}\right) + \cdots + \left(\frac{1}{k} - \frac{1}{k+1}\right)$$

$$= 1 - \frac{1}{k+1}$$

This sequence evidently converges to 1, and so we write

$$1 = \sum_{n=1}^{\infty} \frac{1}{n(n+1)}$$

$$= \tfrac{1}{2} + \tfrac{1}{6} + \tfrac{1}{2} + \tfrac{1}{20} + \tfrac{1}{30} + \tfrac{1}{42} + \cdots \qquad (5.8)$$

The numbers s_k of (5.5) are called the *partial sums* of the series in question, and if they converge to a limit, then that limit (5.6) is called the *sum* of the series. The distinction between a sequence and a series should be firmly kept in mind. A sequence is a string of numbers separated by commas, a series is a string of numbers separated by plus signs. The meaning of the series is that its value is the limit of the sequence of partial sums of its terms, if that limit exists. If the limit does not exist, the series is divergent, and the symbol (5.6) is meaningless.

The series

$$\sum_{j=1}^{\infty} j = 1 + 2 + 3 + 4 + \cdots \qquad (5.9)$$

is clearly divergent, since its nth partial sum is

$$s_n = 1 + 2 + 3 + \cdots + n$$

$$= \frac{n(n+1)}{2}$$

which is a divergent sequence.

The series

$$1 + (-1) + 1 + (-1) + 1 + \cdots$$

also diverges since its sequence of partial sums is

$$1, 0, 1, 0, 1, 0, \ldots$$

which is divergent.

An important class of convergent series are the geometric series with a suitable ratio. A geometric series is a series whose terms are the successive powers of some fixed number, that is, a series of the form

$$1 + r + r^2 + r^3 + r^4 + \cdots \tag{5.10}$$

THEOREM 5.4. The geometric series (5.10) converges if and only if $|r| < 1$. If it converges, its sum is $(1 - r)^{-1}$.

PROOF   The nth partial sum of the geometric series is

$$s_n = 1 + r + r^2 + r^3 + \cdots + r^n$$

But then

$$(1 - r)s_n = (1 - r)(1 + r + r^2 + \cdots + r^n)$$
$$= (1 + r + r^2 + \cdots + r^n) - (r + r^2 + r^3 + \cdots + r^{n+1})$$
$$= 1 - r^{n+1}$$

Hence, the nth partial sum of the series (5.10) is

$$s_n = \frac{1 - r^{n+1}}{1 - r}$$

provided that $r \neq 1$. It is now clear that the sequence $\{s_n\}$ and, hence, the series (5.10) converge if and only if $|r| < 1$ to the sum stated.

We have, for example,

$$\sum_{n=0}^{\infty} 3^{-n} = \tfrac{3}{2}$$

It is clear from the corresponding result for sequences that multiplying each term of a convergent series by the same constant multiplies the sum of the series by that constant, and so we have, for instance,

$$4^{-12} + 4^{-13} + 4^{-14} + \cdots = 4^{-12}(1 + \tfrac{1}{4} + \tfrac{1}{16} + \cdots)$$
$$= 4^{-12}(\tfrac{4}{3})$$
$$= \sum_{n=12}^{\infty} 4^{-n}$$

Exercises

Find the following sums.

(a) $\displaystyle\sum_{k=1}^{n} 1$

(b) $\displaystyle\sum_{j=5}^{9} j^2$

(c) $\displaystyle\sum_{m=3}^{411} 2^m$

(d) $a + ar + ar^2 + ar^3 + \cdots \qquad (|r| < 1)$

(e) $\displaystyle\sum_{k=a}^{\infty} \frac{1}{5^k}$

(f) $\displaystyle\sum_{j=2}^{5} \frac{1}{j}$

(g) $\displaystyle\sum_{n=0}^{\infty} \frac{1}{2^n}$

(h) $\displaystyle\sum_{m=1}^{6} (2m^2 - m + 1)$

(i) $\displaystyle\sum_{s=1}^{11} \left(\frac{1}{s} - \frac{1}{s+1} \right)$

(j) $\displaystyle\sum_{n=1}^{4} \left(n + \frac{1}{n} \right)$

(k) $\displaystyle\sum_{n=1}^{2} \frac{1}{2^n}, \sum_{n=1}^{3} \frac{1}{2^n}, \sum_{n=1}^{4} \frac{1}{2^n}, \ldots, \sum_{n=1}^{8} \frac{1}{2^n}$

5.4. *Tests for Convergence: The Comparison Test*

A central question in the theory of series is the determination of whether or not a given series converges. For this purpose numerous tests have been devised, of which we discuss a few in this and the following sections. One of the most important of these tests is the comparison test. It tells us that, under certain circumstances, if the terms of the given series are *smaller* than those of a series which is known to be *convergent,* then the given series *converges,* while if they are *larger* than the terms of a series which is known to *diverge* then the given series *diverges* also. This test, used in conjunction with a small supply of series with known properties, provides a powerful tool for settling convergence questions.

THEOREM 5.5 (Comparison test for series of positive terms). Let $\Sigma\, a_n$ be a given series of nonnegative terms (all $a_n \geq 0$). Let $\Sigma\, c_n$ be a series which is known to converge. If for all sufficiently large n (i.e., for all n larger than some N) it is true that

$$a_n \leq c_n \tag{5.11}$$

then the series $\Sigma\, a_n$ converges. On the other hand, if $\Sigma\, b_n$ is a series of nonnegative terms which is known to diverge, and if for all sufficiently large n it is true that

$$a_n \geq b_n \tag{5.12}$$

then the given series $\Sigma\, a_n$ diverges also.

PROOF   Let us define the partial sums

$$A_n = a_1 + a_2 + \cdots + a_n$$

and

$$C_n = c_1 + c_2 + \cdots + c_n$$

We are given the sequence $\{C_n\}$ that converges to a limit, say C, and we must show that the sequence $\{A_n\}$ also converges to a limit. Now from (5.11) it is clear that $A_n \leq C_n$, and since the c_n are nonnegative it is equally clear that $C_n \leq C$. Hence, $A_n \leq C$ also. Since the a_n are nonnegative, it follows first that the sequence $\{A_n\}$ is nondecreasing and bounded, and then from Theorem 5.3 that the sequence $\{A_n\}$, and, therefore, the given series $\Sigma\, a_n$ converges. This proves the theorem under the assumption that the inequality (5.11) holds for *every* n. If (5.11) is true only for $n > N$, then throw away the first N terms of both series, which does not alter the convergence or divergence of either of them, thereby reducing the general case to the one already proved.

To prove the second part of the theorem, that if (5.12) holds then the given series diverges, suppose it is false. Then the series $\Sigma\, a_n$ converges. Reading (5.12) from right to left, the series $\Sigma\, b_n$ satisfies the conditions of the part of the theorem which we just proved, and so it converges, contrary to hypothesis, and completes the proof.

Examples
1. Show that the series

$$\sum_{n=1}^{\infty} \frac{1 + 1/n}{2^n}$$

converges.

    Clearly,

$$1 + \frac{1}{n} \leqq 39$$

for every n, and so each term of the given series is less than the corresponding terms of the geometric series

$$39 \sum_{n=1}^{\infty} \frac{1}{2^n}$$

which is known to be convergent. The result now follows from the theorem.

2. Show that the series

$$\sum_{n=1}^{\infty} \frac{\sin^2 (n\pi/7)}{n(n + 1)}$$

converges.

    Since

$$\sin^2 \frac{n\pi}{7} \leqq 15 \qquad (\text{all } n)$$

the terms of the given series are less than the corresponding terms of the series

$$\sum_{n=1}^{\infty} \frac{15}{n(n + 1)}$$

which we know, from (5.8), to be convergent.

3. Show that the series

$$\sum_{n=1}^{\infty} (1.5)^n \log n$$

diverges.

If $n > 300$ then $\log n > 1$, and so for all $n > 300$, the terms of the given series exceed those of the series

$$\sum (1.5)^n$$

which we know, from Theorem 5.4, to be divergent.

(The rather wild estimates which we made in these examples are intended to underscore the fact that there is no need for great precision when the comparison test is used if a crude bound will do the job. Sometimes, as in Example 4, it is not even necessary to identify the exact point in the series at which the comparison begins to be valid, but only to know that it exists.)

4.   Show that the series

$$\sum_{n=1}^{\infty} \frac{1}{n^{2.5}}$$

converges.

It is clear that if n is large enough then

$$n^{2.5} > n(n + 1) = n^2 + n$$

Hence, for all sufficiently large n, the terms of our given series are less than the corresponding terms of the series (5.8), which we know to converge.

Exercises

Test each of the following series for convergence.

(a) $\displaystyle\sum_{n=1}^{\infty} \frac{1 + \cos n}{n^4}$

(b) $\displaystyle\sum_{n=2}^{\infty} \frac{1}{n^5 - 1}$

(c) $\displaystyle\sum_{n=5}^{\infty} \frac{1}{n^2 + n - 6}$

(d) $\displaystyle\sum_{n=0}^{\infty} \frac{1}{2^{n^2}}$

(e) $\displaystyle\sum_{n=0}^{\infty} \frac{1}{(n+1)^4}$

(f) $\displaystyle\sum_{n=2}^{\infty} \frac{1}{3^n \log n}$

(g) $\displaystyle\sum_{n=1}^{\infty} \left\{1 + \frac{1}{2} \sin \frac{n\pi}{3}\right\}$

(h) $\displaystyle\sum_{n=1}^{\infty} \frac{n^2 + 1}{n^5 + 1}$

5.5. *Tests for Convergence: The Integral Test*

An extremely useful test for the convergence of a series is provided by the integral test which permits us to deduce the convergence or divergence of a given infinite series from the convergence or divergence of a certain infinite integral. The test can be used whenever we are given a series whose terms are the values of a function, which is defined for all positive x, at the positive integers, and when that function is nonnegative and decreasing. Thus in the series

$$\sum_{n=2}^{\infty} \frac{1}{n \log n} \tag{5.13}$$

the terms are the values of $f(x) = 1/(x \log x)$ at the positive integers, and that function is indeed nonnegative and decreasing.

In Fig. 5.1, we have sketched the curve $y = f(x)$, and the abscissae a,

Figure 5.1

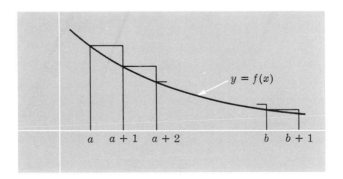

$a + 1$, $a + 2$, ... represent consecutive integers. The base of each rectangle shown is 1, and so the areas of these rectangles are, respectively, $f(a)$, $f(a + 1)$, $f(a + 2)$, ..., $f(b - 1)$, $f(b)$. Since the function f is assumed to be decreasing, it is evident from Fig. 5.1 that the total area of these rectangles is not less than the area under the curve from $x = a$ to $x = b + 1$, that is,

$$\int_a^{b+1} f(x)\,dx \leqq f(a) + f(a + 1) + f(a + 2) + \cdots + f(b)$$
$$= \sum_{m=a}^{b} f(m) \tag{5.14}$$

On the other hand, consider the curve which passes through the upper right-hand corners of these rectangles instead of the upper left-hand corners. This is the curve $y = f(x - 1)$. From Fig. 5.2 it is clear that

Figure 5.2

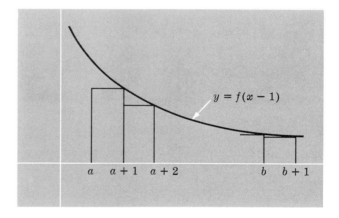

$$\int_a^{b+1} f(x - 1)\,dx \geqq f(a) + f(a + 1) + \cdots + f(b)$$
$$= \sum_{m=a}^{b} f(m) \tag{5.15}$$

and combining (5.14) and (5.15) we have

$$\int_{a-1}^{b} f(x)\,dx \geqq \sum_{m=a}^{b} f(m) \geqq \int_a^{b+1} f(x)\,dx \tag{5.16}$$

where we have made an obvious change of variable in the first integral.

If the infinite integral

$$\int_a^\infty f(x)\,dx \tag{5.17}$$

converges, then from (5.16) each of the partial sums of the infinite series

$$\sum_{m=a}^\infty f(m) \tag{5.18}$$

is less than or equal to the value of that integral, and so the sequence of partial sums of the series (5.18) is nondecreasing [since $f(m)$ is always nonnegative] and bounded, and, therefore, convergent. On the other hand if the infinite integral (5.17) diverges, then by the right-hand inequality in (5.16), the sequence of partial sums of the series (5.18) will grow without bound, and so (5.18) will diverge. We have proved

    THEOREM 5.6.   Let $f(x)$ be defined, nonnegative, and decreasing for $x \geq a$. Then, if the integral (5.17) converges, so does the series (5.18), while if the integral diverges, the series does also.

Where applicable, the integral test of Theorem 5.5 may be the easiest test to use, as the following examples illustrate.

Examples
1.   The harmonic series

$$\sum_{n=1}^\infty \frac{1}{n} = 1 + \frac{1}{2} + \frac{1}{3} + \frac{1}{4} + \cdots \tag{5.19}$$

diverges, because

$$\lim_{A\to\infty} \int_1^A \frac{1}{x}\,dx = \lim_{A\to\infty} \log A$$

does not exist. We have, from (5.16), an even more precise statement, namely, that the sum of the reciprocals of the first n positive integers is at least as large as $\log(n+1)$.

2.   For each fixed positive number d, the series

$$\sum_{n=1}^\infty \frac{1}{n^{1+d}} \tag{5.20}$$

converges. In fact, the integral (5.17) is just

$$\int_1^\infty \frac{1}{x^{1+d}}\, dx = \frac{a^{-d}}{d}$$

though, of course, the exact value of the integral is of no importance since we are interested only in whether it converges.

Comparison of Examples 1 and 2 shows that while the sum of the reciprocals of the first powers of the positive integers diverges, the sum of the reciprocals of any power larger than the first (the 1.0001 power, for instance) converges. It may appear from this that the series of terms n^{-1} is a kind of borderline between convergence and divergence. However, no such borderline exists. We illustrate this by displaying a series whose terms are smaller than n^{-1} but which still diverges.

3. The series (5.13) diverges. In this case, the integral becomes

$$\lim_{A\to\infty} \int_2^A \frac{1}{x \log x}\, dx$$

If we put $x = e^t$ in the integral, it becomes

$$\lim_{A\to\infty} \int_{\log 2}^{\log A} \frac{1}{t}\, dt$$

which diverges, and, therefore, (5.13) does also.

While this example showed that $\Sigma\, n^{-1}$ is not the "smallest possible divergent series," neither are the series $\Sigma\, n^{-1-d}$ the "largest possible convergent series," as the following example shows.

4. The series

$$\sum_{n=2}^\infty \frac{1}{n(\log n)^2} \tag{5.21}$$

converges. Indeed, the integral (5.17) is

$$\lim_{A\to\infty} \int_2^A \frac{1}{x(\log x)^2}\, dx$$

and the substitution $x = e^t$ reduces this to

$$\lim_{A \to \infty} \int_{\log 2}^{\log A} \frac{1}{t^2} \, dt$$

which evidently exists.

It is sad, but true, that there is no universal series against which all other series can be measured. In other words, given any series which diverges, however slowly, there is another series whose terms are even smaller and which still diverges. Further, given any convergent series, there is another one whose terms are even larger, and which still converges. We shall not prove this here, but you should convince yourself that this is precisely the statement that there is no universal series for the comparison test of Theorem 5.5, in either direction.

Exercises

Determine the convergence or divergence of each of the following series.

1. $\sum n e^{-n}$

2. $\sum \dfrac{1}{n(\log n)^{1+d}}$ $(d > 0)$

3. $\sum \dfrac{1}{n^2 + 9}$

4. $\sum \dfrac{1}{n^{1/2}}$

5. $\sum \dfrac{\log n}{n}$

6. $\sum n^{-1/4}$

7. $\sum \dfrac{1}{(n + 4)^3}$

8. $\sum \dfrac{1}{7n^{3/4}}$

9. $\sum \dfrac{1}{(4n + 1)^2}$

10. $\sum \dfrac{1}{(n + 2)^{3/2}}$

5.6.   Tests for Convergence: Order of Magnitude

We have by now accumulated a reasonably large store of reference series against which to measure the convergence of other series. In this section we wish to note that the decisive factor in convergence is the size of the terms of the series when the index of summation is large. That is, if the terms drop off to zero rapidly enough as we go far out in the series, then it will converge, whereas if they go only slowly or not at all to zero, the series will diverge. It is useful to develop some facility for looking beneath superficial complications in the appearance of a series to see which terms really govern the behavior. Consider, for instance, the series

$$\sum_{n=12}^{\infty} \frac{n^4 + \cos{(4n^2 + 3n + 2)}}{(5n + 7)^6}$$

This series presents a formidable appearance, but actually one should be able to see at a glance that it converges. Indeed, when n is large, the numerator is about n^4 (think of $n = 1,000,000$), and the denominator is roughly a constant times n^6. Hence, when n is very large, the nth term of this series is very nearly a constant times $1/n^2$. Since the series $\Sigma \, 1/n^2$ converges we should expect that the given series converges also. In this example, what we did was to find another series, of known convergence, which behaved very much like the given one. The term "behaves very much like" means that the ratio of the nth terms of the given series and of the known series approaches a nonzero limit as n approaches ∞.

Thus, $1/(n + 1)^2$ behaves like $1/n^2$ because their ratio approaches 1 as n becomes large. Similarly,

$$(1 + 4n + 6n^{11})^2$$

behaves like n^{22} in this sense, because their ratio also approaches a limit. Our next theorem says that if one series of positive terms behaves like another, then the series converge or diverge together.

THEOREM 5.7.   Let $\Sigma \, a_n$ and $\Sigma \, b_n$ be two series of positive terms. If

$$\lim_{n \to \infty} \frac{a_n}{b_n} = A \tag{5.22}$$

exists and is not zero, then the series either both converge or both
diverge.

PROOF By (5.22), there is an N such that when $n > N$ we have

$$\left| \frac{a_n}{b_n} - A \right| < \epsilon$$

which is to say that

$$A - \epsilon \leqq \frac{a_n}{b_n} < A + \epsilon$$

If $\Sigma\, a_n$ converges, then since $b_n < a_n/(A - \epsilon)$ for large n, $\Sigma\, b_n$
converges by the comparison test. If $\Sigma\, a_n$ diverges, then since
$b_n > a_n/(A + \epsilon)$, the series $\Sigma\, b_n$ also diverges by the comparison
test. The other two cases are similar.

Exercises

1. Test the following for convergence by any method.

(a) $\displaystyle\sum \frac{1}{an + b}$

(b) $\displaystyle\sum \frac{1}{an^2 + bn + c}$

(c) $\displaystyle\sum \frac{\log n}{2^n}$

(d) $\displaystyle\sum \frac{3 + (-1)^n}{n}$

(e) $\displaystyle\sum \frac{7 - \cos n + \sin (n + 1)}{n^{1/2}}$

(f) $\displaystyle\sum \frac{1}{n^n}$

(g) $\displaystyle\sum \frac{1}{\log n}$

(h) $\displaystyle\sum \frac{\log \log n}{(\log n)^2}$

(i) $\displaystyle\sum \frac{1 + \cos n}{n^2}$

(j) $\sum \dfrac{1}{\log n + 3}$

(k) $\sum \dfrac{1}{\log (n + 3)}$

(l) $\sum \dfrac{1}{(\log n^n)^5}$

(m) $\sum \dfrac{1}{[n(n + 1)(n + 2)]^{1/3}}$

2.   Let us say that $f(n)$ grows faster than $g(n)$ if $g(n) < f(n)$ for all large n. Arrange the following functions in increasing order of their rapidity of growth:

n^2, 2^n, $\log n$, $n^{1/2}$, n^n, e^n, $n!$, $\log \log n$,
$n \log n$, $n(\log \log n)^2$, 2^{n^2}, $e^{n(\log n)^2}$

(Hint: Use L'Hospital's rule.)

5.7.   *Alternating Series*

We have so far concentrated on series of nonnegative terms. In this section the assumption of nonnegativity is dropped, and we discuss a special class of series in which the terms are not all of the same sign, namely, the alternating series. A series is alternating if its terms are alternately positive and negative. Such a series as

$$1 - \frac{1}{2} + \frac{1}{3} - \frac{1}{4} + \frac{1}{5} - \cdots = \sum_{n=1}^{\infty} \frac{(-1)^{n+1}}{n} \tag{5.23}$$

is of this type.

In general, we can write an alternating series as

$$\sum_{n=1}^{\infty} (-1)^{n+1} a_n \tag{5.24}$$

where all the a_n are positive. There is a simple test for convergence of certain alternating series which is often applicable in practice. It is given by

THEOREM 5.8.   If in the series (5.24) the numbers $a_1, a_2, a_3, \ldots$ decrease steadily to zero, then the series converges.

PROOF   Consider the partial sums of the series (5.24)

$$a_1, \quad a_1 - a_2, \quad a_1 - a_2 + a_3, \quad a_1 - a_2 + a_3 - a_4, \quad \cdots$$

Let us ignore, for the moment, the first, third, fifth, etc., of these, and focus attention on the second, fourth, sixth, and so on. These are

$$S_{2n} = a_1 - a_2 + a_3 - a_4 + \cdots + a_{2n-1} - a_{2n} \quad (n = 1, 2, 3, \ldots)$$

We claim that this sequence of even-numbered partial sums is increasing and bounded, and, therefore, convergent. It is increasing because we obtain one from its predecessor by adding $(a_{2n-1} - a_{2n})$, a positive number by hypothesis. It is bounded because

$$S_{2n} = a_1 - (a_2 - a_3) - (a_4 - a_5) - \cdots - (a_{2n-2} - a_{2n-1}) - a_{2n}$$

and the number inside each parenthesis is positive, whence $S_{2n} \leq a_1$. Since the sequence increases, $S_{2n} \geq S_2$ for every n, and so it is bounded. Thus the sequence $\{S_{2n}\}$ converges, as a sequence, to a certain limit, say S. We claim that the odd-numbered partial sums converge to the same limit, and, therefore, the series itself converges to S. Indeed, since

$$S_{2n+1} = S_{2n} + a_{2n+1}$$

and each of the quantities on the right approaches a limit (S and 0, respectively), S_{2n+1} must approach the sum of these limits, which is S, completing the proof.

Since the sequence $1, \frac{1}{2}, \frac{1}{3}, \ldots$ decreases steadily to zero we see that the series (5.23) converges. The series

$$\sum \frac{(-1)^n}{\log n}$$

converges for the same reason, as does

$$1 - \frac{1}{\sqrt{2}} + \frac{1}{\sqrt{3}} - \frac{1}{\sqrt{4}} + \cdots$$

In the series

$$\sum_{n=1}^{\infty} \frac{(-1)^n (100)^n}{n!}$$

the numbers $(100)^n/n!$ increase for a while, but then decrease steadily to zero. Indeed, the ratio

$$\left(\frac{(100)^n}{n!}\right)\Big/\left(\frac{(100)^{n-1}}{(n-1)!}\right) = 100/n$$

shows that the first 100 terms increase in size but that they decrease after that.

We remark that in the hypothesis of Theorem 5.8 the requirement that the individual terms approach zero is actually applicable to every convergent series, alternating or not. That is, a series whose terms do not approach zero cannot converge (though one whose terms do, need not).

THEOREM 5.9.   If $\Sigma\, b_n$ converges, then

$$\lim_{n\to\infty} b_n = 0$$

PROOF   Since the series converges, the sequence

$$S_n = b_1 + b_2 + b_3 + \cdots + b_n$$

approaches a limit, say S. But

$$b_n \doteq S_n - S_{n-1}$$

and each of the terms on the right approaches S, where b_n approaches zero.

Exercises

1.   Test the following series for convergence.

(a) $\displaystyle\sum \frac{(-1)^n}{n^a}$ $(a > 0)$

(b) $\displaystyle\sum \frac{(-1)^n(50)^n}{(2)(4)(6)\ldots(2n)}$

(c) $\displaystyle\sum (-1)^n\left(1 + \sin\frac{3n\pi}{7}\right)$

(d) $\displaystyle\sum (-1)^n \frac{\log n}{n}$

(e) $\sum (-1)^n(e^{1/n} - 1)$

(f) $\sum (-1)^n \sin \frac{\pi}{n}$

2. Let $\{a_n\}_0^\infty$ be a sequence of nonnegative numbers which decreases to zero, and let

$$S = \sum_{n=0}^{\infty} (-1)^n a_n$$

Show that the even-numbered partial sums $S_2, S_4, S_6, \ldots$ increase to S while the odd-numbered partial sums decrease to S, and therefore

$$S_{2k} \leqq S \leqq S_{2k+1} \qquad (k = 0, 1, 2, \ldots)$$

Using this fact, compute the sums of the following series correct to two decimal places:

(a) $\displaystyle\sum_{n=0}^{\infty} \frac{(-1)^n}{(n+1)^3}$

(b) $\displaystyle\sum_{n=0}^{\infty} \frac{(-1)^n}{n!}$

(c) $\displaystyle\sum_{n=0}^{\infty} \frac{(-1)^n}{(n+1)^{n+1}}$

(d) $\displaystyle\sum_{n=0}^{\infty} \frac{n^2}{2^{n^2}}(-1)^n$

(e) $\displaystyle\sum_{n=1}^{\infty} \frac{(-1)^n}{n!n}$

5.8. *Absolute Convergence*

There is a fundamental difference in the nature of the convergence of the two series

$$\sum \frac{(-1)^n}{n}; \qquad \sum \frac{(-1)^n}{n^2}$$

Both converge but, roughly speaking, for different reasons. The first series converges only because of the cancellation between terms of opposite sign. If we gave all terms the same sign, the first series would diverge. In the second series the terms drop off rapidly enough so that the series would converge even without the sign alternation. This distinction has many important consequences, and we formalize it in the following

> **DEFINITION**   The series $\Sigma\ a_n$ is said to converge *absolutely* if $\Sigma\ |a_n|$ converges. If $\Sigma\ a_n$ converges but $\Sigma\ |a_n|$ does not, we speak of *conditional* convergence.

Examples
1.   The series

$$\sum \frac{(-1)^n}{n^2}, \qquad \sum \frac{(-1)^{n(n+1)/2}}{n^3}$$

$$\sum \frac{(-1)^n}{n!}, \qquad \sum \frac{1}{2^n}$$

all converge absolutely, as does any convergent series of nonnegative terms.

2.   The series

$$\sum \frac{(-1)^n}{n}, \qquad \sum \frac{(-1)^n}{\log n}, \qquad \sum \frac{(-1)^n}{n^{1/2}}$$

converge conditionally.

> **THEOREM 5.10.**   A series which converges absolutely, converges.
>
> PROOF   We have to show that, if $\Sigma\ |a_n|$ converges, then so does $\Sigma\ a_n$. Consider the partial sums of each of these series
>
> $$S_n = a_1 + a_2 + \cdots + a_n$$
> $$S_n' = |a_1| + |a_2| + \cdots + |a_n|$$
>
> Since $\Sigma\ |a_n|$ converges, the sequence $\{S_n'\}$ converges. Hence, by the Cauchy criterion, if $\epsilon > 0$ is given, there is an N such that whenever m and n are greater than N we have
>
> $$|S_m' - S_n'| < \epsilon$$
>
> But
>
> $$|S_m' - S_n'| = \sum_{j=n+1}^{m} |a_j| \qquad (m > n)$$

and

$$|S_m - S_n| = \left| \sum_{j=n+1}^{m} a_j \right|$$

$$\leqq \sum_{j=n+1}^{m} |a_j|$$

$$= |S'_m - S'_n|$$

$$< \epsilon$$

if $m, n > N$. Hence, by the Cauchy criterion, the sequence $\{S_m\}$ converges also, which was to be shown.

As an example, the series

$$1 + \tfrac{1}{4} - \tfrac{1}{9} - \tfrac{1}{16} + \tfrac{1}{25} + \tfrac{1}{36} - \cdots$$

is not covered by any of our convergence tests prior to Theorem 5.10. Since this series is absolutely convergent, however, it converges.

A most remarkable and bizarre feature of a conditionally convergent series is that the value of the sum of the series can be changed just by rearranging the order of the terms! The phenomenon has, of course, no analog in finite sums because of the commutative law of addition. To illustrate this point, consider the two series

$$A = 1 - \tfrac{1}{2} + \tfrac{1}{3} - \tfrac{1}{4} + \tfrac{1}{5} - \cdots$$
$$B = (1 + \tfrac{1}{3} - \tfrac{1}{2}) + (\tfrac{1}{5} + \tfrac{1}{7} - \tfrac{1}{4}) + (\tfrac{1}{9} + \tfrac{1}{11} - \tfrac{1}{6}) + \cdots$$

where in B we take two positive terms from A followed by one negative term. We claim that both series converge but to different sums. That A converges is obvious. B converges also because the quantity inside the kth parenthesis is a positive quantity which is less than $1/k^2$. Indeed, inside the kth parenthesis in B is

$$\frac{1}{4k-3} + \frac{1}{4k-1} - \frac{1}{2k} = \frac{8k-3}{2k(4k-1)(4k-3)}$$

which is first clearly positive, and second is

$$< \frac{1}{4k-4} + \frac{1}{4k-4} - \frac{1}{2k} = \frac{1}{2k(k-1)} \leqq \frac{1}{k^2}$$

Hence, the series B converges by the comparison test. Next we show that A and B converge to different sums. The series B converges to a number larger than $\frac{11}{12}$ because the first two parentheses already contribute $\frac{11}{12}$ and the rest of them are positive. On the other hand, the series A can be written

$$1 - (\tfrac{1}{2} - \tfrac{1}{3}) - (\tfrac{1}{4} - \tfrac{1}{5}) - \cdots = 1 - \tfrac{1}{6} - \tfrac{1}{20} - \cdots$$

and it is, therefore, less than $\frac{5}{6}$. Hence, $A < B$ as claimed.

It is a fact that the terms of a given conditionally convergent series can be rearranged so as to make the series converge to *any desired sum,* though we shall not prove this here. Another fact that we will not prove is that for *absolutely* convergent series no such troubles can arise, for we have

THEOREM 5.11.   Let the absolutely convergent series $\Sigma\, a_n$ converge to the sum S. Then every rearrangement of the terms of that series also converges to S.

Exercises

1.   Describe how you might rearrange the terms of the series $\Sigma\, (-1)^n/n$ so that the resulting series would converge to 697.

2.   Test the following for absolute convergence and for convergence.

(a) $\displaystyle\sum \cos \frac{n\pi}{12}$

(b) $\displaystyle\sum (-\tfrac{1}{4})^n$

(c) $\displaystyle\sum \frac{(-1)^n}{\sqrt{\log n}}$

(d) $\displaystyle\sum_{1}^{\infty} \frac{\cos n\pi}{n}$

(e) $\displaystyle\sum_{1}^{\infty} \frac{\sin^3 (n\pi/2)}{n^3}$

(f) $\displaystyle\sum_{1}^{\infty} \frac{(-1)^n}{n \log n}$

3.   About how many terms in the series $\displaystyle\sum_{1}^{\infty} 1/n$ does one need to take before the sum will exceed 1,000,000?

5.9. Sequences and Series of Functions

We have so far considered sequences and series of numbers. Now we broaden these concepts to include sequences and series of functions. Consider, for instance, the sequence

$$1, x, x^2, x^3, x^4, \ldots$$

where x is some fixed real number. If $|x| < 1$, this sequence converges to zero. If $x = 1$, it converges to 1. If $|x| > 1$ or $x = -1$, it diverges. Thus the limit of this sequence depends on x, i.e., is a function of x. This function is

$$f(x) = \begin{cases} 1 & x = 1 \\ 0 & -1 < x < 1 \end{cases}$$

and is undefined for other values of x.

In general, a sequence of functions is a sequence of the form

$$f_1(x), f_2(x), f_3(x), \ldots$$

where the functions $f_j(x)$ have a common domain of definition. The sequence may converge for all x, diverge for all x, or converge for some x and diverge for others. The limit $f(x)$ of such a sequence will then be a function of x whose domain is the set of x on which the given sequence converges.

In a similar way we define a series of functions. The series

$$\sum_{m=1}^{\infty} f_m(x) \tag{5.25}$$

converges, for a certain value of x, if the sequence

$$f_1(x), \quad f_1(x) + f_2(x), \quad f_1(x) + f_2(x) + f_3(x), \ldots \tag{5.26}$$

of partial sums converges, for that value of x. The sum of the series (5.25) is then a function f, whose domain is the set of x for which the sequence (5.26) converges.

Thus the series

$$\sum_{n=0}^{\infty} x^n$$

is, for each fixed x, a geometric series. It converges if $|x| < 1$ to $(1 - x)^{-1}$, and diverges otherwise. Hence, the sum of the series is

$$f(x) = \begin{cases} 1/(1 - x) & -1 < x < 1 \\ \text{undefined} & \text{otherwise} \end{cases}$$

Again, the series

$$\sum_{n=1}^{\infty} \frac{1}{n^2 x + 1}$$

converges for every x except $x = 0$. Indeed, if $x \neq 0$, then this series behaves like

$$\frac{1}{x} \sum_{n=1}^{\infty} \frac{1}{n^2}$$

in the sense of Theorem 5.7, and, therefore, converges. If $x = 0$, the series evidently diverges.

Among all series of functions, we single out for close attention here the power series. A power series is a series of the form

$$\Sigma\, a_n x^n$$

that is, a series of constants multiplied by successive powers of some fixed number. Examples of power series are

$$1 + x + x^2 + \cdots \tag{5.27a}$$
$$3 - 4x + 5x^2 - 6x^3 + 7x^4 - \cdots \tag{5.27b}$$
$$1 + x + \frac{x^2}{2!} + \frac{x^3}{3!} + \cdots \tag{5.27c}$$
$$1 + (x + 1) + (x + 1)^4 + (x + 1)^9 + (x + 1)^{16} + \cdots \tag{5.27d}$$

Recall from our discussion of the theory of contact in Section 4.8 that among all polynomials of degree n, the one which had the highest order of contact with the function e^x at the origin was the polynomial

$$1 + x + \frac{x^2}{2!} + \cdots + \frac{x^n}{n!}$$

At that time we had no machinery for pushing this train of thought to its logical conclusion. We now do have that machinery, and the logical conclusion is the infinite series (5.27c). This infinite series does not provide merely a good approximation to e^x; it is actually equal to e^x for every value of x. Nor is e^x distinguished in this respect. Most of the elementary functions we have studied have power series which converge to the function on a suitable set of x. This possibility of expanding a given function in a convergent power series is of the highest importance, both from a theoretical and a practical standpoint.

To develop the theory further we need to know how to identify the set of x for which a given power series converges. Obviously, every power series converges at $x = 0$. The set of x at which a power series converges cannot be just any set, however. We will see that it must be an *interval* of the x axis. We wish to prove this and to show how we can find out exactly which interval it is for a given series.

5.10. The Radius of Convergence

We begin by considering an example, namely, the series

$$\sum_{n=1}^{\infty} \frac{x^n}{n^2} \tag{5.28}$$

By Theorem 5.9 we know that if (5.28) is to have any chance at all of converging, its terms must approach zero, and so in particular they must be bounded. Thus, if (5.28) converges, there is a K such that

$$\left| \frac{x^n}{n^2} \right| \leq K \qquad (n = 1, 2, 3, \ldots)$$

and so

$$|x| \leq (Kn^2)^{1/n} \qquad (n = 1, 2, 3, \ldots) \tag{5.29}$$

The quantity on the right approaches 1 as n approaches infinity, and, therefore, $|x| \leq 1$. Thus (5.28) surely diverges if $|x| > 1$. It is easy to see by the comparison test that the series converges absolutely when $|x| < 1$, and then by inspection that it converges at $x = \pm 1$.

The success of this method depended on the existence of the limit on the right side of (5.29). In many cases the sequence of coefficients of the powers of x (the numbers which multiply these powers) will be sufficiently irregular that the limit will not exist. For this reason it is necessary to define a slight generalization of the idea of limit, which turns out to be the relevant concept for power series.

> **DEFINITION**   Let $x_1, x_2, x_3, \ldots$ be a given sequence. A number b is called the *limit superior* of the sequence if
>   (a) for every $\epsilon > 0$ there is an N such that $x_n \leq b + \epsilon$ for all $n > N$, and
>   (b) for every $\epsilon > 0$ infinitely many of the x_n are $\geq b - \epsilon$.

Remarks

1. If b is the limit superior of the sequence $\{x_n\}$, we write either

$$b = \limsup_{n \to \infty} x_n$$

or

$$b = \overline{\lim} \, x_n$$

2. If the sequence $\{x_n\}$ actually has a limit, then that limit will also be the limit superior of the sequence.

3. If the sequence contains arbitrarily large numbers (e.g., the sequence $1, 2, 3, \ldots$), it is conventional to write $\overline{\lim} \, x_n = \infty$. If only finitely many of the x_n exceed every fixed number (e.g., the sequence $-1, -2, -3, \ldots$), it is conventional to write $\overline{\lim} \, x_n = -\infty$. With these conventions, every sequence has a limit superior, whether or not it has a limit.

4. A sequence cannot have two different limits superior, for if $b < b'$ are two of these, choose $\epsilon = (b' - b)/3$. Then all x_n from $n = N$ onward are $\leq b + \epsilon$, and so it is impossible for infinitely many of them to exceed $b' - \epsilon$. Thus every sequence has one and only one limit superior.

Examples

1.   For the sequence

$$1, -1, 1, -1, 1, \ldots$$

we have

$$\overline{\lim} \, x_n = 1$$

2. In the case

$$\sin \frac{\pi}{4}, \quad \sin \frac{2\pi}{4}, \quad \sin \frac{3\pi}{4}, \dots$$

the limit superior is 1.

3. In the sequence

$$1, \; 2^{1/2}, \; 3^{1/3}, \; 4^{1/4}, \dots$$

the limit, and, therefore, the limit superior also is 1.

4. If

$$x_n = n \sin \frac{n\pi}{8} \qquad (n = 1, 2, 3, \dots)$$

then

$$\overline{\lim} \, x_n = \infty$$

Equipped with the idea of limit superior we can give a complete answer to the question of determining the interval in which a power series converges.

THEOREM 5.12. Let the power series $\Sigma \, a_n x^n$ be given, and let

$$\mu = \overline{\lim} \, |a_n|^{1/n} \qquad (5.30)$$

Then, if $\mu = 0$, the power series converges for all real x. If $\mu = +\infty$, the series converges only for $x = 0$. Otherwise, if $0 < \mu < \infty$, the series converges absolutely for every x in the interval $-1/\mu < x < 1/\mu$ and diverges for all $|x| > 1/\mu$. The number $R = 1/\mu$ is called the radius of convergence of the power series.

PROOF   First suppose $\mu = 0$. Then, if $\epsilon > 0$ is given, for all large n we have

$$|a_n|^{1/n} < \epsilon$$

Choose a real number $x \neq 0$, and fix it. We will show that the series converges for this value of x. Now, for all large n we have

$$|a_n|^{1/n} < \frac{1}{2x}$$

which is to say that

$$|a_n x^n| < \frac{1}{2^n}$$

whence the given series is absolutely convergent by comparison with the geometric series of ratio $\frac{1}{2}$. Since the value of x was arbitrary, the series converges for all real x.

Next, suppose that $\mu = +\infty$. We will obtain a contradiction from the assumption that the series converges at a certain point $x = x_0 \neq 0$. Indeed, if it does, then by Theorem 5.9 the terms of the series must approach zero, and, therefore, they are bounded. Hence, there is a K such that

$$|a_n x_0^n| \leq K \qquad \text{(all } n\text{)}$$

and so

$$|a_n|^{1/n} \leq \frac{K^{1/n}}{x_0}$$

which implies that

$$\mu = \overline{\lim} \ |a_n|^{1/n} \leq \frac{1}{x_0}$$

contradicting the assumption that $\mu = +\infty$. Hence, there is no $x_0 \neq 0$ at which the series converges, which was to be shown.

Finally, suppose $0 < \mu < \infty$. We claim that the series converges if $|x| < 1/\mu$ and diverges if $|x| > 1/\mu$. Indeed, if x is fixed, $|x| < 1/\mu$, choose $\epsilon > 0$ so small that $|x| < 1/(\mu + 2\epsilon)$. Keeping this x and ϵ fixed, from the definition of limit superior we know that for all large n,

$$|a_n|^{1/n} \leq \mu + \epsilon$$

which is to say that

$$|a_n| \leq (\mu + \epsilon)^n \qquad (n \geq N)$$

Hence,

$$|a_n x^n| \leq (\mu + \epsilon)^n \frac{1}{(\mu + 2\epsilon)^n}$$

$$= \left(\frac{\mu + \epsilon}{\mu + 2\epsilon} \right)^n \qquad (n \geq N)$$

Since the quantity in parentheses is less than 1, the given series converges absolutely at this value of x, by comparison with a convergent geometric series. Since the value of x which we fixed was arbitrary in the interval $(-1/\mu, 1/\mu)$ it follows that the given series converges for all x in that interval.

To show that the series diverges if $|x| > 1/\mu$, choose and fix such a value of x. Then we can find an $\epsilon > 0$ so small that $|x| > 1/(\mu - 2\epsilon)$. Fix such an ϵ. From the definition of limit superior the relation

$$|a_n|^{1/n} \geqq \mu - \epsilon$$

holds for infinitely many values of n, hence,

$$|a_n| \geqq (\mu - \epsilon)^n$$

and

$$|a_n x^n| \geqq (\mu - \epsilon)^n \frac{1}{(\mu - 2\epsilon)^n}$$

$$= \left(\frac{\mu - \epsilon}{\mu - 2\epsilon} \right)^n$$

for such n. Since the quantity in parentheses is greater than 1, it follows that infinitely many terms of the given series exceed 1 in absolute value, hence the sequence of terms does not approach zero. From Theorem 5.9, then, the series cannot converge at the value of x chosen. Hence, the series diverges for every x such that $|x| > 1/\mu$, which was to be shown.

In order to apply this theorem in practice it is necessary to have a good feeling for the behavior of the nth roots of various sequences. The following, for instance, can all be verified by L'Hospital's rule:

$$\lim_{n \to \infty} K^{1/n} = 1 \qquad (K \text{ constant})$$

$$\lim_{n \to \infty} (\log n)^{1/n} = 1$$

$$\lim_{n \to \infty} n^{1/n} = 1$$

$$\lim_{n \to \infty} (n^p)^{1/n} = 1 \qquad (p \text{ constant})$$

Thus, if the coefficients of a power series involve only constants, logarithms of n, and powers of n, then the series will converge if $|x| < 1$ and diverge if $|x| > 1$. For example, each of the following series has radius of convergence equal to 1:

$$\sum (n^2 \log n) x^n, \qquad \sum \left(\frac{n^3 + 1}{n + 1}\right) x^n, \qquad \sum \left(\frac{3n^2 + 2}{n(\log n)^2 + 18}\right) x^n$$

To find a series whose radius of convergence is neither 1 nor 0 nor ∞, we would look for a series in which the behavior of the coefficients is dominated by the nth power of some fixed positive number. Thus the following series all have a radius of convergence equal to 5:

$$\sum \left(\frac{1}{5}\right)^n x^n, \qquad \sum \left(\frac{n^4 + 2n + 1}{3n^5 5^n + 12}\right) x^n, \qquad \sum \frac{n^4}{5^n (\log n)^7} x^n$$

In order that a series should converge for every value of x, its coefficients must approach zero more rapidly than the nth power of any fixed number. The following series converge for every x:

$$\sum \frac{x^n}{n^n}, \qquad \sum \frac{x^n}{2^{n^2}}, \qquad \sum \frac{n^3 + 2n^2 + 5}{4^{n \log n}(6n + 1)} x^n$$

Finally, if a series is to converge for no value of x except $x = 0$, its coefficients must get large very rapidly, faster than the nth power of any fixed number. The following series converge only at $x = 0$:

$$\sum n^n x^n, \qquad \sum 3^{n(n+1)} x^n, \qquad \sum e^{e^n} x^n$$

A little harder to handle are series whose coefficients involve $n!$, because the behavior of $(n!)^{1/n}$ when n is large is not obvious at first glance. Since, as we shall see in the next section, series involving $n!$ are quite important in practice, we now investigate the question of estimating the size of $(n!)^{1/n}$ when n is large. We claim that $(n!)^{1/n}$ behaves like n/e in the sense that

$$\lim_{n \to \infty} \frac{(n!)^{1/n}}{(n/e)} = 1 \tag{5.31}$$

Recall that this means if $\epsilon > 0$ is given we have

$$\frac{n}{e}(1 - \epsilon) \leqq (n!)^{1/n} \leqq \frac{n}{e}(1 + \epsilon) \tag{5.32}$$

for all large n.

To prove (5.31), note that since

$$n! = 1(2)(3)(4) \ldots (n),$$
$$\log n! = \log 1 + \log 2 + \cdots + \log n$$
$$= \sum_{j=1}^{n} \log j$$

and so

$$\log (n!)^{1/n} = \frac{1}{n} \sum_{j=1}^{n} \log j \qquad (5.33)$$

We estimate the size of this last sum by comparing it with

$$\int_{1}^{n} \log t \, dt$$

Indeed, from Fig. 5.3 it is clear that

Figure 5.3

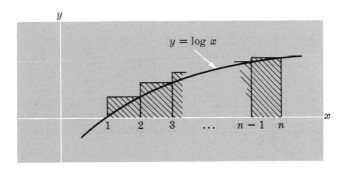

$$\log 2 + \log 3 + \cdots + \log n \geqq \int_{1}^{n} \log t \, dt,$$

while from Fig. 5.4 we see that

$$\log 2 + \log 3 + \cdots + \log n \leqq \int_{1}^{n+1} \log t \, dt$$

Combining these inequalities we obtain, after performing the integration,

$$n \log n - n + 1 \leqq \sum_{j=1}^{n} \log j \leqq (n + 1) \log (n + 1) - (n + 1) + 1$$

Thus, dividing by n

$$\log n - 1 + \frac{1}{n} \leq \log (n!)^{1/n} \leq \left(1 + \frac{1}{n}\right) \log (n + 1) - 1$$

exponentiating

$$\frac{n}{e} e^{1/n} \leq (n!)^{1/n} \leq \frac{n + 1}{e}(n + 1)^{1/n}$$

Figure 5.4

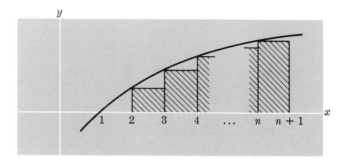

and dividing by n/e we get, finally,

$$e^{1/n} \leq \frac{(n!)^{1/n}}{n/e} \leq \left(1 + \frac{1}{n}\right)(n + 1)^{1/n}$$

Since the first and third members of this last inequality approach 1 as n approaches infinity, the second member must also, which was to be shown.

The point of this last result is that when we are calculating the radius of convergence of a power series we compute

$$\overline{\lim_{n \to \infty}} \, |a_n|^{1/n}$$

and if $(n!)^{1/n}$ occurs as a factor in this expression, it can be replaced by n/e without affecting the value of the limit superior (see Exercise 1 below).

Example
Find the radius of convergence of the series

$$\sum \frac{n^n}{n!} x^n$$

Here we have

$$\varlimsup_{n\to\infty} |a_n|^{1/n} = \varlimsup_{n\to\infty} \left\{ \frac{n}{(n!)^{1/n}} \right\}$$

$$= \varlimsup_{n\to\infty} \left\{ \frac{n}{n/e} \right\}$$

$$= e$$

Hence, the given series converges if $|x| < 1/e$ and diverges if $|x| > 1/e$.

As a final remark we note that Theorem 5.12 gives us no information about the convergence or divergence of the series at the two points $x = \pm 1/\mu$. In fact, anything can happen there, and each case has to be settled individually. The following three series each have radius of convergence 1. The first converges at ± 1, the second diverges at ± 1, and the third converges at -1 and diverges at $+1$ (the reader should verify these assertions):

$$\sum \frac{x^n}{n^2}, \qquad \sum (\log n)\, x^n, \qquad \sum \frac{x^n}{n}$$

Exercises

1. Let $\{b_n\}$ be an arbitrary sequence. Prove that

$$\varlimsup_{n\to\infty} \{(n!)^{1/n}|b_n|\} = \varlimsup_{n\to\infty} \left\{ \frac{n}{e}|b_n| \right\}$$

2. Find the radius of convergence of each of the following series.

   (a) $\sum n^2 x^n$

   (b) $\sum 3^n x^n$

   (c) $\sum \left(1 + \frac{1}{2^n}\right) x^n$

   (d) $\sum (n^3 + \log n)\, x^n$

   (e) $\sum \frac{x^n}{n!}$

   (f) $\sum \frac{(-1)^n x^{2n+1}}{(2n + 1)!}$

(g) $\sum 3^{n^3} x^n$

(h) $\sum \dfrac{(ne)^n}{n!} x^n$

(i) $\sum (\log n)^{15} x^n$

(j) $\sum (4^n + n^4) x^n$

(k) $\sum 1 + x + x^4 + x^9 + x^{16} + x^{25} + x^{36} + \cdots$

3.   Describe precisely the set of *all* numbers x for which each of the following series
     converges. (Careful! Some of these are hard.)

(a) $\sum \dfrac{n^2}{n^3 + 1} (x - 3)^n$

(b) $\sum \dfrac{(x + 2)^n}{(\log n)^4}$

(c) $\sum (6^n + 4)(x^2 - 8)^n$

(d) $\sum (x^2 - 3x + 2)^n 5^n$

(e) $\sum \dfrac{n^n}{n!} (x^2 + 1)^n$

5.11. *Taylor's Theorem*

In our work on the theory of contact we discovered that the best polynomial of given degree n for the approximation of a given function $f(x)$
near a point $x = a$ is the polynomial

$$f(a) + (x - a)f'(a) + (x - a)^2 \frac{f''(a)}{2!} + \cdots + (x - a)^n \frac{f^{(n)}(a)}{n!}$$

$$(5.34)$$

We now wish to ask just how good an approximation to $f(x)$ this polynomial is. For instance, if we used the polynomial

$$1 + x + \frac{x^2}{2} + \frac{x^3}{6}$$

to compute e^x for various small values of x, how much error could we
make? In other words, we want to estimate the size of the difference be-

tween the true value of $f(x)$ and the approximate value (5.34), for some fixed value of n, the degree of the polynomial. Taylor's theorem shows us how to do this.

THEOREM 5.13 (*Taylor's Theorem*). Let f be defined on an interval containing the two points a and b, and suppose that f is n times differentiable for $a \leqq x \leqq b$. Then there is a number ξ such that $a < \xi < b$ and

$$f(b) = f(a) + \sum_{k=1}^{n-1} \frac{(b-a)^k}{k!} f^{(k)}(a) + \frac{(b-a)^n}{n!} f^{(n)}(\xi) \quad (5.35)$$

PROOF Let a number K be defined by the equation

$$f(b) = f(a) + \sum_{k=1}^{n-1} \frac{(b-a)^k}{k!} f^{(k)}(a) + \frac{(b-a)^n}{n!} K$$

Now for $a \leqq x \leqq b$, define a new function F by

$$F(x) = -f(b) + f(x) + \sum_{k=1}^{n-1} \frac{(b-x)^k}{k!} f^{(k)}(x) + K \frac{(b-x)^n}{n!} \quad (5.36)$$

Differentiating (5.36), we find that

$$F'(x) = f'(x) + \sum_{k=1}^{n-1} \left[-\frac{(b-x)^{k-1}}{(k-1)!} f^{(k)}(x) + \frac{(b-x)^k}{k!} f^{(k+1)}(x) \right]$$

$$- \frac{(b-x)^{n-1}}{(n-1)!} K$$

Now, in the sum in the second term, almost everything cancels out, for the sum is

$$[-f'(x) + (b-x)f''(x)] + \left[-(b-x)f''(x) + \frac{(b-x)^2}{2!} f^{(3)}(x) \right]$$

$$+ \left[-\frac{(b-x)^2}{2!} f^{(3)}(x) + \frac{(b-x)^3}{3!} f^{(iv)}(x) \right] + \cdots$$

$$+ \left[-\frac{(b-x)^{n-2}}{(n-2)!} f^{(n-1)}(x) + \frac{(b-x)^{n-1}}{(n-1)!} f^{(n)}(x) \right]$$

in which everything cancels except the first term in the first set of brackets and the second term in the last set of brackets. Hence,

$$F'(x) = \frac{(b-x)^{n-1}}{(n-1)!} f^{(n)}(x) - K \frac{(b-x)^{n-1}}{(n-1)!}$$

$$= \frac{(b-x)^{n-1}}{(n-1)!} [f^{(n)}(x) - K] \tag{5.37}$$

From the definition of $F(x)$, we see that $F(a) = F(b) = 0$, and so by Rolle's theorem there is a point ξ, $a < \xi < b$ where $F'(\xi) = 0$. From (5.37) this means that

$$f^{(n)}(\xi) = K$$

which was to be shown.

The reader should verify that when $n = 1$ this theorem reduces to the mean-value theorem.

As an example of the use of Taylor's theorem, suppose we wish to calculate the number $e^{1/2}$ numerically. The polynomial of degree two (for instance) which has second-order contact with e^x at $x = 0$ is

$$f(0) + xf'(0) + \frac{x^2}{2} f''(0) = 1 + x + \frac{x^2}{2}$$

Hence, we suspect that the number

$$1 + \tfrac{1}{2} + \tfrac{1}{2}(\tfrac{1}{2})^2 = 1.625$$

may be an approximation to $e^{1/2}$. The question is, how good is it? According to Taylor's theorem, there is a number ξ such that $0 < \xi < \tfrac{1}{2}$ and

$$e^{1/2} = 1.625 + \frac{(\tfrac{1}{2} - 0)^3}{3!} e^\xi$$

Therefore,

$$e^{1/2} - 1.625 = \tfrac{1}{48} e^\xi \qquad (0 < \xi < \tfrac{1}{2})$$

and so

$$\begin{aligned}
|e^{1/2} - 1.625| &= \tfrac{1}{48} |e^\xi| \\
&\leq \tfrac{1}{48} e^{1/2} \qquad \text{(since } \xi < \tfrac{1}{2}) \\
&\leq (\tfrac{1}{48})2 \qquad \text{(to be crude)} \\
&= \tfrac{1}{24}
\end{aligned}$$

Hence, the number 1.625 can differ from $e^{1/2}$ by at most $\frac{1}{24} = 0.041$. In fact, it differs by about 0.024.

Yet Taylor's theorem should not be thought of as merely a computational tool since it is in fact of the highest theoretical importance. Let us use it to show that the power series

$$\sum_{n=0}^{\infty} \frac{x^n}{n!} \tag{5.38}$$

converges to the sum e^x for every value of x (that it converges to *something* for every value of x we know from the previous section). Fix an integer n. Then by Taylor's theorem,

$$e^x = \sum_{k=0}^{n-1} \frac{x^k}{k!} + \frac{x^n}{n!} e^\xi$$

since the nth derivative of e^x is e^x, where $0 < \xi < x$. Hence,

$$\left| e^x - \sum_{k=0}^{n-1} \frac{x^k}{k!} \right| \leqq \frac{|x|^n}{n!} e^{|x|}$$

Now as n approaches infinity the quantity on the right approaches zero (x is fixed). This can be shown in many ways, for instance, since $n! \geqq (n/e)^n$,

$$0 \leqq \frac{|x|^n}{n!} e^{|x|} \leqq \frac{|x|^n e^n}{n^n} e^{|x|}$$

$$\leqq \left(\frac{|x|e}{n} \right)^n e^{|x|}$$

which clearly approaches zero when n gets large. It follows that

$$\lim_{n \to \infty} \sum_{k=0}^{n-1} \frac{x^k}{k!} = e^x$$

which is to say that e^x is the limit of the sequence of partial sums of the series (5.38), which proves that

$$e^x = \sum_{n=0}^{\infty} \frac{x^n}{n!} \tag{5.39}$$

for every x, as claimed. The expansion (5.39) is called the Taylor series expansion of e^x. It can be used for many purposes; for instance, the number e can be calculated to any desired degree of accuracy from the rapidly converging series

$$e = 1 + 1 + \frac{1}{2!} + \frac{1}{3!} + \frac{1}{4!} + \cdots$$

$$= \sum_{n=0}^{\infty} \frac{1}{n!} \tag{5.40}$$

In general, if one is given a function $f(x)$ and it is desired to expand it in a Taylor series of the form

$$f(x) = \sum_{k=0}^{\infty} \frac{f^{(k)}(a)}{k!} (x - a)^k \tag{5.41}$$

then Taylor's theorem can be used in order to determine whether or not this series does converge to $f(x)$, and for which values of x it does so.

As another example we find the Taylor's series for $f(x) = \sin x$ about the origin $(a = 0)$. In this case

$$f(0) = 0; \qquad f'(0) = 1; \qquad f''(0) = 0; \qquad f^{(3)}(0) = -1; \ldots$$

and the series (5.41) takes the form

$$x - \frac{x^3}{3!} + \frac{x^5}{5!} - \frac{x^7}{7!} + \cdots \tag{5.42}$$

We claim that this series does indeed converge to $\sin x$ for every value of x, for by Taylor's theorem,

$$\sin x = x - \frac{x^3}{3!} + \cdots + \frac{(-1)^{(n-1)}x^{2n-1}}{(2n-1)!} + \frac{x^{2n}}{(2n)!} K \tag{5.43}$$

where K is the $(2n)$th derivative of $\sin x$, evaluated at some point ξ. Evidently $|K| \leq 1$, and so the term involving K in (5.43) approaches zero as n gets large, completing the proof of the assertion that

$$\sin x = \sum_{k=1}^{\infty} \frac{(-1)^{k-1}}{(2k-1)!} x^{2k-1} \tag{5.44}$$

for every x.

Finally, we give an example of a Taylor series which is valid for some but not for all x, and for which our present methods are not even capable of discovering the whole truth. Consider the function $f(x) =$

log $(1 + x)$. Here

$$f'(x) = \frac{1}{1 + x}; \qquad f''(x) = -\frac{1}{(1 + x)^2};$$

$$f^{(3)}(x) = \frac{2}{(1 + x)^3}; \qquad f^{(iv)}(x) = -\frac{3!}{(1 + x)^4}$$

and, in general,

$$f^{(k)}(x) = \frac{(-1)^{k+1}(k - 1)!}{(1 + x)^k} \qquad (k = 1, 2, 3, \ldots) \qquad (5.45)$$

Hence,

$$f^{(k)}(0) = (-1)^{k+1}(k - 1)! \qquad (k = 1, 2, 3, \ldots)$$

and the series (5.41) becomes

$$f(0) + xf'(0) + \frac{x^2}{2!}f''(0) + \cdots$$

$$= 0 + x + \frac{x^2}{2!}(-1) + \frac{x^3}{3!}(2!) + \frac{x^4}{4!}(-3!) + \cdots$$

$$= x - \frac{x^2}{2} + \frac{x^3}{3} - \frac{x^4}{4} + \cdots$$

We therefore suspect that this last series converges to log $(1 + x)$ for certain values of x. Notice that by Theorem 5.12 we know that this series converges for $|x| < 1$, but we do not know that it converges to log $(1 + x)$ there. To show that, we would try to use Taylor's theorem again, and would find that

$$\log (1 + x) = x - \frac{x^2}{2} + \cdots + (-1)^{n-1}\frac{x^{n-1}}{n - 1} + \frac{x^n}{n!}f^{(n)}(\xi)$$

where ξ lies between 0 and x. From (5.45), the last term is

$$\frac{x^n}{n!}(-1)^{n+1}\frac{(n - 1)!}{(1 + \xi)^n} = (-1)^{n+1}\frac{1}{n}\left(\frac{x}{1 + \xi}\right)^n$$

If $x > 0$, so is $\xi > 0$, and if $x < 1$ also, then $|x/(1 + \xi)| < 1$. Thus, for $0 \leq x < 1$ our series does indeed converge to log $(1 + x)$. If $x < 0$ and ξ lies between 0 and x, then we cannot be sure that $|x/(1 + \xi)| < 1$ unless $-\frac{1}{2} \leq x \leq 0$ (e.g., $x = -\frac{3}{4}$, $\xi = -\frac{1}{2}$). Thus we can prove that

$$\log (1 + x) = x - \frac{x^2}{2} + \frac{x^3}{3} - \cdots \qquad (5.46)$$

is true if $-\frac{1}{2} \le x < 1$. It is, in fact, true if only $-1 < x \le 1$, though we do not find this out by our present method.

Further examples of Taylor's series, and their domains of validity are

$$\cos x = 1 - \frac{x^2}{2!} + \frac{x^4}{4!} - \frac{x^6}{6!} + \cdots$$

$$= \sum_{n=0}^{\infty} (-1)^n \frac{x^{2n}}{(2n)!} \qquad \text{(all } x\text{)} \tag{5.47}$$

$$(1 + x)^{1/2} = 1 + \frac{1}{2}x - \frac{1}{2 \cdot 4}x^2 + \frac{1 \cdot 3}{2 \cdot 4 \cdot 6}x^3 - \cdots - \quad (-1 < x \le 1) \tag{5.48}$$

$$\cosh x = 1 + \frac{x^2}{2!} + \frac{x^4}{4!} + \frac{x^6}{6!} + \cdots \qquad \text{(all } x\text{)} \tag{5.49}$$

$$\sinh x = x + \frac{x^3}{3!} + \frac{x^5}{5!} + \frac{x^7}{7!} + \cdots \qquad \text{(all } x\text{)} \tag{5.50}$$

It is also a fact, which we shall not prove here, that if a certain power series converges on an interval, then that series can be differentiated or integrated term-by-term within the interval of convergence. That is, if

$$f(x) = \sum_{n=0}^{\infty} a_n x^n \qquad (|x| < R) \tag{5.51}$$

then it is true that

$$f'(x) = \sum_{n=0}^{\infty} n a_n x^{n-1} \qquad (|x| < R) \tag{5.52}$$

as one might expect. This should not be taken for granted, however, since after our experiences with rearrangements of conditionally convergent series one should be wary about extrapolating the rules of finite sums to infinite series.

It is also true that from the relation (5.51) there follows

$$\int_0^x f(t)\, dt = \sum_{n=0}^{\infty} \frac{a_n}{n+1} x^{n+1} \qquad (|x| < R) \tag{5.53}$$

Using these facts we can make a new series from the old. Indeed, since

$$\frac{1}{1-x} = 1 + x + x^2 + \cdots \qquad (|x| < 1) \tag{5.54}$$

we find by differentiation that

$$\frac{1}{(1 - x)^2} = 1 + 2x + 3x^2 + 4x^3 + \cdots \qquad (|x| < 1) \qquad (5.55)$$

and by integration from 0 to x that

$$-\log(1 - x) = x + \frac{x^2}{2} + \frac{x^3}{3} + \cdots \qquad (|x| < 1) \qquad (5.56)$$

in agreement with (5.46).

Again, from the geometric series

$$\frac{1}{1 + x^2} = 1 - x^2 + x^4 - x^6 + \cdots \qquad (|x| < 1) \qquad (5.57)$$

we find by integrating from 0 to x

$$\tan^{-1} x = x - \frac{x^3}{3} + \frac{x^5}{5} - \cdots \qquad (5.58)$$

Many other examples can be constructed in this way.

Exercises

1. Compute $\sin \frac{1}{2}$ from the first two nonvanishing terms of the series for $\sin x$ about $x = 0$; estimate the numerical error; compare with the true value.
2. Same as Exercise 1 with $\log \frac{1}{2}$.
3. Find the sums of the following infinite series.

   (a) $\displaystyle\sum_{n=1}^{\infty} \frac{n}{2^n}$

   (b) $\displaystyle\sum_{n=0}^{\infty} \frac{1}{3^n n!}$

   (c) $\displaystyle\sum_{n=0}^{\infty} \frac{(-1)^n}{(2n + 1)!} \left(\frac{\pi}{2}\right)^{2n+1}$

   (d) $\displaystyle\sum_{n=1}^{\infty} \frac{1}{2^n n}$

   (e) $\displaystyle\sum_{n=0}^{\infty} \frac{(\log 2)^{2n}}{(2n)!}$

   (f) $\displaystyle\sum_{n=1}^{\infty} \frac{(-1)^n}{(2n - 1)} \left(\frac{1}{\sqrt{3}}\right)^{2n-1}$

4.   Find the Taylor expansions of each of the following functions in powers of $x - a$, where a is as shown.

   (a) $\sin x$ $(a = \pi/2)$
   (b) e^x $(a = \log 2)$

   (c) $\dfrac{1}{(1 - x)^{1/2}}$ $(a = 0)$

   (d) $\sin^{-1} x$ $(a = 0)$ [Hint: Use the result of (c).]

5.   Find the first four terms of the Taylor series of each of the functions $\log \cos x$, $\tan x$, 3^x, about the origin.

6.   Compute the value of the integral

$$\int_0^{1/2} e^{t^2} \, dt$$

by replacing e^{t^2} by its Taylor series and integrating term-by-term, to three-figure accuracy.

Abstract Mathematical Structures; Groups
Vector Spaces
Mathematical Induction
Linear Independence
Subspaces
Bases
Homomorphisms

6

Vector Spaces

6.1. Abstract Mathematical Structures; Groups

The word "abstraction," in lay usage, often connotes a divorce from reality, an unrecognizable blob, or a train of thought completely unrelated to the physical world. In fact, the word is derived from Latin words meaning "to draw out of," and that literal meaning is the precise sense in which the term is employed in mathematics. Abstraction in mathematics is the process whereby one recognizes the essential similarities between superficially different objects. Having recognized those essential properties, one then studies the family of all objects having those properties. Results thereby obtained then are applicable to any of the original objects, and so a considerable economy of thought is achieved.

Consider, for example, the following two statements:

Statement 1. Let a be a positive integer which is not divisible by 17. Then the number a^{16} leaves a remainder of 1 when divided by 17.

Statement 2. Let S be a set of six objects. Let $f: S \to S$ be a function whose domain and range are both S, and suppose f is 1-1. Let x be one of the six members of S, and consider the following sequence of objects: $f(x)$, $f(f(x))$, $f(f(f(x)))$, ... Then the 720th member of this sequence is x itself!!

Both of these statements are true, though rather unexciting when seen, as now, out of context. What is interesting here, though, is that they are both special cases of the same statement about an abstract class of objects known as *groups,* a statement which has many other consequences of importance. The mechanism which operates in each case is actually the same and has nothing to do with the superficial, specific properties of numbers or 1–1 functions. The operative mechanism, in fact, concerns only the multiplication process, in the first case of a number by itself repeatedly, and in the second case of a function by itself repeatedly. The reader who tries to prove either of these assertions directly soon will see how encumbered by inessential appearances the proof will be, whereas when viewed from the proper abstract standpoint, both statements appear, along with a host of others, as trivial corollaries of a very natural chain of reasoning.

To study the process of abstraction more closely we proceed to develop the concept of an abstract group, first by giving some examples, and then by distilling from ("drawing out of") these examples their essential similarities.

Example 1.   The Nonzero Real Numbers; Multiplicative Structure
Consider the set S whose members are all the real numbers except zero. Besides forming a set, the real numbers have arithmetic structure. Let us concentrate on multiplication. If α and β are two members of S, then so is $\alpha\beta$, for $\alpha\beta$ cannot be zero if $\alpha \neq 0$ and $\beta \neq 0$. There is a number 1 in S with the property that

$$\alpha \cdot 1 = 1 \cdot \alpha = \alpha$$

for all α in S. Further, if α is in S, there is a number α^{-1} in S such that

$$\alpha \cdot \alpha^{-1} = \alpha^{-1} \cdot \alpha = 1$$

(i.e., α has a reciprocal). Finally, multiplication is associative

$$\alpha(\beta\gamma) = (\alpha\beta)\gamma \qquad (\text{all } \alpha, \beta, \gamma \text{ in } S)$$

and commutative

$$\alpha\beta = \beta\alpha \qquad (\text{all } \alpha, \beta \text{ in } S)$$

Example 2. Rotations of the Square
Let a square be given. Consider the following four operations which can
be performed on the square.

Operation I: Leave the square alone.

Operation R_1: Rotate the square counterclockwise 90°.

Operation R_2: Rotate the square counterclockwise 180°.

Operation R_3: Rotate the square counterclockwise 270°.

We next define an operation of multiplication on this set of rotations I,
R_1, R_2, R_3 of the square. By the operation R_1R_2, for instance, we mean
the operation whose effect on the square is the same as doing first R_2 and
then R_1. This results in rotating the square first 180°, then 90°, or 270°
altogether, and so we write

$$R_1R_2 = R_3$$

In a similar way we complete the multiplication table for rotations of the
square as in Table IV. Thus, $R_2{}^2 = I$ means that if we do R_2 twice, the

Table IV

$\cdot$	I	R_1	R_2	R_3
I	I	R_1	R_2	R_3
R_1	R_1	R_2	R_3	I
R_2	R_2	R_3	I	R_1
R_3	R_3	I	R_1	R_2

effect on the square is the same as doing nothing at all. To summarize,
we have

(a) A set S of "objects": I, R_1, R_2, R_3,

(b) An operation, called multiplication, defined on this set S, whereby
the product of two members of S is again in S,

(c) An object I in S such that

$$xI = Ix = x \qquad \text{(all } x \text{ in } S)$$

analogous to the number 1 in Example 1.

(d) A reciprocal x^{-1} for every x in S. Thus, $R_1{}^{-1} = R_3$ because
$R_1R_3 = I$; $R_2{}^{-1} = R_2$ because $R_2R_2 = I$ and $R_3{}^{-1} = R_1$; $I^{-1} = I$ similarly.

(e) The associative and commutative laws for the operation of multiplication on S. In order to check that, for example,

$$R_1(R_2R_3) = (R_1R_2)R_3$$

we note that both sides represent the result of doing R_3, then R_2, then R_1 to the square, and so they must be equal.

Example 3.   Permutations
A *permutation f*, of a set of n objects, is a 1–1 function from the set to itself. For instance, a permutation of the set (a, b, c) is the function $f\colon f(a) = b, f(b) = a, f(c) = c$. As a shorthand notation for a permutation one could write

$$\begin{pmatrix} abc \\ bac \end{pmatrix}$$

in which the values of f appear in the second row, directly beneath the corresponding members of the set. Thus, for example, we can speak of "the permutation" $\begin{pmatrix} 1234 \\ 4312 \end{pmatrix}$, where we mean the function defined on the set 1, 2, 3, 4 with values $f(1) = 4, f(2) = 3, f(3) = 1, f(4) = 2$.

Now suppose that f and g are two permutations of the same set S. By the product fg of f and g we mean the permutation which assigns to each x in S the object $f(g(x))$ in S. That is, fg is the permutation of S which results from first applying g to S, and then f. Thus, if f is $\begin{pmatrix} 1234 \\ 4132 \end{pmatrix}$ and g is $\begin{pmatrix} 1234 \\ 1324 \end{pmatrix}$, then fg is $\begin{pmatrix} 1234 \\ 4312 \end{pmatrix}$ because

$$(fg)(1) = f(g(1)) = f(1) = 4$$
$$(fg)(2) = f(g(2)) = f(3) = 3$$
$$(fg)(3) = f(g(3)) = f(2) = 1$$
$$(fg)(4) = f(g(4)) = f(4) = 2$$

The operation of multiplying permutations is not commutative, for if f and g are as above, then gf is $\begin{pmatrix} 1234 \\ 4123 \end{pmatrix}$ which is different from fg. We do not mean that fg is never equal to gf, but only that the operation is not commutative because fg need not be equal to gf.

If the set S has n objects in it then there are exactly $n!$ different permutations of S. Indeed, the first member of S can be assigned to any one of n places; after this is done, the next member of S can be assigned to any one of $n - 1$ places, etc., whence the total number of possibilities is $n(n - 1)(n - 2) \cdots (1) = n!$ If, for example, S contains the three objects 1, 2, 3, then the six permutations of S are

$$I: \begin{pmatrix} 123 \\ 123 \end{pmatrix} \qquad \sigma_3: \begin{pmatrix} 123 \\ 132 \end{pmatrix}$$

$$\sigma_1: \begin{pmatrix} 123 \\ 213 \end{pmatrix} \qquad \sigma_4: \begin{pmatrix} 123 \\ 231 \end{pmatrix}$$

$$\sigma_2: \begin{pmatrix} 123 \\ 321 \end{pmatrix} \qquad \sigma_5: \begin{pmatrix} 123 \\ 312 \end{pmatrix}$$

We can construct a complete multiplication table for these six permutations. Thus

$$\sigma_1 \sigma_2 = \begin{pmatrix} 123 \\ 312 \end{pmatrix} = \sigma_5$$

$$\sigma_2{}^2 = \begin{pmatrix} 123 \\ 123 \end{pmatrix} = I$$

etc. The complete table is Table V.

Table V

.	I	σ_1	σ_2	σ_3	σ_4	σ_5
I	I	σ_1	σ_2	σ_3	σ_4	σ_5
σ_1	σ_1	I	σ_5	σ_4	σ_3	σ_4
σ_2	σ_2	σ_4	I	σ_5	σ_1	σ_3
σ_3	σ_3	σ_5	σ_4	I	σ_2	σ_1
σ_4	σ_4	σ_2	σ_3	σ_1	σ_5	I
σ_5	σ_5	σ_3	σ_1	σ_2	I	σ_4

The permutation I plays the role of the "neutral element" in the multiplication of permutations. That is to say, if σ is any permutation,

$$\sigma I = I\sigma = \sigma$$

It is furthermore true that every permutation has a reciprocal, or inverse. That is, for every permutation σ there is a permutation σ^{-1} such that

$$\sigma\sigma^{-1} = \sigma^{-1}\sigma = I$$

This is clear since σ^{-1} is just the inverse function of σ, which exists because σ is 1–1. In the case of the permutations in Table V one finds

$$I^{-1} = I; \quad \sigma_1{}^{-1} = \sigma_1; \quad \sigma_2{}^{-1} = \sigma_2; \quad \sigma_3{}^{-1} = \sigma_3; \quad \sigma_4{}^{-1} = \sigma_5; \quad \sigma_5{}^{-1} = \sigma_4$$

That multiplication of permutations is associative can be seen by noticing that both of the symbols

$$\rho(\sigma\tau), \qquad (\rho\sigma)\tau$$

stand for the permutation which assigns to each x in S the member

$$\rho(\sigma(\tau(x)))$$

of S, and so they are equal.

Example 4.   The Integers Modulo a Prime p
As a final example of an algebraic structure which has the properties we have been discussing, we consider a curious way to multiply two positive integers. Let p be a fixed prime number. If a and b are two positive integers, then by the *product of a and b modulo p* we mean the remainder which ab leaves after division by p. Thus, modulo 7, $4 \times 5 = 6$, because 4×5 leaves a remainder of 6 when divided by 7. Also

$$6 \times 4 = 4 \qquad \text{(modulo 5)}$$
$$8 \times 7 = 1 \qquad \text{(modulo 11)}$$
$$3 \times 9 = 6 \qquad \text{(modulo 7)}$$

The complete multiplication table for the integers 1, 2, 3, 4 modulo 5 is Table VI.

Table VI

$\cdot$	1	2	3	4
1	1	2	3	4
2	2	4	1	3
3	3	1	4	2
4	4	3	2	1

It is easy to show that this operation of multiplication modulo a prime is associative and commutative. Furthermore, the number 1 is the neutral element

$$1 \cdot x = x \cdot 1 = x \qquad (\text{all } x = 1, 2, 3, \ldots, p - 1)$$

Also, relative to 1, each integer $1, 2, \ldots, p - 1$ has a reciprocal, though this is not immediately obvious. In the case $p = 5$ of Table VI,

$$1^{-1} = 1; \qquad 2^{-1} = 3; \qquad 3^{-1} = 2; \qquad 4^{-1} = 4$$

Now that we have studied these four examples, we still have to carry out the process of abstraction. That is, we wish to define an abstract algebraic structure which has the essential features of the examples. In this way, by proving theorems about the abstract structure we will simultaneously be proving theorems about the nonzero real numbers, the permutations, the rotations of the square, the integers modulo p, and a great variety of other examples of this kind of a system.

To formulate our abstract definition we recognize first that we want to allow operations other than multiplication to be performed. Addition, for instance, will provide a wealth of examples, as will other operations which we have not yet discussed. Consider the operation of addition. What, in the case of addition of real numbers, plays the role of a neutral element? The distinguishing feature of a neutral element is that if any element operates on it the result is the same element we started with. Just as $x1 = x$ for all x tells us that 1 is the neutral element for multiplication, so $x + 0 = x$ for all x says that 0 is the neutral element for addition. In both cases it is true that

$$x \text{ (operation) (neutral element)} = x \qquad (\text{all } x)$$

Again, if the operation is addition, what is a reciprocal? The distinguishing feature of a reciprocal is that if x is given, then x^{-1} is the object such that

$$x \text{ (operation) } x^{-1} = \text{(neutral element)}$$

If the operation happens to be addition, then this equation reads

$$x + x^{-1} = 0$$

and this shows that x^{-1} is the object which we usually write as $-x$. To sum up, then, in the case of addition, the neutral element is the one which we usually write as 0, and the inverse of x is what we usually call its negative. We state our definition of an abstract group sufficiently generally so that all of these possibilities are covered.

DEFINITION Let there be given a set S. Suppose there is defined on S an operation $\circ$ which assigns to every ordered pair a,b of elements of S a unique member of S, called $a \circ b$. Suppose further that

(i) The associative law is satisfied, that is

$$a \circ (b \circ c) = (a \circ b) \circ c \qquad \text{(all } a, b, c \text{ in } S) \qquad (6.1)$$

(ii) There is an element e of S, called the neutral element, with the property that

$$a \circ e = e \circ a = a \qquad \text{(all } a \text{ in } S) \qquad (6.2)$$

(iii) Relative to e, every element of S has an inverse. That is, for every a in S there is an element a^{-1} of S such that

$$a \circ a^{-1} = a^{-1} \circ a = e \qquad (6.3)$$

Then we say that the set S, together with the operation $\circ$ forms a *group*.

We remark that a group is considerably more than just a set, and indeed it is wise to distinguish carefully between a group and its underlying set. A group is a set *together with* an operation which satisfies certain rules, while a set is just a structureless collection of things. This is typical in abstract algebra. Notice, too, that the group operation $\circ$ need not be commutative. If it is, we speak of a *commutative group,* or an *Abelian group.*

Exercises

1. Construct the multiplication table for the group of rotations of an equilateral triangle. Identify the inverse of each element.
2. How many permutations of $1, 2, \ldots, n$ leave the number 1 fixed? How many leave $1, 2, \ldots, p$ fixed?
3. Check, directly from Table V, that the associative law is satisfied in each of the cases

$$\sigma_1(\sigma_2\sigma_3) = (\sigma_1\sigma_2)\sigma_3; \qquad \sigma_3(\sigma_4\sigma_3) = (\sigma_3\sigma_4)\sigma_3$$

4. Construct the multiplication table for the permutations of two objects.

5. Enumerate the 24 permutations of four objects, and find the inverse of each one.

6. Show that each permutation of three objects can be written as a product of permutations each of whose squares is I.

7. Write out the complete multiplication table of the integers 1, 2, 3, 4, 5, 6 modulo 7. Find the inverse of each element.

8. Write out the complete multiplication table of the integers $1, 2, \ldots, 5$ modulo 6. Do these form a group? Why? Explain why the requirement that p be a prime in the text is essential.

9. Which of the following are groups:

   (a) the rational numbers under addition
   (b) the rational numbers under multiplication
   (c) the numbers of the form $m + n\sqrt{2}$, where m and n are integers not both zero, under multiplication.

10. Suppose the following statement is true (it is): "Let G be a group of n elements. If x is any element of G, then $x^n = e$, where e is the neutral element of G." Show that this implies the truth of Statements 1 and 2 in Section 6.1.

11. Prove that an element of a group cannot have two different inverses.

6.2. *Vector Spaces*

In this section we introduce another kind of abstract mathematical structure, the vector space. The study of vector spaces forms the backbone of linear algebra and leads to a wide variety of applications in mathematics and the sciences. A vector space is roughly a set of elements with an operation of addition defined on it, which satisfies the usual rules of addition, and furthermore (here is the difference between a vector space and an additive group), the elements of the set can be multiplied by real numbers, the result being a member of the set. Before giving a precise definition of a vector space we discuss a few examples.

Example 1. Polynomials of degree $\leqq n$
Let n be a fixed positive integer, and consider the set of all polynomials of degree $\leqq n$, that is, of all expressions

$$a_0 + a_1 x + a_2 x^2 + \cdots + a_n x^n$$

where the a_j are real numbers. On this set of objects we define addition in the usual way:

$$(a_0 + a_1x + \cdots + a_nx^n) + (b_0 + b_1x + \cdots + b_nx^n)$$
$$= (a_0 + b_0) + (a_1 + b_1)x + \cdots + (a_n + b_n)x^n$$

Evidently, the sum of two members of the set is again in the set. Hence, we have an Abelian group under addition. The neutral element is the polynomial all of whose coefficients are zero. The inverse (negative) of the polynomial

$$a_0 + a_1x + a_2x^2 + \cdots + a_nx^n$$

is the polynomial

$$(-a_0) + (-a_1)x + \cdots + (-a_n)x^n$$

and, trivially, addition of polynomials is associative and commutative.

If we stopped here, we would have just another example of an Abelian group, but we continue, by defining the operation of multiplying a polynomial by a real number. This, too, is done in the obvious way, by the relation

$$\alpha(a_0 + a_1x + \cdots + a_nx^n) = (\alpha a_0) + (\alpha a_1)x + \cdots + (\alpha a_n)x^n$$

where α is a real number. If $\mathbf{f}$ and $\mathbf{g}$ are any two polynomials of degree $\leqq n$, and α and β are real numbers, it is easy to check that

$$(\alpha\beta)\mathbf{f} = \alpha(\beta\mathbf{f}) \tag{6.4a}$$
$$\alpha(\mathbf{f} + \mathbf{g}) = \alpha\mathbf{f} + \alpha\mathbf{g} \tag{6.4b}$$
$$0\mathbf{f} = \mathbf{0} \tag{6.4c}$$
$$1 \cdot \mathbf{f} = \mathbf{f} \tag{6.4d}$$

The set of these polynomials, together with the two operations of addition and multiplication by real numbers, forms a vector space. When we think of polynomials as members of a vector space we will use bold-face type for their symbols, as was done in (6.4). In particular, in (6.4c) we carefully distinguished between the number zero and the zero polynomial. This distinction will be maintained.

Example 2.   Euclidean 2-space; the Plane
As another example of a vector space, we begin with the set of all points in the plane. We will then define an operation of addition on these points,

with respect to which they will form an Abelian group. We will then define the multiplication of a point by a real number to complete the vector space structure.

First, we define the operations analytically, then geometrically. Choose x and y axes in the plane. The *sum* of the points (a,b) and (c,d) is defined as the point $(a + c, c + d)$. Thus

$$(2,3) + (-1,4) = (1,7)$$

To multiply the point (x,y) by the real number α we define

$$\alpha(x,y) = (\alpha x, \alpha y)$$

so that

$$3(-4,2) = (-12,6)$$

for instance.

It is easy to see that the points of the plane form an Abelian group under addition, the neutral element being the point $(0,0)$ (the origin). Furthermore, it is clear that the properties 6.4(a)–(d) are satisfied by multiplication.

Geometrically, these same operations can be defined as follows. Given two points P and Q. Draw directed line segments from the origin to P and Q, and then complete the parallelogram which these two segments determine (see Fig. 6.1). The sum $P + Q$ of P and Q is then the point at

Figure 6.1

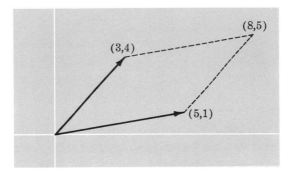

the fourth vertex of this parallelogram. To visualize multiplication by a real number α, let P be a given point. Again draw the directed segment from the origin to P, and call this $\overrightarrow{OP}$. The result of multiplying P by α is the point at the end of a line segment whose length is $|\alpha|$ times the length of $\overrightarrow{OP}$ and whose direction is the same as $\overrightarrow{OP}$ if $\alpha > 0$, opposite if $\alpha < 0$ (Fig. 6.2). The reader should satisfy himself that our analytic and

Figure 6.2

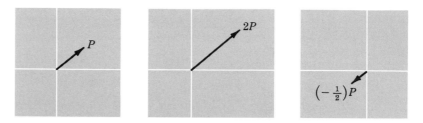

geometric definitions of addition and of multiplication by real numbers are identical.

We proceed with the definition of an abstract vector space over the real numbers ("vector space").

> **DEFINITION**   Let there be given a set S of objects $\mathbf{f}, \mathbf{g}, \ldots$
> Suppose that on this set there is defined an operation of addition under which the set forms an Abelian group. Suppose further that to every real number α and element $\mathbf{f}$ of the set there corresponds an element $\alpha\mathbf{f}$ of the set in such a way that
>
> $$(\alpha\beta)\mathbf{f} = \alpha(\beta\mathbf{f})$$
> $$(\alpha + \beta)\mathbf{f} = \alpha\mathbf{f} + \beta\mathbf{f}$$
> $$\alpha(\mathbf{f} + \mathbf{g}) = \alpha\mathbf{f} + \alpha\mathbf{g}$$
> $$1 \cdot \mathbf{f} = \mathbf{f}$$
>
> for all $\mathbf{f}, \mathbf{g}$ in the set. Then we say that the set S together with the operations of addition and multiplication by real numbers forms a *vector space*. In this case, the elements of the vector space will be called *vectors*, the operation of multiplication by real numbers may be called *scalar multiplication*, and the real numbers themselves may be referred to as *scalars*.

We note for reference that the statement "form an Abelian group under addition" means that

(a) $\mathbf{f} + (\mathbf{g} + \mathbf{h}) = (\mathbf{f} + \mathbf{g}) + \mathbf{h}$ (all $\mathbf{f}$, $\mathbf{g}$, $\mathbf{h}$)
(b) $\mathbf{f} + \mathbf{g} = \mathbf{g} + \mathbf{f}$ (all $\mathbf{f}$, $\mathbf{g}$)
(c) There is a vector $\mathbf{0}$ such that $\mathbf{f} + \mathbf{0} = \mathbf{f}$ (all $\mathbf{f}$)
(d) For every $\mathbf{f}$ there is a vector $-\mathbf{f}$ such that

$$\mathbf{f} + (-\mathbf{f}) = \mathbf{0}$$

Subtraction of vectors is defined by

$$\mathbf{f} - \mathbf{g} = \mathbf{f} + (-\mathbf{g})$$

As another example of a vector space we discuss n-dimensional Euclidean space. This is the natural generalization of Example 2 to higher dimensions, and reduces to Example 2 when $n = 2$. If n is given, consider the set of sequences of n real numbers

$$(\alpha_1, \alpha_2, \alpha_3, \ldots, \alpha_n)$$

This is the set of objects which we shall make into a vector space by defining suitable operations on it. First, the sum of two such sequences is defined by

$$(\alpha_1, \ldots, \alpha_n) + (\beta_1, \ldots, \beta_n) = (\alpha_1 + \beta_1, \alpha_2 + \beta_2, \ldots, \alpha_n + \beta_n)$$

Next, the product of a real number α by such a sequence is

$$\alpha(\gamma_1, \gamma_2, \ldots, \gamma_n) = (\alpha\gamma_1, \alpha\gamma_2, \ldots, \alpha\gamma_n)$$

It is very simple to check off all the axioms of a vector space and see that they are all satisfied. For instance, the zero vector is

$$\mathbf{0} = (0, 0, 0, \ldots, 0)$$

and the negative of a vector is

$$-(\alpha_1, \ldots, \alpha_n) = (-\alpha_1, \ldots, -\alpha_n)$$

This vector space is called n-dimensional Euclidean space, and is denoted symbolically by E^n. If one thinks of the members of the sequence as the coordinates of a point, one can use geometrical language when discussing E^n, though it may be difficult to draw pictures if $n \geq 4$.

Exercises

1. Prove that in an abstract vector space V we have $0\mathbf{f} = \mathbf{0}$ for all $\mathbf{f}$ in V.
2. Prove that $\alpha \cdot \mathbf{0} = \mathbf{0}$ for all real numbers α.
3. Demonstrate the equivalence of the geometric and analytic definitions of addition and scalar multiplication in E^2.
4. Verify that E^n satisfies the axioms for a vector space.
5. Prove that

$$(-\alpha)\mathbf{f} = \alpha(-\mathbf{f}) = -(\alpha\mathbf{f})$$

    for all vectors $\mathbf{f}$ and all scalars α.
6. Do the real numbers form a vector space over the real numbers?

6.3 *Mathematical Induction*

This section forms a digression from the principal developments of the chapter. We wish to introduce here a general method for proving theorems which will be useful in the sequel as well as in virtually all fields of mathematics. Indeed, in our work in calculus, we have already used the method in question, the principle of mathematical induction, *sotto voce,* and we want to make it explicit now.

The following may be taken as an axiom for the positive integers, and is called the *well-ordering principle.*

AXIOM   Let S be a nonempty set of positive integers. Then S contains a smallest element.

Notice that this innocent-looking statement would be false if "integers" were replaced by "real numbers" or "rational numbers" since, for example, the set of all real numbers which are larger than 1 does not have a smallest member. We say that the positive integers are *well ordered.*

THEOREM 6.1.   Let S be a set of positive integers such that

(a) S contains 1.

(b) If m is any member of S, then $m + 1$ also belongs to S.

Then S contains every positive integer.

PROOF   Suppose the contrary. Then the set T of positive integers, which are not in S, is not empty. Therefore, T has a least member, say n_0. By hypothesis (a), $n_0 \geq 2$. Since n_0 is the least element of T, $n_0 - 1$ is not in T and, therefore, is in S. By (b), then, $(n_0 - 1) + 1 = n_0$ is in S also, a contradiction.

THEOREM 6.2 (*The Principle of Mathematical Induction*).   Suppose that there is associated with every positive integer n a proposition P_n. Suppose that (a) P_1 is true and (b) if P_m is true, then so is P_{m+1}. Then all of the propositions $P_1, P_2, \ldots$ are true.

PROOF   The set of positive integers S containing those integers n for which P_n is true satisfies the conditions of Theorem 6.1, Q.E.D.

The beauty of the induction principle lies in the hypothesis (b). We do not need to prove that P_m is true!! We need only show that *if* it is, then P_{m+1} is true also. This point is vital, and should be thoroughly appreciated before going on to the next section.

Example 1.
Prove, by induction, that the sum of the integers $1, 2, \ldots, n$ is $n(n + 1)/2$.

PROOF   With each positive integer n we associate the proposition P_n:

$$1 + 2 + \cdots + n = \frac{n(n + 1)}{2}$$

Then we have an infinite sequence of propositions to prove:

$$P_1: 1 = \frac{(1)(2)}{2}$$

$$P_2: 1 + 2 = \frac{(2)(3)}{2}$$

$$P_3: 1 + 2 + 3 = \frac{(3)(4)}{2}$$

etc. We use the principle of induction. First, P_1 is obviously true.

Next, *suppose P_m is true.* Then

$$1 + 2 + 3 + \cdots + (m + 1)$$
$$= 1 + 2 + \cdots + m + (m + 1)$$
$$= \frac{m(m + 1)}{2} + (m + 1) \qquad \text{(since } P_m \text{ is true)}$$
$$= \frac{(m + 1)(m + 2)}{2}$$

and we have indeed proved that, if P_m is true, then so is P_{m+1}. Our proof is now complete. The key step in the proof was the use of the very same formula which we were trying to prove in the second line of the preceding equations. This is typical of a proof by induction, since in the middle of such a proof we always suppose that the theorem we are trying to prove is true for a certain value of n and then try to prove it for the next value.

Example 2.
Given that $\log (ab) = \log a + \log b$, prove that

$$\log (a^n) = n \log a \qquad\qquad (6.5)$$

for every positive integer n.

PROOF   The proposition P_n is (6.5). P_1 is clearly true. Now suppose P_m is true. Then

$$\log (a^{m+1}) = \log (a^m a)$$
$$= \log a^m + \log a$$
$$= m \log a + \log a$$
$$= (m + 1) \log a$$

and P_{m+1} is true also, Q.E.D.

The principle of induction is useful not only in proving theorems, but also in making definitions. If we wish to define a family of objects, one for each positive integer, we can (a) define the first object and (b) tell how to obtain any object from its predecessor. By induction, we shall have defined the entire family.

Example 3.

Pretend that we had never seen the symbol $n!$ before. To define it we could say that

(a) $1! = 1$
(b) $n! = n(n - 1)!$ $(n = 2, 3, 4, \ldots)$

Based on this definition of $n!$ we could then prove as a theorem the fact that $n! = 1(2)(3)(4) \ldots (n)$. The proof of this theorem would, of course, be by induction.

Example 4.

We define a certain sequence of numbers $\{x_n\}$ by saying that

(a) $x_1 = 2$
(b) $x_{n+1} = 2x_n$ $(n = 1, 2, 3, \ldots)$

If we wrote out the first few members of this sequence, we would find $1, 2, 4, 8, 16, 32, \ldots$. We might then conjecture that $x_n = 2^n$ for every n, and prove the conjecture by induction.

Exercises

1. A sequence $\{x_n\}_1^\infty$ is defined by

    (a) $x_1 = 1$
    (b) $x_{n+1} = x_n + (n + 1)$ $(n = 1, 2, 3, \ldots)$

    Find a formula for x_n and prove it by induction.
2. Prove the theorem referred to in Example 3.
3. Prove the conjecture referred to in Example 4.
4. Prove that

$$1^2 + 2^2 + 3^2 + \cdots + n^2 = \frac{n(2n + 1)(n + 1)}{6}$$

5. Prove by induction that

$$\sum_{j=0}^{n} r^j = \frac{r^{n+1} - 1}{r - 1} \quad (n = 1, 2, 3, \ldots)$$

6.   A sequence $\{y_n\}_1^\infty$ is defined by

    (a) $y_1 = 2$
    (b) $y_{n+1} = y_n^2$ $(n = 1, 2, 3, \ldots)$

Find a formula for y_n, and prove it by induction.

7.   Suppose $x_1 = 2$, $x_2 = 3$, and, in general, x_n is the smallest positive integer which is not divisible by any of $x_1, x_2, \ldots, x_{n-1}$. Write out the first ten members of the sequence.

6.4.   *Linear Independence*

We return now to the mainstream of the development by taking up the study of vector spaces. Let V be a given vector space over the real numbers, and let $\mathbf{u}_1, \mathbf{u}_2, \ldots, \mathbf{u}_n$ be a finite set of vectors in V. By a *linear combination* of the vectors $\mathbf{u}_1, \mathbf{u}_2, \ldots, \mathbf{u}_n$ we mean a vector of the form

$$\alpha_1 \mathbf{u}_1 + \alpha_2 \mathbf{u}_2 + \cdots + \alpha_n \mathbf{u}_n$$

where $\alpha_1, \ldots, \alpha_n$ are scalars (real numbers). Thus

$$2\mathbf{u}_1 - \mathbf{u}_2, \mathbf{u}_1 + \mathbf{u}_2 + \cdots + \mathbf{u}_n, \mathbf{u}_1 + 2\mathbf{u}_2 + \cdots + n\mathbf{u}_n$$

are each linear combinations of $\mathbf{u}_1, \mathbf{u}_2, \mathbf{u}_3, \ldots, \mathbf{u}_n$.

> **DEFINITION**   We say that the vectors $\mathbf{u}_1, \mathbf{u}_2, \ldots, \mathbf{u}_n$ are *linearly dependent* if there exist scalars $\alpha_1, \ldots, \alpha_n$ *not all zero* such that
>
> $$\alpha_1 \mathbf{u}_1 + \alpha_2 \mathbf{u}_2 + \cdots + \alpha_n \mathbf{u}_n = \mathbf{0} \tag{6.6}$$

If no such scalars exist, the set is called a *linearly independent* set. To put it positively, $\mathbf{u}_1, \mathbf{u}_2, \ldots, \mathbf{u}_n$ are a linearly independent set if from (6.6) it follows that

$$\alpha_1 = \alpha_2 = \cdots = \alpha_n = 0$$

Example 1.
In the vector space of polynomials of degree 2, the two vectors

$$\mathbf{u}_1 = 1 + 0x + 0x^2$$
$$\mathbf{u}_2 = 0 + x + x^2$$

are linearly independent, for if $\alpha_1 u_1 + \alpha_2 u_2$ is the zero vector (i.e., the polynomial of second degree all of whose coefficients are zero), then

$$\alpha_1(1 + 0 \cdot x + 0 \cdot x^2) + \alpha_2(0 + 1 \cdot x + 0 \cdot x^2) = \alpha_1 + \alpha_2 x + 0 \cdot x^2$$
$$= 0 + 0 \cdot x + 0 \cdot x^2$$

and so $\alpha_1 = \alpha_2 = 0$.

In this same vector space, the four vectors

$$\mathbf{u}_1 = 1 + x + x^2$$
$$\mathbf{u}_2 = 1 - 2x + x^2$$
$$\mathbf{u}_3 = 2 + 3x - x^2$$
$$\mathbf{u}_4 = 4 + 2x + x^2$$

are linearly *dependent* because

$$\mathbf{u}_1 + \mathbf{u}_2 + \mathbf{u}_3 - \mathbf{u}_4 = \mathbf{0}$$

Example 2.

In the Euclidean plane E^2, the vectors

$$\mathbf{u}_1 = (2,1)$$
$$\mathbf{u}_2 = (-3,4)$$

are independent because if

$$\alpha_1 \mathbf{u}_1 + \alpha_2 \mathbf{u}_2 = (0,0)$$

then by computing the left side we see that

$$2\alpha_1 - 3\alpha_2 = 0$$
$$\alpha_1 + \alpha_2 = 0$$

and solving these equations, $\alpha_1 = \alpha_2 = 0$, which was to be shown.

The vectors $(3,5) = \mathbf{u}_1$ and $(-9,-15) = \mathbf{u}_2$ are dependent because $3\mathbf{u}_1 + \mathbf{u}_2 = \mathbf{0}$. In the space E^2 it is easy to check that two vectors are dependent if and only if they lie on the same straight line through the origin. In Theorem 6.5 (Section 6.5) we will prove, among other things, that any set of more than two vectors in E^2 is necessarily dependent.

We have so far defined independence only for finite sets of vectors. An infinite set of vectors is linearly independent if and only if every finite subset of them is linearly independent. In the vector space of all polynomials (of whatever degree) the vectors $1, x, x^2, x^3, \ldots$ form an infinite, linearly independent set, while the vectors 1, x, x^2, $(x - 1)^2$, x^3, $(x - 1)^3$, ... are linearly dependent.

THEOREM 6.3. A set $\mathbf{u}_1, \mathbf{u}_2, \ldots, \mathbf{u}_n$ is linearly dependent if and only if one of the $\mathbf{u}_j$ can be expressed as a linear combination of the others.

PROOF Suppose $\mathbf{u}_1, \mathbf{u}_2, \ldots, \mathbf{u}_n$ are linearly dependent. Then

$$\alpha_1 \mathbf{u}_1 + \cdots + \alpha_n \mathbf{u}_n = \mathbf{0}$$

for some set of scalars $\alpha_1, \ldots, \alpha_n$ not all of which are zero. Suppose $\alpha_p \neq 0$. Then

$$\mathbf{u}_p = \left(-\frac{\alpha_1}{\alpha_p}\right)\mathbf{u}_1 + \cdots + \left(-\frac{\alpha_{p-1}}{\alpha_p}\right)\mathbf{u}_{p-1}$$
$$+ \left(-\frac{\alpha_{p+1}}{\alpha_p}\right)\mathbf{u}_{p+1} + \cdots + \left(-\frac{\alpha_n}{\alpha_p}\right)\mathbf{u}_n$$

which was to be shown. The converse is trivial.

THEOREM 6.4. Let $\mathbf{u}_1, \ldots, \mathbf{u}_n$ be linearly independent. If

$$\alpha_1 \mathbf{u}_1 + \cdots + \alpha_n \mathbf{u}_n = \beta_1 \mathbf{u}_1 + \cdots + \beta_n \mathbf{u}_n$$

then $\alpha_1 = \beta_1$, $\alpha_2 = \beta_2, \ldots, \alpha_n = \beta_n$.

PROOF Left as an exercise.

Theorem 6.4 shows that any vector which can be written as a linear combination of the given independent vectors can be so written in exactly one way.

DEFINITION Let V be a vector space. Suppose there exists a nonnegative integer m such that

(a) V contains a set of m linearly independent vectors, and
(b) every set of $m + 1$ vectors in V is linearly dependent.

Then m is called the *dimension* of the space V. If no such m exists, we say that V is *infinite-dimensional*.

The dimension of a vector space is therefore the maximum number of linearly independent vectors which can be found in the space, or ∞.

Example 3.
The vector space of all polynomials of degree 2 is three-dimensional. It contains three independent vectors, e.g., 1, x, x^2, and it is easy to show that any four quadratic polynomials are dependent.

Example 4.
The Euclidean plane is two-dimensional. It contains two independent vectors, for example, $\mathbf{i} = (1,0)$ and $\mathbf{j} = (0,1)$, and it is easy to show that any three vectors in this space are dependent.

Example 5.
The vector space of all polynomials is infinite-dimensional.

Exercises

1. Prove the "it is easy to show" assertions in Examples 3 and 4.
2. Prove Theorem 6.4.
3. Let V be a vector space of dimension n. If $r > n$, show that any set of r vectors is linearly dependent.
4. Let $\mathbf{f}_1, \mathbf{f}_2, \ldots, \mathbf{f}_n$ be n independent polynomials. Are their derivatives necessarily independent? Prove your answer. If the derivatives are independent, must the polynomials be? Prove.
5. (a) Are $(3,2)$ and $(1,4)$ independent vectors in E^2?
   (b) Are $(1,3)$ and $(-2,-6)$ independent vectors in E^2?
   (c) Under what conditions on the numbers a,b,c,d are the vectors (a,b) and (c,d) independent in E^2?
6. (a) Are $1 + x$, $2x - 3$, $x^2 + 1$ independent polynomials?
   (b) Are 2, $3 + x$, $x^2 - x + 1$ independent?
   (c) Under what conditions on the numbers a, b, c, d are the polynomials $a + bx$ and $c + dx$ independent?
7. Find three independent vectors in E^3. Find three dependent vectors in E^3.
8. In E^n show that the following n vectors are independent: $\mathbf{e}_1 = (1, 0, 0, \ldots, 0)$, $\mathbf{e}_2 = (0, 1, 0, \ldots, 0), \ldots, \mathbf{e}_n = (0, 0, 0, \ldots, 0, 1)$.

6.5.　Subspaces

Let V be a vector space, and suppose S is a subset of V. Then S inherits from V the operations of addition and scalar multiplication. However, S need not be closed under these operations. That is, if $\mathbf{x}$ and $\mathbf{y}$ are in S, $\mathbf{x} + \mathbf{y}$ need not be, and $\alpha\mathbf{x}$ need not be in S. If, on the other hand, S *is* closed under these operations we call S a *subspace* of V.

> **DEFINITION**　A subset S of a vector space V is a *subspace* of V if S is itself a vector space under the operations of addition and scalar multiplication inherited from V.

To prove that a certain subset is, in fact, a subspace one need only show that, if $\mathbf{x}$ and $\mathbf{y}$ are in S and α is a real number, then $\mathbf{x} + \mathbf{y}$ and $\alpha\mathbf{x}$ are both in S. The remaining axioms for a vector space are automatically satisfied.

Examples
1.　In the vector space of all polynomials of degree ≤ 13, the set of polynomials of degree ≤ 9 forms a subspace, as does the set of polynomials whose constant term is zero. The polynomials of degree ≤ 13 all of whose coefficients are integers do not form a subspace of this space. Why?
2.　In Euclidean three-dimensional space E^3, the vectors of the form $(x,y,0)$ form a subspace as do the vectors $(x,0,0)$, or the set of vectors (x,y,x).

> **DEFINITION**　Let V be a vector space, and let $\mathbf{u}_1, \mathbf{u}_2, \ldots, \mathbf{u}_m$ be a set of vectors in V. By the *subspace generated by* $\mathbf{u}_1, \mathbf{u}_2, \ldots, \mathbf{u}_m$ we mean the totality of finite linear combinations of the $\mathbf{u}_i$, that is, the set of all vectors of the form
>
> $$\alpha_1\mathbf{u}_1 + \alpha_2\mathbf{u}_2 + \cdots + \alpha_m\mathbf{u}_m$$
>
> as the α_i range over the real numbers.

3.　In the space of all polynomials, the subspace generated by 1, x, x^2 is the space of quadratic polynomials.

4. In E^3, the vectors $(1,0,0)$, $(0,1,0)$ generate the set of all vectors $(\alpha,\beta,0)$, whose third coordinate is zero.

Notice that in the space of all polynomials, the vectors 1, x, x^2 generate the quadratic polynomials, and the vectors

$$1, \ x, \ x^2, \ 2x - 1, \ 3x^2 - 2, \ (x + 1)^2$$

generate the quadratic polynomials also. In the second set of vectors, we gained no advantage from having the last three on the list; the subspace generated by them did not change. The reason for this is, of course, that the second set of six vectors is not a linearly independent set. Therefore, a linear combination of all six of them

$$\alpha_1 \cdot 1 + \alpha_2 \cdot x + \alpha_3 x^2 + \alpha_4(2x - 1) + \alpha_5(3x^2 - 2) + \alpha_6(x + 1)^2$$

is also a linear combination of just the first three

$$(\alpha_1 - \alpha_4 - 2\alpha_5 + \alpha_6) \cdot 1 + (\alpha_2 + 2\alpha_4 + 2\alpha_6) \cdot x + (\alpha_3 + 3\alpha_5 + \alpha_6) \cdot x^2$$

and so the totality of all linear combinations of the six is identical with the totality of linear combinations of the first three.

In view of the foregoing remarks it should be clear that one cannot hope to deduce the dimension of the space generated by a set of vectors merely by counting the vectors, since the set may have "extra" members. We wish to show that, in any case, the dimension of the space generated cannot exceed the number of generating vectors and will be equal to that number if the vectors are independent. To do this we need first a result about simultaneous linear equations.

Consider one equation in two unknowns, say

$$2x - 3y = 0$$

Such an equation is said to be *homogeneous,* which means simply that the choice $x = y = 0$ satisfies it. This equation also has solutions in which not both x and y are zero, for instance, $x = 3, y = 2$. Next consider two equations in three unknowns,

$$\begin{cases} 2x + 3y - z = 0 \\ \ x + y + z = 0 \end{cases} \tag{6.7}$$

which are also homogeneous because $x = y = z = 0$ satisfies them both at once. Again, there are other ways to satisfy them both at once, say by taking $x = -4$, $y = 3$, $z = 1$. We would like to show that if one is given n equations in $n + 1$ unknowns, and if these equations are homogeneous, then they can be simultaneously satisfied by choosing certain values for the unknowns, not all of which are zero. This proposition can be restated in the language of vectors. For example, the two equations (6.7) can be written

$$x(2,1) + y(3,1) + z(-1,1) = (0,0)$$

and to say that the equations have a solution in which not all of x, y, z are zero, is to say that the three vectors $(2,1)$, $(3,1)$, $(-1,1)$ are linearly dependent.

The following theorem generalizes this remark by showing that any $n + 1$ vectors in E^n are linearly dependent. Since there obviously are n independent vectors in E^n, say the n vectors

$$(1,0,0, \ldots , 0)$$
$$(0,1,0, \ldots , 0)$$
$$(0,0,1, \ldots , 0)$$
$$(0,0,0, \ldots , 1)$$

we will have shown that the dimension of E^n is n.

THEOREM 6.5.   Let there be given n simultaneous linear homogeneous equations in $n + 1$ unknowns $x_1, x_2, \ldots , x_{n+1}$

$$\begin{cases} a_{11}x_1 + a_{12}x_2 + \cdots + a_{1,n+1}x_{n+1} = 0 \\ a_{21}x_1 + a_{22}x_2 + \cdots + a_{2,n+1}x_{n+1} = 0 \\ \qquad\qquad \cdots \\ a_{n1}x_1 + a_{n2}x_2 + \cdots + a_{n,n+1}x_{n+1} = 0 \end{cases}$$

or briefly

$$\sum_{j=1}^{n+1} a_{ij}x_j = 0 \qquad (i = 1, 2, \ldots , n)$$

Then these have a solution (that is, there exists a set of values for the unknowns which satisfies all the equations at once) other than the trivial one in which all the unknowns have the value 0.

PROOF   The proof is by induction. First, the theorem is true if $n = 1$, for in that case it asserts that we can solve

$$a_{11}x_1 + a_{12}x_2 = 0$$

nontrivially (i.e., without taking both x_1 and x_2 to be zero). This is clear, for if both a_{11} and a_{12} are zero, then any values of x_1 and x_2 will do. If one of a_{11}, a_{12} is not zero, say $a_{11} \neq 0$, take $x_2 = 1$ and

$$x_1 = -\frac{a_{12}}{a_{11}}$$

for a nontrivial solution.

Inductively, suppose the theorem has been proved for $n - 1$ equations in n unknowns. We will show that this implies its truth for n equations in $n + 1$ unknowns. Let

$$\sum_{j=1}^{n+1} a_{ij}x_j = 0 \qquad (i = 1, 2, \ldots, n) \tag{6.8}$$

be such a set of equations. If all the coefficients a_{ij} arc zcro, then obviously we can find values for the unknowns, not all zero, to satisfy (6.8) since any set of values will do. Suppose then that not all the a_{ij} are zero. Then, by renumbering the equations and unknowns if necessary, we can assume that $a_{n,n+1}$ is a coefficient which is not zero. Then the last equation $[i = n$ in (6.8)] can be written

$$x_{n+1} = -\frac{1}{a_{n,n+1}}\{a_{n1}x_1 + \cdots + a_{nn}x_n\} \tag{6.9}$$

that is, we can solve for x_{n+1} in terms of the remaining x's.

Substituting (6.9) into (6.8) we find

$$\sum_{j=1}^{n}\left\{a_{ij} - \frac{a_{nj}}{a_{n,n+1}}\right\}x_j = 0 \qquad (i = 1, 2, \ldots, n - 1). \tag{6.10}$$

This, however, is a system of only $n - 1$ equations in n unknowns. Since we are assuming that the theorem has been proved in this case, it follows that there are numbers $x_1, x_2, \ldots, x_n$ not all zero which satisfy (6.10). If we take such a set $x_1, \ldots, x_n$ and calculate x_{n+1} from (6.9), we have a set $x_1, \ldots, x_{n+1}$ of numbers not all of which are zero and which satisfy (6.8), completing the proof. If you feel that such a proof is somehow "cheating" because we assumed something in the middle of it, please restudy Section 6.3.

COROLLARY 1   The dimension of E^n is n.

COROLLARY 2   A system of n homogeneous equations in $n + k$ unknowns $(k \geq 1)$ has a nontrivial solution.

PROOF   We have to show that $n + k$ vectors in E^n are dependent no matter how they are chosen. Choose such a set of vectors. There is already a dependence among the first $n + 1$ of them, by Theorem 6.5. Introducing the remaining $k - 1$ vectors into this dependence with zero coefficients, we find a dependence among all $n + k$ of them.

THEOREM 6.6.   Let V be an abstract vector space, and let $\mathbf{f}_1, \mathbf{f}_2, \ldots, \mathbf{f}_r$ be r linearly independent vectors in V. Then the dimension of the subspace generated by $\mathbf{f}_1, \mathbf{f}_2, \ldots, \mathbf{f}_r$ is exactly r.

PROOF   The dimension is at least r because the subspace surely contains a set of r linearly independent vectors, namely, $\mathbf{f}_1, \mathbf{f}_2, \ldots, \mathbf{f}_r$ themselves (why must they be in the subspace?). We have to show that any set of $r + 1$ vectors must be dependent.

Let $\mathbf{g}_1, \mathbf{g}_2, \ldots, \mathbf{g}_{r+1}$ be a set of $r + 1$ vectors lying in the subspace in question. We will show that they must be dependent. First, these vectors are in the subspace by virtue of the fact that each of them is a linear combination of $\mathbf{f}_1, \mathbf{f}_2, \ldots, \mathbf{f}_r$. That is, there are numbers a_{ij} such that

$$\mathbf{g}_1 = a_{11}\mathbf{f}_1 + \cdots + a_{1r}\mathbf{f}_r$$

$$\vdots \qquad \vdots \qquad \qquad \vdots$$

$$\mathbf{g}_{r+1} = a_{r+1,1}\mathbf{f}_1 + \cdots + a_{r+1,r}\mathbf{f}_r \qquad (6.11)$$

Choose and fix such a set of numbers a_{ij}. Then, for that set of a_{ij}'s, contemplate the system of linear homogeneous equations

$$\begin{cases} a_{11}x_1 + a_{21}x_2 + \cdots + a_{r+1,1}x_{r+1} = 0 \\ \qquad\qquad \cdots \\ a_{1r}x_1 + a_{2r}x_2 + \cdots + a_{r+1,r}x_{r+1} = 0 \end{cases} \qquad (6.12)$$

By Theorem 6.5 there are numbers $x_1, \ldots, x_{r+1}$, not all zero, which satisfy the system (6.12) of simultaneous equations. Choose and fix such a set of numbers $x_1, x_2, \ldots, x_{r+1}$. We claim that

$$x_1\mathbf{g}_1 + x_2\mathbf{g}_2 + \cdots + x_{r+1}\mathbf{g}_{r+1} = \mathbf{0}$$

which will show that the vectors $\mathbf{g}_1, \mathbf{g}_2, \ldots, \mathbf{g}_{r+1}$ are indeed linearly dependent and will complete the proof of the theorem. To show this we have

$$x_1\mathbf{g}_1 + \cdots + x_{r+1}\mathbf{g}_{r+1}$$
$$= x_1(a_{11}\mathbf{f}_1 + \cdots + a_{1r}\mathbf{f}_r) + \cdots + x_{r+1}(a_{r+1,1}\mathbf{f}_1 + \cdots + a_{r+1,r}\mathbf{f}_r)$$
$$= (a_{11}x_1 + \cdots + a_{r+1,1}x_{r+1})\,\mathbf{f}_1 + \cdots + (a_{1r}x_1 + \cdots + a_{r+1,r}x_{r+1})\,\mathbf{f}_r$$
$$= 0\mathbf{f}_1 + \cdots + 0\mathbf{f}_r$$
$$= \mathbf{0}$$

as required.

Exercises

1. Show directly that the four vectors

$$(1,0,1), \qquad (2,1,1), \qquad (3,-1,1), \qquad (4,1,2)$$

  in E^3 are dependent.
2. Prove that if $\mathbf{f}_1, \ldots, \mathbf{f}_r$ are not linearly dependent, then the dimension of the space they generate is equal to the largest number of independent $\mathbf{f}$'s which can be chosen from among them.
3. Describe geometrically the subspace of E^3 generated by $(2,1,0)$ and $(1,1,0)$.
4. Describe the subspace of the vector space of polynomials which is generated by $1, x^2, x^4, \ldots$.
5. Prove that the intersection of two subspaces is a subspace. Is the union?
6. Which of the following are *subspaces* of E^n (give reasons):

  (a) The set of all $(x_1, \ldots, x_n)$ where the x_i are all integers.
  (b) The set of all vectors $(0, x_2, x_3, \ldots, x_n)$.
  (c) The set of all $(x_1, \ldots, x_n)$ where all $x_i \geqq 2$.
  (d) The set of all $(x_1, \ldots, x_n)$ such that $2x_1 - x_3 = 0$.
  (e) The set of all $(x_1, \ldots, x_n)$ such that all $x_i \neq 0$.
  (f) The set of all $(x_1, \ldots, x_n)$ such that $x_1 \geqq x_2 \geqq x_3 \geqq \cdots \geqq x_n$.
  (g) The set of all $(x_1, \ldots, x_n)$ such that $x_1 + x_2 + \cdots + x_n = 0$.
  (h) The set of all $(x_1, \ldots, x_n)$ such that the polynomial

$$f(t) = x_1 + x_2 t + x_3 t^2 + \cdots + x_n t^{n-1}$$

  satisfies $f(2) = 0$.

6.6.   Bases

A basis for a vector space is an independent set of vectors which gener-
ates the whole space. That is, a set $\mathbf{f}_1, \ldots, \mathbf{f}_n$ of vectors is a basis for
a vector space V if (a) $\mathbf{f}_1, \ldots, \mathbf{f}_n$ are linearly independent and (b) if $\mathbf{x}$ is
any vector of V then

$$\mathbf{x} = \alpha_1 \mathbf{f}_1 + \cdots + \alpha_n \mathbf{f}_n \tag{6.13}$$

for some scalars $\alpha_1, \ldots, \alpha_n$. By Theorem 6.4 we know that for each $\mathbf{x}$ in
V the set of scalars $\alpha_1, \ldots, \alpha_n$ in (6.13) is unique. These scalars are
called the coordinates of $\mathbf{x}$ relative to the basis $\mathbf{f}_1, \ldots, \mathbf{f}_n$.

Examples
1. $(1,0)$ and $(0,1)$ form a basis for E^2. They are clearly independent, and
      if (α, β) is any vector of E^2 then

$$(\alpha, \beta) = \alpha(1,0) + \beta(0,1)$$

   as required by (6.13).

2. $(2,3)$ and $(1,-4)$ form a basis for E^2 also. They are independent
      because if

$$\alpha(2,3) + \beta(1,-4) = (0,0)$$

   then

$$2\alpha + \beta = 0$$
$$3\alpha - 4\beta = 0$$

   and so $\alpha = \beta = 0$. Further, if (a,b) is any vector of E^2 then

$$(a,b) = \frac{4a + b}{11}(2,3) + \frac{3a - 2b}{11}(1,-4)$$

   which completes the proof.
3. $1, x, x^2$ are a basis for the quadratic polynomials. Another basis for
      them is $1, x, 2x^2 - 1$.

> **THEOREM 6.7.**   Let V be a vector space of finite dimension n.
> Then any set of n linearly independent vectors in V is a basis for V.
> Further, every basis for V contains exactly n vectors.

PROOF   Let $\mathbf{f}_1, \ldots, \mathbf{f}_n$ be linearly independent. We claim they are a basis, for suppose $\mathbf{x}$ is any vector of V. The set of $n + 1$ vectors

$$\mathbf{x}, \mathbf{f}_1, \ldots, \mathbf{f}_n$$

must be dependent, since n is the dimension of V. Hence, there are scalars $\alpha_1, \ldots, \alpha_{n+1}$, not all zero such that

$$\alpha_1 \mathbf{f}_1 + \cdots + \alpha_n \mathbf{f}_n + \alpha_{n+1} \mathbf{x} = \mathbf{0} \qquad (6.14)$$

Now $\alpha_{n+1} \neq 0$, for if it were zero, (6.14) would be a linear dependence among $\mathbf{f}_1, \mathbf{f}_2, \ldots, \mathbf{f}_n$, contradicting their assumed independence. Thus,

$$\mathbf{x} = \left(-\frac{\alpha_1}{\alpha_{n+1}}\right)\mathbf{f}_1 + \cdots + \left(-\frac{\alpha_n}{\alpha_{n+1}}\right)\mathbf{f}_n$$

as required by (6.13).

The second part of the theorem follows easily, for let $\mathbf{f}_1, \ldots, \mathbf{f}_r$ be any basis for V. We claim $r = n$. Since they are independent, by Theorem 6.6 the dimension of the subspace they generate is r. Since they are a basis, that subspace is in fact the whole vector space V, of dimension n. Hence $n = r$.

As a result of this theorem we see that a definition of dimension entirely equivalent to the one we gave is: the dimension of a vector space is the number of vectors in any basis for V, or ∞ if no finite basis exists.

If, given a vector space, one tried to construct a basis for it, a reasonable way to proceed would be to choose, first, an arbitrary vector $\mathbf{f}_1$. Next one would find a vector $\mathbf{f}_2$ independent of $\mathbf{f}_1$ and attempt to continue this process until a number of independent vectors equal to the dimension of the vector space had been found. By Theorem 6.7, these vectors would constitute a basis for V. The success of this process does not depend on just how we happen to choose the first few vectors. The next theorem shows that any set of independent vectors can be extended to a basis by adjoining more vectors to it.

THEOREM 6.8   Let V be a vector space of finite dimension n. Let $\mathbf{f}_1, \ldots, \mathbf{f}_r$ be given independent vectors of V, $r < n$. Then there exist vectors $\mathbf{f}_{r+1}, \ldots, \mathbf{f}_n$ such that the set

$$\mathbf{f}_1, \mathbf{f}_2, \ldots, \mathbf{f}_r, \mathbf{f}_{r+1}, \ldots, \mathbf{f}_n \qquad (6.15)$$

is a basis for V.

PROOF   Consider the subspace generated by $\mathbf{f}_1, \ldots, \mathbf{f}_r$. By Theorem 6.6, this has dimension r. Since $r < n$, there must be vectors of V which are not in this subspace. Let $\mathbf{f}_{r+1}$ be such a vector. Then the set

$$\mathbf{f}_1, \mathbf{f}_2, \ldots, \mathbf{f}_r, \mathbf{f}_{r+1} \tag{6.16}$$

is linearly independent, for if not, then $\mathbf{f}_{r+1}$ would be a linear combination of the other $\mathbf{f}$'s and so would be in the subspace they generate, contradicting its choice outside that subspace. We have now enlarged the original set to a new set with one more independent vector. The process may be repeated as above until a basis is obtained.

Exercises

1. Find three different basis sets for the cubic polynomials.
2. Find four sets of basis vectors for E^3. Describe all pairs of vectors in E^2 which do not form a basis for E^2.
3. Relative to each of the bases you found in Exercise 2, find the coordinates of the vector $(1,2,3)$.
4. Consider the set of all triples of numbers (a,b,c) which satisfy the simultaneous equations

$$2a - b + c = 0$$
$$a + b + c = 0$$

Show that this set is a *subspace* of E^3, and find a basis for it. Thus find all possible solutions of the given set of equations. What is the dimension of the subspace? Describe it geometrically.
5. Let U be a vector space of dimension n. Let V be a subspace of U, also of dimension n. Show that $V = U$.

6.7.   Homomorphisms

Until now we have been studying vector spaces as more or less static structures. In this section we introduce a dynamic element into the discussion in the form of certain operators which act on vector spaces by carrying given vectors into new ones. The concept of a homomorphism lies at the center of this circle of ideas as well as at the center of much of modern mathematics. It will reappear continually, in various guises, in advanced mathematical studies. A homomorphism is, roughly, a function with a college education. That is, a homomorphism is first of all a function, a rule which assigns to members of one set members of another set, but it is more intelligent than most functions because it pays attention to whatever algebraic structure may be present on the sets in question.

Suppose, as an example, that we are given a pair of multiplicative groups, say G and H. A function $f: G \to H$ would just be a rule which assigns to each element g of G an element $f(g)$ in H. Yet these groups are more than just sets. Each of them has an operation of multiplication defined on it. An intelligent function, then, would recognize the existence of the multiplicative structure of the groups and would *preserve* that structure. To say that a function preserves the multiplicative structure is to say that f assigns to the product (in G) of two group elements g and g' the product (in H) of the elements which it assigns to g and g'. In symbols we would have

$$f(gg') = f(g)f(g') \tag{6.17}$$

for every pair of elements g, g' in the group G. Note that the product gg' on the left side of this equation takes place in G, while the product $f(g)f(g')$ on the right is a product of two elements of H. A function $f: G \to H$ with the property (6.17) would be called a homomorphism. We shall not pause here to give examples of group homomorphisms because our primary concern rests with homomorphisms of vector spaces. We remark only that, speaking quite generally, a homomorphism of a pair of algebraic structures is a function from one to the other which preserves whatever operations are defined on those structures.

Turning to the case of our present interest, we wish to define a homomorphism between a pair of given vector spaces U and V. Each of them consists, of course, of a set of vectors together with an operation of vector addition and an operation of scalar multiplication. Let $T: U \to V$ be a function from U to V. That is, T assigns to each vector $\mathbf{f}$ of U a vector $T\mathbf{f}$ of V. If it is true that

$$T(\mathbf{f} + \mathbf{g}) = T\mathbf{f} + T\mathbf{g} \tag{6.18}$$

and

$$T(\alpha\mathbf{f}) = \alpha T\mathbf{f} \tag{6.19}$$

for all vectors **f**, **g** in U and all scalars α, then we will say that T is a *homomorphism,* or a *linear mapping,* or a *linear transformation,* or a *linear operator* from U to V.

Equations (6.18) and (6.19) say only that T preserves the algebraic structure of the vector spaces U and V. In Eq. (6.18) the plus sign on the left is addition in the space U, on the right is addition in the space V. We do not, of course, rule out the possibility that U and V are the same, and indeed this is quite an important special case.

Example 1.
Let U be the vector space of polynomials of degree ≤ 20 and V the space of polynomials of degree ≤ 35. Consider the mapping $T: U \to V$ which assigns to each polynomial **f** in U its derivative **f**$'$ in V, that is

$$T(a_0 + a_1x + \cdots + a_{20}x^{20}) = a_1 + 2a_2x + \cdots + 20a_{20}x^{19}$$

It is clear that (6.18) and (6.19) are satisfied, and so T is a homomorphism.

Example 2.
Let U be the vector space E^n, and let V be the space of polynomials of degree $\leq n - 1$. Let $T: U \to V$ be the function which assigns to the vector $(\alpha_1, \alpha_2, \ldots, \alpha_n)$ in U the polynomial $\alpha_1 + \alpha_2x + \cdots + \alpha_nx^{n-1}$ in V. Again (6.18) and (6.19) are satisfied, and T is a homomorphism.

Example 3.
Let U and V both be E^2, Euclidean 2-space. Let $T: E^2 \to E^2$ be the function which assigns to the vector (α,β) the vector $(\alpha,0)$. Then T is a homomorphism of E^2 into itself. Geometrically, T is a projection of the vector (α,β) onto the x axis (Fig. 6.3).

Figure 6.3

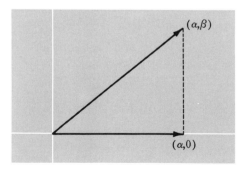

Example 4.
Let U be E^n, and let V be E^m, for some fixed integers m and n. Let a_{ij} ($i = 1, 2, \ldots, m; j = 1, 2, \ldots, n$) be a given set of mn real numbers. Define a linear mapping $A: E^n \to E^m$ as the function which assigns to the vector $(\alpha_1, \alpha_2, \ldots, \alpha_n)$ of E^n the vector $(\beta_1, \beta_2, \ldots, \beta_m)$ of E^m where

$$\beta_i = \sum_{j=1}^{n} a_{ij}\alpha_j \qquad (i = 1, 2, \ldots, m) \tag{6.20}$$

Then A is a homomorphism of E^n to E^m. As a very particular example of such a homomorphism, consider the map $A: E^3 \to E^2$ which assigns to $(\alpha_1, \alpha_2, \alpha_3)$ of E^3 the vector (β_1, β_2) of E^2 where

$$\beta_1 = \alpha_1 - 2\alpha_2 + 3\alpha_3$$
$$\beta_2 = 4\alpha_1 + \alpha_2 - 2\alpha_3$$

so that

$$A(1, 2, -3) = (-12, 12)$$
$$A(1, 1, 1) = (2, 3)$$

etc. It is simple to verify that such maps are homomorphisms.

THEOREM 6.9. Let $T: U \to V$ be a homomorphism. Let $\mathbf{0}_U$ and $\mathbf{0}_V$ denote, respectively, the zero vector of the space U and of the space V. Then

$$T\mathbf{0}_U = \mathbf{0}_V \tag{6.21}$$

PROOF The theorem asserts that a homomorphism must assign the zero vector of the first space to the zero vector of the second. To prove the theorem notice that if, in any vector space, a certain vector $\mathbf{h}$ satisfies the relation $\mathbf{h} = \mathbf{h} + \mathbf{h}$, then by subtracting $\mathbf{h}$ from both sides one sees that $\mathbf{h}$ must be the zero vector of the space in question. To apply this remark, we have

$$T\mathbf{0}_U = T(\mathbf{0}_U + \mathbf{0}_U)$$
$$= T\mathbf{0}_U + T\mathbf{0}_U$$

where (6.18) has been used. Hence, the vector $T\mathbf{0}_U$ does what the vector $\mathbf{h}$ in the preceding remark did, and, therefore, $T\mathbf{0}_U$ must be the zero vector of the space in which it lies, i.e., the zero vector of V, as required.

DEFINITION   Let $T: U \to V$ be a homomorphism from U to V. The *kernel* of T is the set of all vectors $\mathbf{f}$ of U such that $T\mathbf{f} = \mathbf{0}_V$. It is denoted by the symbol Ker T.

The *image* of T, or more precisely the image of U under the map T, is the totality of vectors in V which are assigned by T to some vector in U. That is, the image of T is the totality of vectors $T\mathbf{f}$ in V as $\mathbf{f}$ runs over the whole space U. It is denoted by the symbol Im T.

Thus, Ker T is a subset of U and Im T is a subset of V. As a bit of abstract art which may be useful in remembering these concepts, refer to Fig. 6.4.

Figure 6.4

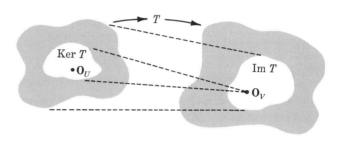

Theorem 6.9 asserts just that $\mathbf{0}_U$ always belongs to Ker T, as is shown in Fig. 6.4. $\mathbf{0}_U$ may or may not be the only vector of U in Ker T.

Example 5.
If T is the mapping of Example 1, then Ker T consists of all polynomials in which $a_1 = a_2 = \cdots = a_{20} = 0$ and a_0 is arbitrary, i.e., of the constant polynomials. Im T consists of all polynomials of degree ≤ 19 since every such polynomial "comes from" some vector of U.

Example 6.
If T is the homomorphism of Example 2, then Ker T consists solely of the zero polynomial of U, and Im T is the entire space V.

Example 7.
If T is the mapping of Example 3, then Ker T consists of all vectors of the form $(0,\beta)$, i.e., Ker T is the whole y axis in the plane. Im T consists of all vectors $(\alpha,0)$, that is, Im T is the x axis of the plane.

The reader may have noted from the examples that Ker T and Im T were not merely *subsets* of U and V, respectively, but were actually *subspaces*. This is true in general, as is shown by

THEOREM 6.10 Let $T: U \to V$ be a homomorphism. Then Ker T is a subspace of U and Im T is a subspace of V.

PROOF They are obviously subsets. What we need to prove, then, is that each of them is closed under vector addition and scalar multiplication. Suppose $\mathbf{x}$ and $\mathbf{y}$ are both in Ker T. Then

$$T\mathbf{x} = \mathbf{0}_V$$
$$T\mathbf{y} = \mathbf{0}_V$$

and so

$$
\begin{aligned}
T(\mathbf{x} + \mathbf{y}) &= T\mathbf{x} + T\mathbf{y} \\
&= \mathbf{0}_V + \mathbf{0}_V \\
&= \mathbf{0}_V
\end{aligned}
\tag{6.22}
$$

whence $\mathbf{x} + \mathbf{y}$ is also in Ker T. If $\mathbf{x}$ is in Ker T and α is a scalar, then

$$
\begin{aligned}
T(\alpha\mathbf{x}) &= \alpha T\mathbf{x} \\
&- \alpha\mathbf{0}_V \\
&= \mathbf{0}_V
\end{aligned}
\tag{6.23}
$$

and so $\alpha\mathbf{x}$ is in Ker T. Thus Ker T is a subspace of U.

Let $\mathbf{x}$ and $\mathbf{y}$ be in Im T. Then

$$\mathbf{x} = T\mathbf{f}, \qquad \mathbf{y} = T\mathbf{g}$$

for some $\mathbf{f}$ and $\mathbf{g}$ of U. Hence,

$$
\begin{aligned}
\mathbf{x} + \mathbf{y} &= T\mathbf{f} + T\mathbf{g} \\
&= T(\mathbf{f} + \mathbf{g})
\end{aligned}
$$

and so $\mathbf{x} + \mathbf{y}$ is in Im T also. Further, if $\mathbf{x}$ is in Im T and α is a scalar, then

$$\mathbf{x} = T\mathbf{f}$$

for some $\mathbf{f}$ in U and so

$$
\begin{aligned}
\alpha\mathbf{x} &= \alpha T\mathbf{f} \\
&= T(\alpha\mathbf{f})
\end{aligned}
$$

and $\alpha\mathbf{x}$ is in Im T also, completing the proof.

Since Ker T and Im T are subspaces of U and V it makes sense to talk about their dimensions. Thus we formulate the

DEFINITION   Let $T: U \to V$ be a homomorphism. The *rank* of T, written $r(T)$, is the dimension of the subspace Im T, while the *nullity* of T, written $\nu(T)$, is the dimension of the subspace Ker T.

Example 8.

The mapping T of Examples 1 and 5 has

$$r(T) = 20, \qquad \nu(T) = 1$$

For the mapping T of Examples 2 and 6 we have

$$r(T) = n, \qquad \nu(T) = 0$$

Finally, if T is the map in Examples 3 and 7,

$$r(T) = 1, \qquad \nu(T) = 1$$

We have now progressed far enough so that a few remarks can be made about the applications of the ideas developed so far. More of these will appear as we progress. Suppose that in the course of a certain investigation we encounter a certain set of four quantities x, y, z, w which satisfy two equations

$$\begin{aligned} 2x + y + z + w &= 0 \\ x - 2y + z - w &= 0 \end{aligned} \tag{6.24}$$

It would then be natural to ask for a description of all possible sets of these quantities which satisfy both of the conditions (6.24). In a simple case like this, of course, one could grind out the answer by eliminating unknowns. It is often fruitful, however, to approach such a question from the point of view of operators on vector spaces. Consider the homomorphism $T: E^4 \to E^2$ which assigns to a vector (x,y,z,w) of E^4 the vector $(2x + y + z + w, x - 2y + z - w)$ of E^2. To ask for all possible solutions of Eq. (6.24), then, is to ask for all possible vectors $\mathbf{f}$ of E^4 such that

$$T\mathbf{f} = \mathbf{0} \tag{6.25}$$

where T is the mapping just defined, and $\mathbf{0}$ is the zero vector of E^2, i.e., the vector $(0,0)$.

In other words, a complete description of the solutions of (6.24) is a complete description of the kernel of T! But Ker T is a certain subspace

of E^4. To give a complete description of a subspace, one could first determine the dimension of the subspace (the nullity of T) and then give a
basis for the subspace. The subspace would then be described as the
totality of linear combinations of the basis vectors. We do not yet have
a systematic way to go about this, though we will later on. At the
moment all we have (and it is quite a lot) is an appropriate language in
which to express the answer. It turns out that in this case the nullity of
T is 2, therefore, the dimension of Ker T is 2, and, therefore, to find a
basis for Ker T we need only find two linearly independent solution
vectors. By inspection or otherwise, two such vectors are

$$(x,y,z,w) = (1,3,0,-5)$$
$$(x,y,z,w) = (0,2,1,-3)$$

Therefore, the *complete* answer to our question of determining all possible solutions of (6.24) is that any solution (x,y,z,w) is of the form

$$(x,y,z,w) = \alpha(1,3,0,-5) + \beta(0,2,1,-3) \tag{6.26}$$

where α and β are real numbers. That is, if we choose any pair of real
numbers α,β and take

$$x = \alpha$$
$$y = 3\alpha + 2\beta$$
$$z = \beta$$
$$w = -5\alpha - 3\beta$$

then we have a solution of (6.24), and, further, every solution of (6.24)
arises in this way. Of the steps in the process just described, the one which
we will be able to mechanize later is the key step of determining the
nullity of a given linear mapping, but for the moment the reader should
be aware that he is in possession of a natural point of view from which
such questions may be considered, as well as of the correct language in
which to express the answers.

Now we refer to the three situations of Example 8, and construct a
strongly suggestive table of the results in that example (Table VII). The
theorem which Table VII suggests is

Table VII

Dimension of U	$r(T)$	$\nu(T)$
21	20	1
n	n	0
2	1	1

THEOREM 6.11.   Let T be a linear mapping from U to V, where U is of finite dimension n. Then

$$r(T) + \nu(T) = n \tag{6.27}$$

PROOF   The vector space Ker T has dimension $\nu(T) \equiv \nu$. Therefore, it has a basis, say

$$\mathbf{f}_1, \mathbf{f}_2, \ldots, \mathbf{f}_\nu \tag{6.28}$$

of exactly ν vectors. By Theorem 6.8, we can extend this set of vectors to a basis for the whole space U:

$$\mathbf{f}_1, \mathbf{f}_2, \ldots, \mathbf{f}_\nu, \mathbf{f}_{\nu+1}, \ldots, \mathbf{f}_n \tag{6.29}$$

Having done this, we now claim that the vectors

$$T\mathbf{f}_{\nu+1}, \ldots, T\mathbf{f}_n \tag{6.30}$$

form a basis for the space Im T. To prove this we must show that they are linearly independent and that they generate Im T. Suppose they are linearly dependent. Then there exist scalars $\alpha_{\nu+1}, \ldots, \alpha_n$ not all zero, such that

$$\alpha_{\nu+1} T\mathbf{f}_{\nu+1} + \cdots + \alpha_n T\mathbf{f}_n = \mathbf{0}_V$$

and so

$$T(\alpha_{\nu+1}\mathbf{f}_{\nu+1} + \cdots + \alpha_n\mathbf{f}_n) = \mathbf{0}_V \tag{6.31}$$

Hence, the vector $\alpha_{\nu+1}\mathbf{f}_{\nu+1} + \cdots + \alpha_n\mathbf{f}_n$ is carried by T into the zero vector of V, and, therefore, lies in the kernel of T. It is, therefore, expressible as a linear combination of the basis vectors (6.28) of Ker T, that is

$$\alpha_{\nu+1}\mathbf{f}_{\nu+1} + \cdots + \alpha_n\mathbf{f}_n = \alpha_1\mathbf{f}_1 + \cdots + \alpha_\nu\mathbf{f}_\nu$$

But this is a dependence among the whole set (6.29), contradicting the assumed independence of that set. Therefore, the vectors (6.30) are independent.

To prove that (6.30) generates Im T, let $\mathbf{y}$ be any vector in Im T. Then $\mathbf{y} = T\mathbf{x}$ for some $\mathbf{x}$ in U. Since (6.29) is a basis for U,

$$\mathbf{x} = \beta_1\mathbf{f}_1 + \cdots + \beta_n\mathbf{f}_n$$

for some scalars $\beta_1, \ldots, \beta_n$. But then

$$\begin{aligned}
\mathbf{y} = T\mathbf{x} &= T(\beta_1\mathbf{f}_1 + \cdots + \beta_n\mathbf{f}_n) \\
&= \beta_1 T\mathbf{f}_1 + \cdots + \beta_n T\mathbf{f}_n \\
&= 0 + 0 + \cdots + 0 + \beta_{\nu+1}T\mathbf{f}_{\nu+1} + \cdots + \beta_n T\mathbf{f}_n \quad\quad (6.32)
\end{aligned}$$

since $\mathbf{f}_1, \ldots, \mathbf{f}_\nu$ [see (6.28)] all lie in Ker T. Equation (6.32) is pre-cisely the assertion that every vector in Im T is a linear combina-tion of the vectors (6.30), i.e., that the set (6.30) generates Im T. Thus the vectors in (6.30) are independent, and they generate Im T, and, therefore, they form a basis for Im T. To find the dimension of Im T we have, by Theorem 6.7, only to count the vectors in any basis for Im T. Counting the vectors in (6.30) we discover that the dimension of Im T, the rank of T, is equal to $n - \nu$, which was to be shown.

Exercises

1. Which of the following mappings of $E^3 \to E^3$ is a homomorphism?

   (a) $T(\alpha,\beta,\gamma) = (\alpha + a, \beta + a, a + \gamma)$ $(a \neq 0)$
   (b) $T(\alpha,\beta,\gamma) = (\gamma,\alpha,\beta)$
   (c) $T(\alpha,\beta,\gamma) = (\alpha^2,\beta^2,\gamma^2)$
   (d) $T(\alpha,\beta,\gamma) = (-\alpha,\beta,\gamma)$
   (e) $T(\alpha,\beta,\gamma) = (\alpha + \gamma, 0, \alpha + \beta)$

2. Find the kernel, image, rank, and nullity of each of the following.

   (a) $T(\alpha,\beta,\gamma) = (\alpha,\beta,0)$ $(E^3 \to E^3)$
   (b) $T(\alpha_1, \ldots, \alpha_n) = (\alpha_1,\alpha_2)$ $(E^n \to E^2)$
   (c) $T(\alpha_1, \ldots, \alpha_n) = (\alpha_n,\alpha_1,\alpha_2, \ldots, \alpha_{n-1})$ $(E^n \to E^n)$
   (d) $T(\alpha,\beta) = (2\alpha - \beta, \alpha + \beta)$ $(E^2 \to E^2)$
   (e) $T(\alpha,\beta) = (\alpha,\beta,0,0)$ $(E^2 \to E^4)$

3. Show that if $\mathbf{x}$ and $\mathbf{y}$ are two vectors each of which is carried into $\mathbf{f}$ by a cer-tain homomorphism, then $\mathbf{x} - \mathbf{y}$ belongs to the kernel of that homomorphism.

4. Prove by induction that if T is a homomorphism $U \to V$ then

$$T(\alpha_1\mathbf{x}_1 + \alpha_2\mathbf{x}_2 + \cdots + \alpha_n\mathbf{x}_n) = \alpha_1 T\mathbf{x}_1 + \cdots + \alpha_n T\mathbf{x}_n$$

   for every set of vectors $\mathbf{x}_1, \ldots, \mathbf{x}_n$ of U and scalars $\alpha_1, \ldots, \alpha_n$.

5. Let p, n be given positive integers. Construct a homomorphism of two vector spaces whose rank is p and whose nullity is n.

6. Find a basis for the kernel of each of the operators of Exercise 2.

7. Find a basis for the image of each operator of Exercise 2.

8. Prove that the functions in Examples 1–4 are indeed homomorphisms.

The Algebra of Linear Mappings
Matrices
Matrix Algebra
Determinants and Simultaneous Linear Equations
More on Permutations
Determinant Functions
Properties of Determinants
Solution of Linear Equations
Computational Methods
Applications

7

Matrices, Determinants, and Linear Equations

7.1. The Algebra of Linear Mappings

In the preceding chapter we studied vector spaces and linear mappings. We continue this study in the present chapter by developing a somewhat more concrete view of linear mappings, namely, the theory of matrices, and by giving some applications to linear equations. Matrices are a convenient computational tool for solving problems connected with linear mappings. They are also fun to manipulate, and so a word of caution seems advisable to the effect that many problems about linear operators can best be solved without ever reaching for a matrix. Indeed, the use of matrices can, on occasion, hide rather than illuminate the essential features of a problem. Aside from this slight precaution, it is surely true that the study of matrices is a most useful and delightful sport, to which we now turn our attention.

Let U and V be a fixed pair of vector spaces. We now contemplate the collection of *all* linear mappings from U to V. Let $A: U \to V$ and $B: U \to V$ be two such mappings. By the *sum* of the mappings A and B we mean the mapping which assigns to each vector $\mathbf{f}$ of U the vector $A\mathbf{f} + B\mathbf{f}$ of V. That is, $A + B$ is the map from $U \to V$ defined by

$$(A + B)\mathbf{f} = A\mathbf{f} + B\mathbf{f} \qquad \text{(all } \mathbf{f} \text{ in } U) \tag{7.1}$$

277

We check that $A + B$ is a homomorphism by the following computation:

$$(A + B)(\alpha\mathbf{f}) = A(\alpha\mathbf{f}) + B(\alpha\mathbf{f})$$
$$= \alpha A\mathbf{f} + \alpha B\mathbf{f}$$
$$= \alpha(A\mathbf{f} + B\mathbf{f})$$
$$= \alpha(A + B)\mathbf{f}$$

and

$$(A + B)(\mathbf{f} + \mathbf{g}) = A(\mathbf{f} + \mathbf{g}) + B(\mathbf{f} + \mathbf{g})$$
$$= A\mathbf{f} + A\mathbf{g} + B\mathbf{f} + B\mathbf{g}$$
$$= (A + B)\mathbf{f} + (A + B)\mathbf{g}$$

This shows that $A + B$ is a linear mapping if A and B are, and, therefore, shows that the collection of all linear mappings from U to V is closed under the operation of addition just defined.

Next, if A is a map from $U \to V$ and α is a real number, we define a map αA by the relation

$$(\alpha A)\mathbf{f} = \alpha(A\mathbf{f}) \qquad \text{(all } \mathbf{f} \text{ in } U) \tag{7.2}$$

It is simple to check that αA is a linear map if A is, and so the collection of all linear maps $U \to V$ is closed under scalar multiplication.

The zero mapping $O: U \to V$ is defined by

$$O\mathbf{f} = \mathbf{0}_V \qquad \text{(all } \mathbf{f} \text{ in } U) \tag{7.3}$$

and it is a linear map. To say that two mappings A, B of $U \to V$ are equal is to say that they agree on every vector of U. That is, $A = B$ means that

$$A\mathbf{f} = B\mathbf{f} \qquad \text{(all } \mathbf{f} \text{ in } U) \tag{7.4}$$

Relative to the operation of addition and the zero map just defined, every map has a negative. Precisely, if $A: U \to V$ is given, then $-A$ is the map

$$(-A)\mathbf{f} = -(A\mathbf{f}) \qquad \text{(all } \mathbf{f} \text{ in } U) \tag{7.5}$$

because one sees easily that $A + (-A) = O$ for every linear map A.

We have now done almost all the work contained in the statement of

THEOREM 7.1.   Let U and V be a given pair of vector spaces. The collection of all linear mappings $U \to V$ forms a vector space over the real numbers, when endowed with the operations of addition as in (7.1), and scalar multiplication as in (7.2).

The complete proof of this theorem is left as an exercise. It is remarkable that from a given pair of vector spaces one can construct a new vector space on the collection of mappings between them. This new vector space is usually denoted by the symbol Hom (U,V), which stands for the space of all homomorphisms from U to V.

Example 1.
Consider the collection of linear maps from $E^3 \to E^2$. One such map is

$$A(\alpha_1,\alpha_2,\alpha_3) = (0,\alpha_2)$$

and another one is

$$B(\alpha_1,\alpha_2,\alpha_3) = (\alpha_1 + \alpha_2, \alpha_3)$$

Then the mapping $A + B$ is given by

$$(A + B)(\alpha_1,\alpha_2,\alpha_3) = (\alpha_1 + \alpha_2, \alpha_2 + \alpha_3)$$

and, if γ is a real number, the map γA is

$$(\gamma A)(\alpha_1,\alpha_2,\alpha_3) = (0,\gamma\alpha_2)$$

The zero map $O: E^3 \to E^2$ is

$$O(\alpha_1,\alpha_2,\alpha_3) = (0,0)$$

Hom (E^3,E^2) is the vector space of all linear mappings $E^3 \to E^2$.

There is still more algebraic structure in the theory of homomorphisms than just the vector space structure so far described. We now discuss the circumstances under which two mappings A and B can be "multiplied," to form a new mapping AB. Hence, suppose $A: U \to V$ and $B: W \to X$ are two given homomorphisms, where U, V, W, X are vector spaces. One reasonable way to define a map AB is by the usual composition rule, which decrees that AB is the map which assigns to a vector $\mathbf{f}$ the vector $A(B\mathbf{f})$. The need for caution is at once apparent: since B maps $W \to X$, the vector $B\mathbf{f}$ makes sense only if $\mathbf{f}$ lies in the space W, and then $B\mathbf{f}$ will lie in X. In order for $A(B\mathbf{f})$ to make sense, however, $B\mathbf{f}$ must lie in U, the domain of A.

To summarize, $A(B\mathbf{f})$ is meaningful if $\mathbf{f}$ belongs to W, and, for all $\mathbf{f}$ in W, $B\mathbf{f}$ belongs to X. We assume, therefore, that the spaces U and X are the same, and we have the following diagram:

$$W \xrightarrow{B} X \xrightarrow{A} V \qquad\qquad (7.6)$$

The diagram means that B is a map from W to X and A is a map from the same X to V. Under these circumstances we make the

> **DEFINITION**   Let W, X, V be three given vector spaces, and let $B\colon W \to X$, $A\colon X \to V$ be given mappings. By the mapping $AB\colon W \to V$ we mean the map which assigns to each $\mathbf{f}$ in W the vector
>
> $$(AB)\mathbf{f} = A(B\mathbf{f}) \tag{7.7}$$
>
> of V.

The diagram (7.6) could be slightly enlarged as follows:

$$
\begin{array}{ccc}
W & \xrightarrow{\ B\ } & X \\
& {\scriptstyle AB}\searrow & \downarrow {\scriptstyle A} \\
& & V
\end{array}
\tag{7.8}
$$

Example 2.

Let $B\colon E^4 \to E^3$ be given by

$$B(\alpha_1,\alpha_2,\alpha_3,\alpha_4) = (\alpha_1,\ \alpha_1 + \alpha_2,\ 0)$$

and let $A\colon E^3 \to E^2$ be defined by

$$A(\alpha_1,\alpha_2,\alpha_3) = (0,\alpha_3)$$

Then $AB\colon E^4 \to E^2$ is the map

$$
\begin{aligned}
(AB)(\alpha_1,\alpha_2,\alpha_3,\alpha_4) &= A(B(\alpha_1,\alpha_2,\alpha_3,\alpha_4)) \\
&= A(\alpha_1,\ \alpha_1 + \alpha_2,\ 0) \\
&= (0,0)
\end{aligned}
$$

Hence, AB is the map from E^4 to E^2 which sends every vector of E^4 into the zero vector of E^2, i.e., $AB = O\colon E^4 \to E^2$, even though neither A nor B is itself a zero map. In this example the symbol BA is meaningless because if $B(A\mathbf{f})$ is to make sense, $\mathbf{f}$ must be in E^3, then $A\mathbf{f}$ is in E^2, and B does not know where to send $A\mathbf{f}$ because B is defined only on E^4!

One very important special case, in which both of the products AB and BA are well defined, occurs when all three of the vector spaces in (7.6) are identical. If $A\colon U \to U$ is a linear map of a vector space U *to itself*, we will say that A is a linear mapping on U or a linear operator on U or a homomorphism of U. The space Hom (U,U) of all linear mappings on U can be endowed with a richer algebraic structure than that of a vector space. Indeed, if A and B are any pair of linear operators on U, their product, in either order, is well defined by the rule (6.7). Of course, we do not imply that $AB = BA$, for this is generally not true.

Example 3.
On the space U of polynomials of degree $\leqq 3$, let A and B be the linear operators defined by

$$A(a_0 + a_1x + a_2x^2 + a_3x^3) = a_0 + a_3x^3$$
$$B(a_0 + a_1x + a_2x^2 + a_3x^3) = (a_2 + a_3)x^2 + a_3x^3$$

It is easy to see that

$$(AB)(a_0 + a_1x + a_2x^2 + a_3x^3) = a_3x^3$$

while

$$(BA)(a_0 + a_1x + a_2x^2 + a_3x^3) = a_3x^2 + a_3x^3$$

Thus AB and BA are both well-defined linear operators on U, but $AB \neq BA$.

If $A: U \to U$ is a linear map, its powers $A^2, A^3, \ldots$ are defined in the obvious way,

$$A^2 = AA$$
$$A^3 = A \cdot A^2$$
$$\cdots$$

The identity mapping $I: U \to U$ of a vector space to itself is the linear operator which leaves every vector alone,

$$I\mathbf{f} = \mathbf{f} \qquad \text{(all } \mathbf{f} \text{ in } U) \tag{7.9}$$

If $A: U \to U$ is an operator on U, there may or may not exist an operator $A^{-1}: U \to U$ such that

$$AA^{-1} = A^{-1}A = I \tag{7.10}$$

If such an operator A^{-1} exists, it is called the *inverse* of the operator A, and A is said to be *nonsingular*. Otherwise, we say that A is *singular* if it has no inverse.

THEOREM 7.2.   Multiplication of operators on U is associative. That is, if A, B, C are three maps $U \to U$ then

$$A(BC) = (AB)C$$

PROOF $A(BC)$ is the map which assigns to each $\mathbf{f}$ the vector

$$(A(BC))\mathbf{f} = A((BC)\mathbf{f}) = A(B(C\mathbf{f}))$$

while $(AB)C$ assigns to $\mathbf{f}$ the vector

$$((AB)C)\mathbf{f} = (AB)(C\mathbf{f}) = A(B(C\mathbf{f}))$$

and so they are identical.

Let U be a finite-dimensional vector space.

THEOREM 7.3.   A map $A : U \to U$ is nonsingular if and only if Ker A consists of $\mathbf{0}$ alone.

PROOF   First suppose A is nonsingular. Then A^{-1} exists. If $\mathbf{f}$ is any vector in Ker A, then

$$A\mathbf{f} = \mathbf{0}$$

Multiplying by A^{-1}, we find

$$
\begin{aligned}
A^{-1}(A\mathbf{f}) = A^{-1}\mathbf{0} &= \mathbf{0} \\
&= (A^{-1}A)\mathbf{f} \\
&= I\mathbf{f} \\
&= \mathbf{f}
\end{aligned}
$$

and so $\mathbf{f} = \mathbf{0}$ as required.

Conversely, suppose Ker A consists of $\mathbf{0}$ alone. Let $\mathbf{g}$ be a given vector of U. We claim that there is exactly one vector $\mathbf{f}$ in U such that

$$A\mathbf{f} = \mathbf{g}$$

For if there were two, say $\mathbf{f}_1$ and $\mathbf{f}_2$, then $A\mathbf{f}_1 = \mathbf{g}$, $A\mathbf{f}_2 = \mathbf{g}$ imply that

$$\mathbf{0} = A\mathbf{f}_1 - A\mathbf{f}_2 = A(\mathbf{f}_1 - \mathbf{f}_2).$$

Thus $\mathbf{f}_1 - \mathbf{f}_2$ is in Ker A, and, therefore, $\mathbf{f}_1 - \mathbf{f}_2 = \mathbf{0}$ whence $\mathbf{f}_1 = \mathbf{f}_2$ as claimed. We have shown that there is at most one vector $\mathbf{f}$ such that $A\mathbf{f} = \mathbf{g}$. To see that there is one, since Ker $A = \mathbf{0}$ the nullity of A is $\nu(A) = 0$. Hence by Theorem 6.11, the rank of A is $r(A) = n$, the dimension of U. Hence, the image of A, Im A, is identical with the whole space U, and, therefore, every vector $\mathbf{g}$ in U is the result of A acting on some vector $\mathbf{f}$. Hence, for each $\mathbf{g}$ in U, there is exactly one $\mathbf{f}$ such that $A\mathbf{f} = \mathbf{g}$.

Consider, then, the function A^{-1} which assigns to each $\mathbf{f}$ in U the unique $\mathbf{g}$ such that $A\mathbf{g} = \mathbf{f}$.

We leave it as an exercise to show that A^{-1} as defined is a linear operator on U, and that $AA^{-1} = A^{-1}A = I$, completing the proof of the theorem.

COROLLARY   Let U be of finite dimension n. An operator A on U is nonsingular if any only if $r(A) = n$.

THEOREM 7.4.   Let A, B be linear operators on a vector space U. If A and B are nonsingular, then so is AB and

$$(AB)^{-1} = B^{-1}A^{-1}$$

PROOF $(AB)(B^{-1}A^{-1}) = A(BB^{-1})A^{-1}$
$$= AIA^{-1}$$
$$- AA^{-1}$$
$$= I$$

and

$$(B^{-1}A^{-1})(AB) = B^{-1}(A^{-1}A)B$$
$$= B^{-1}IB$$
$$= B^{-1}B$$
$$= I \quad \text{Q.E.D.}$$

Exercises

1. Perform the "simple check" following Eq. (7.2).
2. Prove that the zero map (7.3) is a linear mapping.
3. Prove that $(-1)A = -A$, if $A: U \to V$ is a linear map.
4. Prove Theorem 7.1.
5. Show that A^{-1} defined in the proof of Theorem 7.3 is a linear map and that it satisfies (7.10).

6. Let $A: E^3 \to E^3$ be given by

$$A(\alpha_1,\alpha_2,\alpha_3) = (\alpha_1, \alpha_1 + \alpha_2, \alpha_1 + \alpha_2 + \alpha_3)$$

and let $B: E^3 \to E^3$ be defined by

$$B(\alpha_1,\alpha_2,\alpha_3) = (\alpha_3,\alpha_1,\alpha_2)$$

    (a) Describe the operator A^2 [i.e., what is $A^2(\alpha_1,\alpha_2,\alpha_3)$?].
    (b) Describe AB [i.e., what is $AB(\alpha_1,\alpha_2,\alpha_3)$?].
    (c) Describe BA.
    (d) Show that $B^3 = I$, and, therefore, that $B^{-1} = B^2$.
    (e) Show that A is nonsingular, and describe A^{-1}.
    (f) Show that $I - 3A + 3A^2 - A^3 = 0$.
    (g) Describe $(AB)^{-1}$ and $(BA)^{-1}$.

7. Let θ be a fixed real number. Define an operator $A_\theta: E^2 \to E^2$ by

$$A_\theta(\alpha_1,\alpha_2) = (\alpha_1 \cos \theta - \alpha_2 \sin \theta, \alpha_1 \sin \theta + \alpha_2 \cos \theta)$$

    (a) Show that $A_\theta A_\varphi = A_{\theta+\varphi}$ for any real numbers θ, φ.
    (b) Describe geometrically the effect of A_θ on a vector in the plane.
    (c) Show that A_θ is nonsingular and describe A_θ^{-1}.

8. Let $A: E^n \to E^n$ be nonsingular, and let $\mathbf{u}_1, \ldots, \mathbf{u}_r$ be a set of independent vectors in E^n. Show that the vectors $A\mathbf{u}_1, A\mathbf{u}_2, \ldots, A\mathbf{u}_r$ are also independent.

7.2. Matrices

Suppose we wish to describe a linear mapping $A: U \to V$. One way to do this is to describe the effect of A on *every* vector of U, and this is the approach which we have so far followed. A more economical method would give the effect of A on only *some* vectors of U. If these vectors are cleverly chosen, then we will, in fact, have given a complete description of A.

To illustrate this point, suppose we consider a map $A: E^2 \to E^2$ by giving its action on just two vectors of E^2, namely, $(1,0)$ and $(0,1)$. To be specific, suppose that

$$A(1,0) = (3,2)$$
$$A(0,1) = (-2,0) \tag{7.11}$$

We claim that just these two pieces of information, together with the requirement that A be a linear mapping, describe A completely. Indeed, suppose (x,y) is an arbitrary vector of E^2. Then

$$(x,y) = x(1,0) + y(0,1) \tag{7.12}$$

and so

$$\begin{aligned} A(x,y) &= Ax(1,0) + Ay(0,1) \\ &= xA(1,0) + yA(0,1) \\ &= x(3,2) + y(-2,0) \\ &= (3x,2x) + (-2y,0) \\ &= (3x - 2y, 2x) \end{aligned}$$

We have discovered that a linear operator which acts on $(1,0)$ and $(0,1)$ as in (7.11), is completely determined, and must carry (x,y) into $(3x - 2y, 2x)$. The key step in this argument is the statement (7.12), to the effect that every vector (x,y) is a linear combination of $(1,0)$ and $(0,1)$. In other words, the method succeeds because the vectors $(1,0)$, $(0,1)$ are a basis for E^2. In general, we have

THEOREM 7.5. Let $e_1, e_2, \ldots, e_n$ be a basis for a vector space U. A linear operator $A: U \to V$ is completely determined by giving the n vectors $Ae_1, \ldots, Ae_n$, in V.

PROOF Let x be any vector of U. Then there is a *unique* set of real numbers $\alpha_1, \ldots, \alpha_n$ such that

$$x = \alpha_1 e_1 + \cdots + \alpha_n e_n$$

Then

$$Ax = \alpha_1 Ae_1 + \cdots + \alpha_n Ae_n$$

which describes the action of A on every vector of the space.

We propose next to carry this process of economization one step further. In order to describe A completely, we need only give the n vectors $Ae_1, \ldots, Ae_n$. How shall we "give" these vectors? Each of them lies in the vector space V. Hence, suppose we choose a basis $f_1, f_2, \ldots, f_m$ for V. Then each of the vectors $Ae_1, \ldots, Ae_n$ is uniquely expressible as a linear combination of $f_1, \ldots, f_m$. That is, there is a unique set of mn

real numbers $a_{11}, a_{12}, \ldots, a_{1n}, a_{21}, \ldots, a_{2n}, \ldots, a_{mn}$ such that

$$A\mathbf{e}_1 = a_{11}\mathbf{f}_1 + a_{21}\mathbf{f}_2 + \cdots + a_{m1}\mathbf{f}_m$$

$$A\mathbf{e}_n = a_{1n}\mathbf{f}_1 + a_{2n}\mathbf{f}_2 + \cdots + a_{mn}\mathbf{f}_m \tag{7.13}$$

The linear operator A is now completely described by the *numbers* a_{ij} $(i = 1, \ldots, m; j = 1, \ldots, n)$, for let $\mathbf{x}$ be any vector of U. Then there are unique scalars $\alpha_1, \ldots, \alpha_n$ such that

$$\mathbf{x} = \alpha_1\mathbf{e}_1 + \cdots + \alpha_n\mathbf{e}_n \tag{7.14}$$

and

$$
\begin{aligned}
A\mathbf{x} &= \alpha_1 A\mathbf{e}_1 + \cdots + \alpha_n A\mathbf{e}_n \\
&= \alpha_1(a_{11}\mathbf{f}_1 + \cdots + a_{m1}\mathbf{f}_m) + \cdots + \alpha_n(a_{1n}\mathbf{f}_1 + \cdots + a_{mn}\mathbf{f}_m) \\
&= (a_{11}\alpha_1 + \cdots + a_{1n}\alpha_n)\mathbf{f}_1 + \cdots + (a_{m1}\alpha_1 + \cdots + a_{mn}\alpha_n)\mathbf{f}_m \quad (7.15)
\end{aligned}
$$

If the numbers a_{ij} are all given, then we can express $A\mathbf{x}$ in terms of the basis for V as soon as $\mathbf{x}$ is expressed in terms of the basis for U.

It is convenient to display the numbers a_{ij} in a rectangular array

$$
\begin{pmatrix}
a_{11} & a_{12} & \cdots & a_{1n} \\
a_{21} & a_{22} & \cdots & a_{2n} \\
\cdot & \cdot & & \cdot \\
\cdot & \cdot & & \cdot \\
\cdot & \cdot & & \cdot \\
a_{m1} & a_{m2} & \cdots & a_{mn}
\end{pmatrix} \tag{7.16}
$$

in which the number in the ith row and jth column is a_{ij}. Such an array is called a *matrix* of m rows and n columns, or an $m \times n$ ("m by n") matrix.

A matrix represents a linear operator $A: U \to V$ relative to a fixed pair of bases, $\mathbf{e}_1, \ldots, \mathbf{e}_n$ in U and $\mathbf{f}_1, \ldots, \mathbf{f}_m$ in V. The same linear operator A would be represented by a different matrix if either of the sets of basis vectors were changed. We review the mechanism whereby a matrix represents a linear operator relative to a fixed pair of bases. Given the linear operator $A: U \to V$ and the pair of bases, determine all the numbers a_{ij} by Eqs. (7.13), and write out the matrix (7.16).

Then, given any vector $\mathbf{x}$ in U, with coordinates $(\alpha_1, \ldots, \alpha_n)$ relative to the basis $\mathbf{e}_1, \ldots, \mathbf{e}_n$ of U [this means that (7.14) is true], $A\mathbf{x}$ is the vector of V whose coordinates relative to the basis $\mathbf{f}_1, \ldots, \mathbf{f}_m$ of V are $(\beta_1, \ldots, \beta_m)$ where

$$\beta_i = \sum_{j=1}^{n} a_{ij}\alpha_j \qquad (i = 1, 2, \ldots, m) \qquad (7.17)$$

according to Eq. (7.15).

It is helpful to visualize the operator A acting on a vector $\mathbf{x}$ to produce a new vector $A\mathbf{x}$ by thinking of the matrix which represents A relative to the given pair of bases acting on the coordinates of $\mathbf{x}$ to produce the coordinates of $A\mathbf{x}$. To visualize this process, which is analytically given in (7.17), think of the matrix as written to the left of a column of the coordinates of $\mathbf{x}$, thus:

$$\begin{pmatrix} a_{11} & a_{12} & \cdots & a_{1n} \\ a_{21} & a_{22} & \cdots & a_{2n} \\ \cdot & \cdot & & \cdot \\ \cdot & \cdot & & \cdot \\ \cdot & \cdot & & \cdot \\ a_{m1} & a_{m2} & \cdots & a_{mn} \end{pmatrix} \begin{pmatrix} \alpha_1 \\ \alpha_2 \\ \cdot \\ \cdot \\ \cdot \\ \alpha_m \end{pmatrix} = \begin{pmatrix} \beta_1 \\ \beta_2 \\ \cdot \\ \cdot \\ \cdot \\ \beta_m \end{pmatrix} \qquad (7.18)$$

Then, according to (7.17), the number β_1 is obtained by multiplying the entries in the first row of the matrix by the corresponding coordinates α_i and adding. β_2 is obtained similarly from the second row of the matrix and the α's, etc.

Example

Let the vector spaces U and V be, respectively, E^3 and E^2. Consider the basis

$$\begin{aligned} \mathbf{e}_1 &= (1,0,0) \\ \mathbf{e}_2 &= (0,1,0) \\ \mathbf{e}_3 &= (0,0,1) \end{aligned}$$

of E^3 and the basis

$$\begin{aligned} \mathbf{f}_1 &= (1,1) \\ \mathbf{f}_2 &= (2,1) \end{aligned}$$

of E_2.

We define an operator $A: E^3 \rightarrow E^2$ by describing its effect on the basis vectors of E^3. Suppose

$$A\mathbf{e}_1 = (0,0)$$
$$A\mathbf{e}_2 = (1,1)$$
$$A\mathbf{e}_3 = (1,-1)$$

We wish to find the matrix which represents this operator relative to the given bases. Equations (7.13), in this case, are

$$(0,0) = a_{11}(1,1) + a_{21}(2,1) \tag{7.19a}$$
$$(1,1) = a_{12}(1,1) + a_{22}(2,1) \tag{7.19b}$$
$$(1,-1) = a_{13}(1,1) + a_{23}(2,1) \tag{7.19c}$$

From (7.19a), $a_{11} = a_{21} = 0$. From (7.19b), $a_{12} = 1$, $a_{22} = 0$, and from (7.19c) $a_{13} = -3$, $a_{23} = 2$. Hence, relative to the given pair of bases, the operator A is represented by the 2×3 matrix

$$\begin{pmatrix} 0 & 1 & -3 \\ 0 & 0 & 2 \end{pmatrix}$$

To find the effect of this operator on any vector $\mathbf{x}$, suppose the coordinates of $\mathbf{x}$ relative to the base $\mathbf{e}_1$, $\mathbf{e}_2$, $\mathbf{e}_3$ are α_1, α_2, α_3, then the coordinates β_1, β_2 of $A\mathbf{x}$ relative to the base $\mathbf{f}_1$, $\mathbf{f}_2$ are given by

$$\begin{pmatrix} 0 & 1 & -3 \\ 0 & 0 & 2 \end{pmatrix} \begin{pmatrix} \alpha_1 \\ \alpha_2 \\ \alpha_3 \end{pmatrix} = \begin{pmatrix} \beta_1 \\ \beta_2 \end{pmatrix} \tag{7.20}$$

This last equation is to be interpreted according to (7.17), and it means that

$$\beta_1 = \alpha_2 - 3\alpha_3$$
$$\beta_2 = 2\alpha_3$$

For instance,

$$\begin{pmatrix} 0 & 1 & -3 \\ 0 & 0 & 2 \end{pmatrix} \begin{pmatrix} 5 \\ 2 \\ 7 \end{pmatrix} = \begin{pmatrix} 0 \cdot 5 + 1 \cdot 2 - 3 \cdot 7 \\ 0 \cdot 5 + 0 \cdot 2 + 2 \cdot 7 \end{pmatrix}$$

$$= \begin{pmatrix} -19 \\ 14 \end{pmatrix}$$

$$\begin{pmatrix} 0 & 1 & -3 \\ 0 & 0 & 2 \end{pmatrix} \begin{pmatrix} 1 \\ 3 \\ 3 \end{pmatrix} = \begin{pmatrix} -6 \\ 6 \end{pmatrix} \tag{7.21}$$

and so on. We see here quite clearly how the given matrix acts on vectors of E^3 and transforms them into vectors of E^2. It is most important, however, to keep in mind the underlying bases. These bases do not appear explicitly, say in (7.21), but the vectors (1,3,3) and ($-6,6$) on the two sides of (7.21) refer to the vectors

$$1 \cdot \mathbf{e}_1 + 3\mathbf{e}_2 + 3\mathbf{e}_3$$

and

$$-6\mathbf{f}_1 + 6\mathbf{f}_2$$

respectively.

Exercises

1. Find the coordinates of each of the following vectors of E^2 relative to the basis $\mathbf{e}_1 = (2,4)$, $\mathbf{e}_2 = (3,1)$.

   (a) (0,0)
   (b) (1,1)
   (c) ($-1,3$)
   (d) (x,y)

2. If a matrix is square, what can you say about the operator which it represents?

3. Let D be the linear operator which assigns to every polynomial of degree $\leq n$ its derivative. Regard D as a map from the space U of polynomials of degree $\leq n$ to the space V of polynomials of degree $\leq n - 1$. Relative to the basis

$$1, x, x^2, \ldots, x^n$$

of U and the basis

$$1, x, x^2, \ldots, x^{n-1}$$

of V find the matrix which represents D.

4. Carry out the transformations indicated:

   (a) $\begin{pmatrix} 1 & 0 \\ 2 & 1 \end{pmatrix} \begin{pmatrix} 3 \\ 2 \end{pmatrix} =$

   (b) $\begin{pmatrix} 2 & 4 & 1 \\ 2 & 3 & 2 \end{pmatrix} \begin{pmatrix} 1 \\ 2 \\ 3 \end{pmatrix} =$

   (c) $\begin{pmatrix} 0 & 1 \\ 0 & 0 \end{pmatrix} \begin{pmatrix} a \\ 0 \end{pmatrix} =$

(d) $\begin{pmatrix} a & a & a \\ b & b & b \\ c & c & c \end{pmatrix} \begin{pmatrix} 1 \\ 2 \\ 3 \end{pmatrix} =$

(e) $(3 \quad 1 \quad 2) \begin{pmatrix} 2 \\ 5 \\ -6 \end{pmatrix} =$

In each case state the dimensions of the two vector spaces between which the matrix acts.

5. A certain linear operator $A\colon E^2 \to E^2$ satisfies

$$A(-1,-1) = (2,2)$$
$$A(1,4) = (3,3)$$

What is $A(x,y)$?

6. A certain function $A\colon E^2 \to E^2$ satisfies

$$A(2,3) = (1,1)$$
$$A(1,-1) = (2,0)$$
$$A(3,1) = (1,4)$$

Is A a linear operator?

7. An operator $A\colon E^2 \to E^2$ is defined by

$$A(\alpha_1,\alpha_2) = (3\alpha_1 - \alpha_2, \alpha_1)$$

Find the matrix which represents A relative to

   (a) The basis $(1,0)$, $(0,1)$ of E^2.
   (b) The basis $(2,3)$, $(3,2)$ of E^2.

8. An operator $T\colon E^3 \to E^2$ is defined by

$$T(\alpha_1,\alpha_2,\alpha_3) = (\alpha_1 - \alpha_3, \alpha_1)$$

Find the matrix which represents T relative to

   (a) The basis $(1,0,0)$, $(0,1,0)$, $(0,0,1)$ of E^3 and the basis $(1,0)$, $(0,1)$ of E^2.
   (b) The basis $(1,1,1)$, $(1,1,0)$, $(1,0,0)$ of E^3 and the basis $(2,0)$, $(1,3)$ of E^2.

7.3.   *Matrix Algebra*

We have found that a matrix is a rectangular array of numbers which represents a linear operator between two vector spaces relative to a choice of basis vectors in those spaces. The fact that linear operators can be added, multiplied by scalars, and multiplied together under certain circumstances, induces corresponding operations on matrices. Thus matrices can be added, multiplied by scalars, and multiplied together, under suitable conditions. In this section we discuss these operations on matrices, and show how they are forced by the underlying linear operators. It is then possible to "cut loose" the matrices from their *alter egos,* the linear operators, and study them for their own sake, however, we will not have space here to follow them extensively.

Consider first the addition of matrices. Let U_m and U_n be two vector spaces, of dimension m and n, respectively, and let $A\colon U_n \to U_m$ and $B\colon U_n \to U_m$ be two linear operators from U_n to U_m. Fix a pair of bases, one in U_n and one in U_m. Then the operators A and B are represented by $m \times n$ matrices, which we will also call A and B. The operator $A + B\colon U_n \to U_m$ is well defined, and our definition of the matrix $A + B$ will be the matrix which represents the operator $A + B$ relative to the same pair of bases. It remains, then, to discover how the matrix $A + B$ is related to the matrices A and B.

Let $\mathbf{x}$ be a vector in U_n whose coordinates relative to the chosen basis in U_n are $(\alpha_1, \alpha_2, \ldots, \alpha_n)$. Then the ith coordinate of $A\mathbf{x}$ relative to the basis in U_m is

$$(A\mathbf{x})_i = \sum_{j=1}^n a_{ij}\alpha_j \qquad (i = 1, \ldots, m)$$

and the ith coordinate of $B\mathbf{x}$ is

$$(B\mathbf{x})_i = \sum_{j=1}^n b_{ij}\alpha_j \qquad (i = 1, \ldots, m)$$

Hence, the ith coordinate of $(A + B)\mathbf{x}$ is

$$
\begin{aligned}
(A + B)\mathbf{x}_i &= (A\mathbf{x})_i + (B\mathbf{x})_i \\
&= \sum_{j=1}^n a_{ij}\alpha_j + \sum_{j=1}^n b_{ij}\alpha_j \\
&= \sum_{j=1}^n (a_{ij} + b_{ij})\alpha_j \qquad (i = 1, \ldots, m)
\end{aligned}
$$

This equation tells us that the operator $A + B$ is represented by the matrix which has the number $a_{ij} + b_{ij}$ in its ith row and jth column, for each $i = 1, \ldots, m; j = 1, \ldots, n$. Hence, we formulate the

Rule for Matrix Addition. Let A and B be two $m \times n$ matrices with entries a_{ij}, b_{ij} $(i = 1, \ldots, m; j = 1, \ldots, n)$. Then the matrix $A + B$ has entries $a_{ij} + b_{ij}$ $(i = 1, \ldots, m; j = 1, \ldots, n)$.

Thus

$$\begin{pmatrix} 1 & 2 \\ 0 & 3 \end{pmatrix} + \begin{pmatrix} 3 & -2 \\ 4 & 1 \end{pmatrix} = \begin{pmatrix} 4 & 0 \\ 4 & 4 \end{pmatrix}$$

$$\begin{pmatrix} 2 & 3 & 4 \\ 1 & 2 & 3 \end{pmatrix} + \begin{pmatrix} 0 & 2 & 1 \\ 1 & 2 & 3 \end{pmatrix} = \begin{pmatrix} 2 & 5 & 5 \\ 2 & 4 & 0 \end{pmatrix}$$

Note that addition is defined only for matrices of the same size.

We turn next to matrix multiplication. Again the question is one of discovering, rather than decreeing, the rule, for the law of multiplication of matrices is implicitly contained in what has already been said. Indeed, let $B: U_n \to U_m$ and $A: U_m \to U_r$ be given linear operators, where the dimensions of the spaces are as indicated by the subscripts. If we choose a set of three bases, one in each space, B and A are represented by matrices B and A, which are, respectively, $m \times n$ and $r \times m$. The operator AB is well defined, and the matrix AB will be the one which represents the operator. It remains to discover the relationship of the matrix AB to the matrices A and B.

Let $\mathbf{x}$ be a vector in U_n with coordinates $(\alpha_1, \ldots, \alpha_n)$ relative to the chosen basis there. Then $B\mathbf{x}$ has coordinates

$$(B\mathbf{x})_i = \sum_{j=1}^{n} b_{ij}\alpha_j \qquad (i = 1, \ldots, m)$$

relative to the basis in U_m, and $A(B\mathbf{x})$, therefore, has coordinates

$$\{A(B\mathbf{x})\}_i = \sum_{j=1}^{m} a_{ij}(A\mathbf{x})_j$$

$$= \sum_{j=1}^{m} a_{ij} \left(\sum_{k=1}^{n} b_{jk}\alpha_k \right)$$

$$= \sum_{k=1}^{n} \left(\sum_{j=1}^{m} a_{ij}b_{jk} \right)\alpha_k$$

To find the entry in the ith row and the kth column of the matrix AB we need only look inside the parenthesis on the right-hand side of this last equation, for there we find the entries of the matrix which represents AB. Looking there we find the

Rule for Matrix Multiplication. Let A and B be matrices which are, respectively, $r \times m$ and $m \times n$. Then the matrix AB is the $r \times n$

matrix which has in its ith row and jth column the number

$$\sum_{k=1}^{m} a_{ik}b_{kj} \qquad (i = 1, \ldots, r; j = 1, \ldots, n) \qquad (7.22)$$

Thus, to find the product of matrices A and B we require first that A have as many columns as B has rows, for otherwise the product is undefined. This is a direct reflection of the fact that the product of two linear operators is undefined unless the image space of one operator is the domain space of the other. The rather formidable-looking rule (7.22) can easily be remembered, with a little practice, as follows: to compute the number in the ith row and the jth column of the product, go across the ith row of A and down the jth column of B multiplying corresponding numbers and adding. Thus

$$\begin{pmatrix} 1 & 0 & 4 \\ 2 & -2 & 5 \end{pmatrix}\begin{pmatrix} 3 & 1 \\ 0 & 2 \\ 1 & 4 \end{pmatrix}$$
$$= \begin{pmatrix} 1\cdot 3 + & 0\cdot 0 + 4\cdot 1 & 1\cdot 1 + & 0\cdot 2 + 4\cdot 4 \\ 2\cdot 3 + (-2)\cdot 0 + 5\cdot 1 & 2\cdot 1 + (-2)\ \cdot 2 + 5\cdot 4 \end{pmatrix}$$
$$= \begin{pmatrix} 7 & 18 \\ 11 & 18 \end{pmatrix}$$

and

$$\begin{pmatrix} 1 & -1 & 0 \\ -1 & 1 & 0 \\ 0 & 1 & 1 \end{pmatrix}\begin{pmatrix} a & d \\ b & e \\ c & f \end{pmatrix} = \begin{pmatrix} a - b & d - e \\ b - a & e - d \\ b + c & e + f \end{pmatrix}$$

If A is a square $(n \times n)$ matrix, then $A \cdot A$ is meaningful, and it is called A^2. A^3 and higher powers of A are defined in the obvious way.

The square matrix

$$I_n = \begin{pmatrix} 1 & 0 & 0 \cdots 0 \\ 0 & 1 & 0 \cdots 0 \\ 0 & 0 & 1 \cdots 0 \\ & \cdot & \cdot & \cdot \\ & \cdot & \cdot & \cdot \\ & \cdot & \cdot & \cdot \\ 0 & 0 & 0 \cdots 1 \end{pmatrix} \qquad (7.23)$$

which has 1's down the main diagonal and zeros elsewhere is called the $n \times n$ unit matrix or identity matrix. It is easy to check that it has the property

$$AI_n = I_nA = A \tag{7.24}$$

for every $n \times n$ matrix A. It plays the role of a neutral element in matrix multiplication. The $m \times n$ matrix all of whose entries are 0 is called the zero matrix, and it plays the role of a neutral element in the addition of $m \times n$ matrices:

$$A + O = O + A = A \tag{7.25}$$

Addition of matrices is commutative. Multiplication of matrices need not be commutative even where both of the products AB and BA are defined (i.e., when A is $m \times n$ and B is $n \times m$). Thus

$$\begin{pmatrix} 1 & 2 \\ 3 & 4 \end{pmatrix}\begin{pmatrix} 2 & 3 \\ 1 & 4 \end{pmatrix} = \begin{pmatrix} 4 & 11 \\ 10 & 25 \end{pmatrix}$$

but

$$\begin{pmatrix} 2 & 3 \\ 1 & 4 \end{pmatrix}\begin{pmatrix} 1 & 2 \\ 3 & 4 \end{pmatrix} = \begin{pmatrix} 11 & 16 \\ 13 & 18 \end{pmatrix}$$

It is quite possible to have $AB = O$ without either A or B being the zero matrix, thus

$$\begin{pmatrix} 1 & 0 \\ 2 & 0 \end{pmatrix}\begin{pmatrix} 0 & 0 \\ 3 & 5 \end{pmatrix} = \begin{pmatrix} 0 & 0 \\ 0 & 0 \end{pmatrix}$$

and, in fact, if

$$A = \begin{pmatrix} 0 & 1 \\ 0 & 0 \end{pmatrix}$$

then $A^2 = 0$.

One final operation on matrices concerns the multiplication of a matrix A by a scalar α. We leave it as an exercise to show that the result is to multiply each of the entries of A by α. Hence,

$$3\begin{pmatrix} 5 & 7 & 8 \\ 2 & 1 & 4 \end{pmatrix} = \begin{pmatrix} 15 & 21 & 24 \\ 6 & 3 & 12 \end{pmatrix}$$

etc.

Exercises

1. If

$$A = \begin{pmatrix} 1 & -1 \\ 2 & 3 \end{pmatrix}$$

    calculate $3A, A^2, A^3, A^3 - 2A + I_2$.

2. Prove that multiplication of a matrix by a scalar is performed as described in the last paragraph above.

3. Let U and V be vector spaces of dimensions m and n respectively. What is the dimension of Hom (U,V)?

4. Compute the following matrix products:

    (a) $(3,2,2) \begin{pmatrix} 4 \\ 1 \\ 1 \end{pmatrix}$

    (b) $\begin{pmatrix} 1 & 3 & 6 \\ 2 & 0 & 1 \\ 4 & 1 & 2 \end{pmatrix} \begin{pmatrix} 3 \\ 1 \\ 3 \end{pmatrix}$

    (c) $\begin{pmatrix} 1 \\ 2 \\ 4 \end{pmatrix} (2 \quad 3 \quad -1)$

    (d) $\begin{pmatrix} 1 & 3 & -2 \\ 2 & 0 & 1 \\ 1 & 0 & 2 \end{pmatrix} \begin{pmatrix} 2 & 4 \\ 2 & 4 \\ 2 & 5 \end{pmatrix}$

5. If

$$A = \begin{pmatrix} 0 & 1 & 0 \\ 0 & 0 & 1 \\ 1 & 0 & 0 \end{pmatrix}$$

    show that A^3 is I_3.

6. Find 2^n different $n \times n$ matrices A such that $A^2 = I_n$.

7. Find two 2×2 matrices A, B, neither of them being O or I_2, such that $AB = BA$.

8. Let A and B be two diagonal matrices (i.e., their only nonzero entries are on the diagonal). Show that $AB = BA$.

9. Find two matrices A, B such that $AB = O$ while neither A nor B is O.

7.4.   Determinants and Simultaneous Linear Equations

Many problems in mathematics and the sciences can ultimately be brought into the form of a system of simultaneous linear equations for which it is desired to find the solution or solutions. By a system of simultaneous linear equations we mean a set of equations of the form

$$a_{11}x_1 + a_{12}x_2 + \cdots + a_{1n}x_n = b_1$$
$$a_{21}x_1 + a_{22}x_2 + \cdots + a_{2n}x_n = b_2$$
$$\cdots$$
$$a_{m1}x_1 + a_{m2}x_2 + \cdots + a_{mn}x_n = b_m \tag{7.26}$$

in which all the numbers a_{ij} and b_i are given and we want to determine the "unknowns" $x_1, x_2, \ldots, x_n$ in such a way that all the equations are satisfied at once (simultaneously). If all $b_i = 0$, we say the system is *homogeneous*. A homogeneous system invariably admits the "trivial" solution $x_1 = x_2 = \cdots = x_n = 0$, and in such cases interest usually attaches to the question of whether or not the system has nontrivial solutions, and if so, how to describe them all. This problem was partly answered in Theorem 6.5.

The connection between such questions and the theory of vector spaces can be made as follows. Let us call a matrix with one column and m rows a *column vector*. The collection of all such column vectors, for m given, is evidently a vector space which is identical with E^m except that we write the coordinates of the vectors vertically rather than horizontally. We shall, therefore, not distinguish between this space and E^m.

Now if A is the matrix whose entries are a_{ij} $(i = 1, \ldots, m; j = 1, \ldots, n)$, and if $\mathbf{x}$ is the column vector of unknowns $x_1, x_2, \ldots, x_n$, and if $\mathbf{b}$ is the column vector of $b_1, b_2, \ldots, b_m$, then the system (7.26) can be written as

$$A\mathbf{x} = \mathbf{b} \tag{7.27}$$

The matrix A is, of course, a linear operator $E^n \to E^m$, and so the question of finding the solutions of (7.26) is identical with the question of determining all vectors $\mathbf{x}$ which are carried into the given vector $\mathbf{b}$ by the operator A.

Consider a pair of linear equations in two unknowns, say

$$2x_1 + 3x_2 = 1$$
$$x_1 - 2x_2 = 2$$

To solve these, one would normally eliminate one unknown. If we eliminate x_1 by means of the second equation,

$$x_1 = 2 + 2x_2$$

and substitute in the first

$$2(2 + 2x_2) + 3x_2 = 1$$

we obtain

$$7x_2 = -3$$

and so $x_2 = -\frac{3}{7}$, $x_1 = \frac{8}{7}$ is the unique solution.

Next consider the system

$$\begin{cases} 2x_1 - 3x_2 = 1 & \text{(7.28a)} \\ -6x_1 + 9x_2 = 2 & \text{(7.28b)} \end{cases}$$

If we solve the second equation for x_1,

$$x_1 = \tfrac{3}{2}x_2 - \tfrac{1}{3}$$

and substitute in the first equation,

$$2(\tfrac{3}{2}x_2 - \tfrac{1}{3}) - 3x_2 = 1$$

we get the appealing result that

$$-\tfrac{2}{3} = 1$$

and so (7.28) has no solution at all.

Finally, if the right-hand side of (7.28b) is changed from 2 to -3, we obtain infinitely many solutions: choose any number x_2 at all, and then take $x_1 = \tfrac{1}{2} + \tfrac{3}{2}x_2$, and both equations will be satisfied.

Now consider the general case of two equations in two unknowns

$$\begin{align} a_{11}x_1 + a_{12}x_2 = b_1 & \qquad \text{(7.29a)} \\ a_{21}x_1 + a_{22}x_2 = b_2 & \qquad \text{(7.29b)} \end{align}$$

To eliminate x_2, we can multiply the first equation by a_{22}, the second by a_{12}, and subtract, obtaining

$$(a_{11}a_{22} - a_{12}a_{21})x_1 = a_{22}b_1 - a_{12}b_2 \qquad \text{(7.30)}$$

The description of the solutions hinges upon the number

$$\Delta = a_{11}a_{22} - a_{12}a_{21} \qquad \text{(7.31)}$$

If $\Delta \neq 0$, we can find x_1 from (7.30) and then x_2 from either (7.29a) or (7.29b). Hence, there is a unique solution if $\Delta \neq 0$. If $\Delta = 0$, then, according to (7.30), there will be no solution at all unless $a_{22}b_1 - a_{12}b_2$ happens to be zero also. In the latter case, (7.30) is satisfied by any choice of x_1 and there will be infinitely many solutions.

The number Δ in (7.31) is called the *determinant* of the 2×2 matrix

$$A = \begin{pmatrix} a_{11} & a_{12} \\ a_{21} & a_{22} \end{pmatrix} \tag{7.32}$$

and is written $\det A$. Thus, the determinant of

$$\begin{pmatrix} 1 & 1 \\ 3 & 5 \end{pmatrix}$$

is $\Delta = 2$. The determinant of a 2×2 matrix has the following properties:

(A)   If any vector is added to the first column of A, the result being the new first column of A, the value of the determinant changes linearly, that is,

$$\det \begin{pmatrix} a_{11} + b_1 & a_{12} \\ a_{21} + b_2 & a_{22} \end{pmatrix} = \det \begin{pmatrix} a_{11} & a_{12} \\ a_{21} & a_{22} \end{pmatrix} + \det \begin{pmatrix} b_1 & a_{12} \\ b_2 & a_{22} \end{pmatrix}$$

(B)   If a column of A is multiplied by a scalar α, the value of the determinant is multiplied by α, e.g.,

$$\det \begin{pmatrix} \alpha a_{11} & a_{12} \\ \alpha a_{21} & a_{22} \end{pmatrix} = \alpha \det \begin{pmatrix} a_{11} & a_{12} \\ a_{21} & a_{22} \end{pmatrix}$$

(C)   If two columns of A are interchanged, the determinant changes sign.

(D)   We have $\det \begin{pmatrix} 1 & 0 \\ 0 & 1 \end{pmatrix} = 1$, that is, the determinant of the identity matrix is 1.

The truth of these assertions can be checked by the obvious simple computations. What is most remarkable, however, is that the properties (A)–(D) can be taken as the *definition* of a determinant because the *only* function from 2×2 matrices to real numbers which satisfies (A)–(D) is the function (7.31)! In formulating a definition of the determinant of an $n \times n$ matrix, a wide choice is available. That is, there are several fully equivalent ways of stating such a definition. Once a choice is made, all of the other useful properties of determinants must then be proved as theorems. The test of a good definition, then, is the simplicity of the chain of argument which deduces all of the properties of determinants from the definition. By this test, the most elegant definition of a determinant which has yet been found is the one which says that a determinant is the unique function which has the analogs of properties (A)–(D) in the $n \times n$ case. One of the alternatives which we reject, for example, is writing out the formula analogous to (7.31) in the $n \times n$ case, since the proofs from that starting point seem enormously complex.

As a matter of notation, it will be convenient in what follows to think of an $n \times n$ matrix in terms of its columns by letting $\mathbf{a}_1$ stand for the first column, $\mathbf{a}_2$ the second column, etc. Consider a function D, which assigns to every $n \times n$ matrix A a real number $D(A)$, in such a way that

(I)   If a column of A is multiplied by a scalar α, then $D(A)$ is multiplied by α, that is

$$D(\mathbf{a}_1, \ldots, \mathbf{a}_{j-1}, \alpha\mathbf{a}_j, \mathbf{a}_{j+1}, \ldots, \mathbf{a}_n)$$
$$= \alpha D(\mathbf{a}_1, \ldots, \mathbf{a}_{j-1}, \mathbf{a}_j, \mathbf{a}_{j+1}, \ldots, \mathbf{a}_n) \quad (7.33)$$

(II)   If a certain vector $\mathbf{b}$ is added to a column of A, then $D(A)$ changes linearly, that is,

$$D(\mathbf{a}_1, \ldots, \mathbf{a}_{j-1}, \mathbf{a}_j + \mathbf{b}, \mathbf{a}_{j+1}, \ldots, \mathbf{a}_n)$$
$$= D(\mathbf{a}_1, \ldots, \mathbf{a}_{j-1}, \mathbf{a}_j, \ldots, \mathbf{a}_m)$$
$$+ D(\mathbf{a}_1, \ldots, \mathbf{a}_{j-1}, \mathbf{b}, \mathbf{a}_{j+1}, \ldots, \mathbf{a}_n) \quad (7.34)$$

(III)   The value of D on the identity matrix I_n is 1.

(IV)   If two columns of the matrix A are interchanged, then $D(A)$ changes sign, that is,

$$D(\mathbf{a}_1, \ldots, \mathbf{a}_{p-1}, \mathbf{a}_p, \mathbf{a}_{p+1}, \ldots, \mathbf{a}_{q-1}, \mathbf{a}_q, \mathbf{a}_{q+1}, \ldots, \mathbf{a}_n)$$
$$= -D(\mathbf{a}_1, \ldots, \mathbf{a}_{p-1}, \mathbf{a}_q, \mathbf{a}_{p+1}, \ldots, \mathbf{a}_{q-1}, \mathbf{a}_p, \mathbf{a}_{q+1}, \ldots, \mathbf{a}_n)$$

A function D which satisfies (I)–(IV) will be called a *determinant function*. We will show that there is precisely one determinant function, and will derive an explicit formula for it as well as a number of its properties.

Exercises

1. Solve

$$3x - 2y + z = 4$$
$$x + y + z = 6$$
$$x - y - z = 2$$

2. If

$$A = \begin{pmatrix} 1 & 3 \\ 3 & 1 \end{pmatrix}$$

calculate det A, det (A^2), $(\det A)^2$.

3. If

$$A = \begin{pmatrix} 2 & -1 \\ 1 & 2 \end{pmatrix}, \qquad B = \begin{pmatrix} 3 & 2 \\ 2 & 2 \end{pmatrix}$$

calculate

(a) AB
(b) BA
(c) det AB
(d) det BA
(e) $(\det A)(\det B)$

4. If

$$A = \begin{pmatrix} a & b \\ c & d \end{pmatrix}, \qquad B = \begin{pmatrix} e & f \\ g & h \end{pmatrix}$$

repeat (a)–(e) of Exercise 3, thus proving that, for 2×2 matrices,

$$\det (AB) = \det (BA) = \det A \det B$$

5. If

$$A = \begin{pmatrix} a_{11} & a_{12} & a_{13} \\ a_{21} & a_{22} & a_{23} \\ a_{31} & a_{32} & a_{33} \end{pmatrix}$$

find det A by attempting to solve the equations

$$A \begin{pmatrix} x_1 \\ x_2 \\ x_3 \end{pmatrix} = \begin{pmatrix} b_1 \\ b_2 \\ b_3 \end{pmatrix}$$

and identifying a number which cannot be zero if a unique solution is to exist.

6. Show that the inverse of the matrix

$$A = \begin{pmatrix} 3 & 3 \\ 1 & 2 \end{pmatrix}$$

is the matrix

$$A^{-1} = \begin{pmatrix} \frac{2}{3} & -1 \\ -\frac{1}{3} & 1 \end{pmatrix}$$

Calculate $\det A$, $\det A^{-1}$, $(\det A)^{-1}$.

7. Show that the inverse of the matrix

$$A = \begin{pmatrix} a & b \\ c & d \end{pmatrix}$$

is the matrix

$$A^{-1} = \begin{pmatrix} \dfrac{d}{\Delta} & -\dfrac{b}{\Delta} \\ -\dfrac{c}{\Delta} & \dfrac{a}{\Delta} \end{pmatrix}$$

where $\Delta = \det A$, provided $\Delta \neq 0$. Show that

$$\det (A^{-1}) = \frac{1}{(\det A)}$$

for a 2×2 matrix with nonzero determinant.

8. Consider the function J which assigns to each $n \times n$ matrix the product of the sums of the entries in each row. That is,

$$J(A) = (a_{11} + a_{12} + \cdots + a_{1n})(a_{21} + a_{22} + \cdots + a_{2n}) \cdots (a_{n1} + a_{n2} + \cdots + a_{nn})$$

Is this a determinant function? Which axioms for determinant functions are satisfied by J?

7.5.   *More on Permutations*

In order to carry out the program described at the end of the last section we need to introduce one more concept concerning permutations of n objects, the idea of "even" and "odd" permutations. Consider the permutations $\begin{pmatrix} 1234 \\ 4312 \end{pmatrix}$ of the objects 1, 2, 3, 4. Let us put the numbers back in their original order by permitting ourselves, at each step, only to inter-change two of the symbols, leaving the others alone.

One way to do this is by the path

$$(4312) \rightarrow (2314) \rightarrow (1324) \rightarrow (1234) \tag{7.35}$$

Another way is via the route

$$(4312) \rightarrow (3412) \rightarrow (3142) \rightarrow (1342) \rightarrow (1324) \rightarrow (1234) \quad (7.36)$$

By (7.35) we achieve our aim in three steps. By (7.36), five interchanges are required. Is there some way in which four steps would do the job? The answer is no. Furthermore, there is no way which requires exactly two steps, or six steps, or any even number of steps. For this reason, we say that $\begin{pmatrix} 1234 \\ 4312 \end{pmatrix}$ is an "odd" permutation.

In order to prove that, for any given permutation, the number of "switches" required to get the numbers back in order is either always even, or always odd, it is necessary to give a definition of even and odd permutations which looks quite different from what we have been discussing, and then to prove equivalence.

DEFINITION   Let σ be a permutation of $1, 2, 3, \ldots, n$. Calculate the number

$$h(\sigma) = \frac{\sigma(2) - \sigma(1)}{2 - 1} \frac{\sigma(3) - \sigma(1)}{3 - 1} \cdots \frac{\sigma(n) - \sigma(1)}{n - 1} \frac{\sigma(3) - \sigma(2)}{3 - 2}$$

$$\cdots \frac{\sigma(n) - \sigma(2)}{n - 2} \cdots \frac{\sigma(n) - \sigma(n - 1)}{n - (n - 1)} \tag{7.37}$$

If $h(\sigma) = +1$, σ is an *even* permutation. If $h(\sigma) = -1$, σ is an *odd* permutation [$h(\sigma)$ must be either $+1$ or -1 because each numerator is the same as some denominator, except possibly for the sign].

Example

Let σ be the permutation $\begin{pmatrix} 123 \\ 312 \end{pmatrix}$, i.e., $\sigma(1) = 3$, $\sigma(2) = 1$, $\sigma(3) = 2$. Then,

$$h(\sigma) = \frac{\sigma(2) - \sigma(1)}{2 - 1} \frac{\sigma(3) - \sigma(1)}{3 - 1} \frac{\sigma(3) - \sigma(2)}{3 - 2}$$

$$= \frac{1-3}{2-1} \cdot \frac{2-3}{3-1} \cdot \frac{2-1}{3-2}$$

$$= +1$$

and so $\begin{pmatrix} 123 \\ 312 \end{pmatrix}$ is an even permutation.

The principal property of $h(\sigma)$ is given by

THEOREM 7.6. Let σ and τ be two permutations of $1, 2, 3, \ldots, n$. Then

$$h(\sigma\tau) = h(\sigma)h(\tau) \tag{7.38}$$

PROOF The product $\sigma\tau$ on the left side of (7.38) is the product of two permutations in the sense of Section 6.1. Now, by the definition of h in (7.37) we have

$$h(\sigma\tau) = \frac{\sigma\tau(2) - \sigma\tau(1)}{2-1} \cdots \frac{\sigma\tau(n) - \sigma\tau(1)}{n-1} \cdots \frac{\sigma\tau(n) - \sigma\tau(n-1)}{n-(n-1)}$$

$$= \left[\frac{\sigma\tau(2) - \sigma\tau(1)}{\sigma(2) - \sigma(1)} \cdots \frac{\sigma\tau(n) - \sigma\tau(1)}{\sigma(n) - \sigma(1)} \cdots \frac{\sigma\tau(n) - \sigma\tau(n-1)}{\sigma(n) - \sigma(n-1)} \right]$$

$$\times \left[\frac{\sigma(2) - \sigma(1)}{2-1} \cdots \frac{\sigma(n) - \sigma(1)}{n-1} \cdots \frac{\sigma(n) - \sigma(n-1)}{n-(n-1)} \right]$$

The quantity in the second bracket is exactly $h(\sigma)$. We claim that the quantity in the first bracket is $h(\tau)$. Indeed, if in the first bracket we cross out the letter σ wherever it appears, the result would obviously be $h(\tau)$. We cannot do this, but the remark shows us that a term in the product in the first bracket is obtained from the corresponding term in the definition of $h(\tau)$ by applying the permutation σ to each number appearing in the term. This means, however, that the terms in the first bracket are just a rearrangement of the terms in $h(\tau)$, completing the proof.

DEFINITION By a *transposition* we mean a permutation of n letters which leaves $n-2$ of the letters alone and interchanges the other two.

Examples

The permutations $\begin{pmatrix} 123 \\ 213 \end{pmatrix}$, $\begin{pmatrix} 12345678 \\ 12745638 \end{pmatrix}$, and $\begin{pmatrix} 1234 \\ 4231 \end{pmatrix}$ are all transpositions.

THEOREM 7.7.   Every permutation can be expressed as a product of transpositions.

PROOF   The theorem asserts that, starting with the integers $1, 2, \ldots, n$ in order, we can arrive at any desired permutation by successively interchanging pairs of integers. The proof is by induction. For $n = 2$, i.e., for permutations of $1, 2$, the result is clear. Suppose the theorem has been proved for permutations of $1, 2, \ldots,$ $n - 1$. Let σ be a permutation of $1, 2, \ldots, n$. By a single transposition, τ_0, we can put the letter n back where it belongs, at the end. By the inductive assumption, the remaining $n - 1$ letters can be put back in order by a sequence of transpositions. Q.E.D.

THEOREM 7.8.   The permutation σ is even (respectively, odd) if and only if when we write

$$\sigma = \tau_1 \tau_2 \ldots \tau_m$$

where each τ_i is a transposition, the integer m is always even (respectively, odd).

PROOF   We have now arrived at the "definition" of even and odd permutations given at the beginning of the section. Suppose σ is even. If

$$\sigma = \tau_1 \tau_2 \ldots \tau_m$$

then

$$h(\sigma) = h(\tau_1)h(\tau_2) \ldots h(\tau_m) \tag{7.39}$$

by Theorem 7.6. For a transposition τ, however, $h(\tau) = -1$ (see Exercise 1). Thus every term on the right-hand side of (7.39) is (-1) and so

$$h(\sigma) = (-1)^m$$

Since σ is even, $h(\sigma) = +1$, hence, m is even. If m is always even, the same argument in reverse shows that σ is even. If m is always odd, the proof is similar. Q.E.D.

Exercises

1. Prove, from (7.37), that $h(\sigma) = -1$ if σ is a transposition.
2. Prove that a set of two objects $1, -1$ with the multiplication table below is a group.

$\cdot$	1	-1
1	1	-1
-1	-1	1

3. Show that the function $h: \sigma \to h(\sigma)$ is a group homomorphism from the group of permutations of n letters to the group in Exercise 2.
4. If $h: G \to G'$ is a homomorphism of the group G to the group G', the kernel of h, Ker h, is the set of elements of G which are assigned, by h, to the neutral element of G'. Show that Ker h is itself a group. Identify Ker h for the homomorphism of Exercise 3. Do the odd permutations form a group? Why?
5. Which of the following permutations are even?

   (a) $\begin{pmatrix} 12345678 \\ 32147658 \end{pmatrix}$

   (b) $\begin{pmatrix} 12345678 \\ 84312576 \end{pmatrix}$

   (c) $\begin{pmatrix} 123456 \\ 654321 \end{pmatrix}$

   (d) $\begin{pmatrix} 1234567 \\ 7162534 \end{pmatrix}$

6. Find *all* the even permutations of 1, 2, 3, 4.
7. Express each of the following permutations as a product of transpositions in two different ways:

   (a) $\begin{pmatrix} 12345 \\ 23451 \end{pmatrix}$

   (b) $\begin{pmatrix} 1234 \\ 2143 \end{pmatrix}$

   (c) $\begin{pmatrix} 12345 \\ 14523 \end{pmatrix}$

   (d) $\begin{pmatrix} 1234 \\ 4321 \end{pmatrix}$

7.6. Determinant Functions

We now return to the problem of finding all determinant functions, that is, all functions D from $n \times n$ matrices to the real numbers which satisfy axioms (I)–(IV) of Section 7.4. Hence, suppose that a particular $n \times n$ matrix is given, say

$$A = \begin{pmatrix} a_{11} & a_{12} & \cdots & a_{1n} \\ a_{21} & a_{22} & \cdots & a_{2n} \\ & & & \\ & & & \\ a_{n1} & a_{n2} & \cdots & a_{nn} \end{pmatrix} \tag{7.40}$$

Let D be a determinant function, and let us proceed to compute the value of D on the matrix A.

We first introduce the natural basis for the space E^n of column vectors, namely, the basis

$$\mathbf{e}_1 = \begin{pmatrix} 1 \\ 0 \\ 0 \\ \cdot \\ \cdot \\ 0 \end{pmatrix} ; \quad \mathbf{e}_2 = \begin{pmatrix} 0 \\ 1 \\ 0 \\ \cdot \\ \cdot \\ 0 \end{pmatrix} ; \quad \ldots ; \quad \mathbf{e}_n = \begin{pmatrix} 0 \\ 0 \\ 0 \\ \cdot \\ \cdot \\ 1 \end{pmatrix} \tag{7.41}$$

so that if

$$\mathbf{x} = \begin{pmatrix} \alpha_1 \\ \alpha_2 \\ \cdot \\ \cdot \\ \alpha_n \end{pmatrix}$$

is any column vector, then clearly

$$\mathbf{x} = \alpha_1 \mathbf{e}_1 + \alpha_2 \mathbf{e}_2 + \cdots + \alpha_n \mathbf{e}_n$$

In particular, if $\mathbf{a}_j$ denotes the jth column of the given matrix (7.40), then obviously

$$\mathbf{a}_j = a_{1j}\mathbf{e}_1 + a_{2j}\mathbf{e}_2 + \cdots + a_{nj}\mathbf{e}_n$$

Hence, the value of D at the matrix A is

$$D(\mathbf{a}_1, \mathbf{a}_2, \mathbf{a}_3, \ldots, \mathbf{a}_n) = D(a_{11}\mathbf{e}_1 + a_{21}\mathbf{e}_2 + \cdots + a_{n1}\mathbf{e}_n, \mathbf{a}_2, \ldots, \mathbf{a}_n)$$

We invoke Axioms I and II, which express the linearity of D in the columns of A, and find

$$D(\mathbf{a}_1, \mathbf{a}_2, \ldots, \mathbf{a}_n) = a_{11}D(\mathbf{e}_1, \mathbf{a}_2, \ldots, \mathbf{a}_n) + a_{21}D(\mathbf{e}_2, \mathbf{a}_2, \ldots, \mathbf{a}_n) + \cdots$$
$$+ a_{n1}D(\mathbf{e}_n, \mathbf{a}_2, \ldots, \mathbf{a}_n) \quad (7.42)$$

What we have so far accomplished is to express $D(A)$ in terms of the value of D on matrices which are slightly simpler than A in that their first columns are the vectors (7.41). We want to repeat this process on the second and succeeding columns. The calculation will get quite messy, and so we had better take refuge in the summation symbols, by writing (7.42) as

$$D(\mathbf{a}_1, \ldots, \mathbf{a}_n) = \sum_{i=1}^{n} a_{i1}D(\mathbf{e}_i, \mathbf{a}_2, \ldots, \mathbf{a}_n) \quad (7.43)$$

Now

$$\mathbf{a}_2 = a_{12}\mathbf{e}_1 + \cdots + a_{n2}\mathbf{e}_n$$

and substituting this into (7.43) we obtain

$$D(\mathbf{a}_1, \ldots, \mathbf{a}_n) = \sum_{i=1}^{n} a_{i1}D(\mathbf{e}_i, a_{12}\mathbf{e}_1 + \cdots + a_{n2}\mathbf{e}_n, \mathbf{a}_3, \ldots, \mathbf{a}_n)$$

We again use Axioms I and II to expand the right-hand side, and get

$$D(\mathbf{a}_1, \ldots, \mathbf{a}_n) = \sum_{i=1}^{n} a_{i1} \sum_{k=1}^{n} a_{k2}D(\mathbf{e}_i, \mathbf{e}_k, \mathbf{a}_3, \ldots, \mathbf{a}_n) \quad (7.44)$$

We have now expressed $D(\mathbf{a}_1, \ldots, \mathbf{a}_n)$ in terms of the value of D on a collection of matrices which are simpler than before, because the first *two* columns of the matrices on the right-hand side of (7.44) have been standardized. Next, the process of reduction must be continued to all the remaining columns. The notation, however, will pose an insuperable block to this continuation if we insist on introducing new letters of the alphabet [as i and k in (7.44)] every time a new sum has to be done. Hence, we rewrite (7.44), changing the letter i to i_1 and k to i_2 so that subsequent summations will be over $i_3, i_4, \ldots, i_n$:

$$D(\mathbf{a}_1, \ldots, \mathbf{a}_n) = \sum_{i_1=1}^{n} \sum_{i_2=1}^{n} a_{i_11} a_{i_22} D(\mathbf{e}_{i_1}, \mathbf{e}_{i_2}, \mathbf{a}_3, \ldots, \mathbf{a}_n) \qquad (7.44)'$$

Now

$$\mathbf{a}_3 = \sum_{i_3=1}^{n} a_{i_33} \mathbf{e}_{i_3}$$

and substituting this in (7.44)' we get

$$D(\mathbf{a}_1, \ldots, \mathbf{a}_n) = \sum_{i_1=1}^{n} \sum_{i_2=1}^{n} a_{i_11} a_{i_22} D\left(\mathbf{e}_{i_1}, \mathbf{e}_{i_2}, \sum_{i_3=1}^{n} a_{i_33} \mathbf{e}_{i_3}, \ldots, \mathbf{a}_n\right)$$

$$= \sum_{i_1=1}^{n} \sum_{i_2=1}^{n} \sum_{i_3=1}^{n} a_{i_11} a_{i_22} a_{i_33} D(\mathbf{e}_{i_1}, \mathbf{e}_{i_2}, \mathbf{e}_{i_3}, \mathbf{a}_4, \ldots, \mathbf{a}_n)$$

where Axioms I and II have again been used.

Continuation of this process through all of the columns of A leads to the result that

$$D(\mathbf{a}_1, \ldots, \mathbf{a}_n) = \sum_{i_1, \ldots, i_n = 1}^{n} a_{i_11} a_{i_22} \ldots a_{i_nn} D(\mathbf{e}_{i_1}, \mathbf{e}_{i_2}, \ldots, \mathbf{e}_{i_n}) \qquad (7.45)$$

This equation shows that the value of D is known on any matrix if it is known on matrices whose columns are some arrangement of the standard vectors (7.41). The sum on the right-hand side of (7.45) apparently contains n^n terms, one for each possible choice of the indices $i_1, i_2, \ldots, i_n$. We claim, however, that if some integer occurs more than once among the indices $i_1, \ldots, i_n$ then $D(\mathbf{e}_{i_1}, \ldots, \mathbf{e}_{i_n}) = 0$, so such a term will not contribute to the right-hand side of (7.45). This will follow from

THEOREM 7.9.   Let D be a determinant function. If A is a matrix with two identical columns, then $D(A) = 0$.

PROOF   Interchange the two identical columns. Since A is unaltered, $D(A)$ is unaltered. By Axiom IV for determinant functions, $D(A)$ also changes sign. $D(A)$ must, therefore, be a number which is unaltered when its sign is changed. Q.E.D.

Hence, in Eq. (7.45) we need not extend the sum over all n^n possible choices of $i_1, \ldots, i_n$, but only over those $n!$ choices in which $i_1, \ldots, i_n$ are all different, in other words, over the *permutations* of the integers

1, 2, . . . , n. To take account of this remark we rewrite (7.45) in slightly different notation:

$$D(\mathbf{a}_1, \ldots, \mathbf{a}_n) = \sum_{(!)} a_{i_1 1} a_{i_2 2} \ldots a_{i_n n} D(\mathbf{e}_{i_1}, \ldots, \mathbf{e}_{in}) \qquad (7.45)'$$

where the factorial symbol (!) under the Σ is to remind us that the sum extends only over permutations.

Now consider just one of the terms in (7.45)', say the term involving

$$D(\mathbf{e}_{i_1}, \ldots, \mathbf{e}_{i_n}) \qquad (7.46)$$

where $(i_1 \ldots i_n)$ is some fixed permutation of $(1, 2, \ldots, n)$.

The expression (7.46) denotes the value of the determinant function D on a very special kind of matrix, namely, an $n \times n$ matrix whose columns are some rearrangement of the special vectors (7.41). Consider a sequence of transpositions which puts the permutation $\begin{pmatrix} 1, & 2 & \ldots n \\ i_1, & i_2 & \ldots i_n \end{pmatrix}$ back in the order $\begin{pmatrix} 1, & 2 \ldots n \\ 1, & 2 \ldots n \end{pmatrix}$. By successively interchanging pairs of columns in the matrix $(\mathbf{e}_{i_1}, \ldots, \mathbf{e}_{i_n})$ according to that sequence of transpositions we will bring the matrix into the form $(\mathbf{e}_1, \mathbf{e}_2, \ldots, \mathbf{e}_n)$, that is, into the form

$$I_n = \begin{pmatrix} 1 & 0 & 0 & \cdots & 0 \\ 0 & 1 & 0 & \cdots & 0 \\ 0 & 0 & 1 & \cdots & 0 \\ & \cdot & \cdot & \cdot & & \cdot \\ & \cdot & \cdot & \cdot & & \cdot \\ & \cdot & \cdot & \cdot & & \cdot \\ 0 & 0 & 0 & \cdots & 1 \end{pmatrix} \qquad (7.47)$$

of the $n \times n$ identity matrix I_n. Each time we interchange a pair of columns, according to Axiom IV for determinant functions, the quantity (7.46) will change sign. Hence, the value of (7.46) is either equal to $D(I_n)$ or $-D(I_n)$ according to whether the given permutation $\begin{pmatrix} 1 & \ldots & n \\ i_1 & \ldots & i_n \end{pmatrix}$ is even or odd, respectively. That is,

$$D(\mathbf{e}_{i_1}, \ldots, \mathbf{e}_{i_n}) = h\begin{pmatrix} 1 & \ldots & n \\ i & \ldots & i_n \end{pmatrix} D(I_n) \qquad (7.48)$$

where $h\begin{pmatrix} 1 & \cdots & n \\ i_1 & \cdots & i_n \end{pmatrix}$ is the sign of the permutation $\begin{pmatrix} 1 & \cdots & n \\ i_1 & \cdots & i_n \end{pmatrix}$, and is $+1$ for even permutations, -1 for odd ones.

Substituting (7.48) in (7.45)' and factoring out $D(I_n)$, we find

$$D(\mathbf{a}_1, \ldots, \mathbf{a}_n) = D(I_n) \sum_{(!)} h\begin{pmatrix} 1 & \cdots & n \\ i_1 & \cdots & i_n \end{pmatrix} a_{1i_1} a_{2i_2} \cdots a_{ni_n} \qquad (7.49)$$

We note, for future reference, that in deducing (7.49) we have made no use of Axiom III. Equation (7.49), therefore, tells us that if we have a function D which satisfies I, II, IV, then its value on every matrix is known as soon as its value on the single matrix (7.47) is specified.

We now invoke Axiom III for determinant functions, and obtain

THEOREM 7.10.   Let D be a determinant function. Then $D(A)$ has the value

$$D(A) = \sum_{(!)} h\begin{pmatrix} 1 & \cdots & n \\ i_1 & \cdots & i_n \end{pmatrix} a_{1i_1} a_{2i_2} \cdots a_{ni_n} \qquad (7.50)$$

on an $n \times n$ matrix A.

Example
Let $n = 2$, and

$$A = \begin{pmatrix} a_{11} & a_{12} \\ a_{21} & a_{22} \end{pmatrix}$$

There are just two permutations of 1, 2, namely, $\begin{pmatrix} 12 \\ 12 \end{pmatrix}$ and $\begin{pmatrix} 12 \\ 21 \end{pmatrix}$, the first being even, the second odd. The sum in (7.50) has just two terms,

$$D(A) = h\begin{pmatrix} 12 \\ 12 \end{pmatrix} a_{11} a_{22} + h\begin{pmatrix} 12 \\ 21 \end{pmatrix} a_{12} a_{21}$$

$$= (+1)a_{11}a_{22} + (-1)a_{12}a_{21}$$

$$= a_{11}a_{22} - a_{12}a_{21}$$

the usual determinant of A.

We leave the case of 3×3 matrices for an exercise. Our argument has shown that, if D is a determinant function, then its value is given by

(7.50), i.e., that there exists at most one determinant function. To show that there is a determinant function we would have to show that (7.50) satisfies Axioms I–IV. This is true, but the proof, by straightforward but lengthy calculations, is omitted. The function (7.50) will simply be called "the determinant of A," written det A.

Exercises

1. Find the determinant of

$$\begin{pmatrix} a_{11} & a_{12} & a_{13} \\ a_{21} & a_{22} & a_{23} \\ a_{31} & a_{32} & a_{33} \end{pmatrix}$$

2. Compute the determinants of

$$\begin{pmatrix} 1 & 3 & 1 \\ 2 & 1 & 2 \\ 1 & 2 & 1 \end{pmatrix}, \quad \begin{pmatrix} 1 & 0 & 0 \\ 2 & 1 & 3 \\ 3 & 1 & 2 \end{pmatrix}$$

3. Suppose that a certain matrix has only zeros above the main diagonal (i.e., $a_{ij} = 0$ if $i < j$). Prove that its determinant is equal to the product of its diagonal elements: $a_{11}a_{22}a_{33} \ldots a_{nn}$.

4. If $A = I_n$, show that the expression (7.50) has the value 1.

5. Show, directly from (7.50), that if a matrix A has a whole row or column of zeros then $D(A) = 0$.

7.7. Properties of Determinants

The formula (7.50) is usually ill-suited to calculation. There are many other methods for computing determinants, some of which are quite efficient. The expansion of Laplace, which we now discuss, has an air of simplicity about it which is not really justified by its computational power. We should think of it as a method which is useful for small matrices, is easy to remember, and is of importance in further theoretical developments.

Let an $n \times n$ matrix A be given. By the *minor* of the entry a_{ij}

we mean the determinant of the $(n-1) \times (n-1)$ matrix which is obtained from A by striking out the ith row and the jth column. We will denote this minor by the symbol a^{ij}. Thus, if

$$A = \begin{pmatrix} 1 & 1 & -2 \\ -1 & 2 & -1 \\ 3 & 2 & 1 \end{pmatrix}$$

then

$$a^{11} = \det \begin{pmatrix} 2 & -1 \\ 2 & 1 \end{pmatrix} = 4$$

$$a^{31} = \det \begin{pmatrix} 1 & -2 \\ 2 & -1 \end{pmatrix} = 3$$

$$a^{23} = \det \begin{pmatrix} 1 & 1 \\ 3 & 2 \end{pmatrix} = -1$$

etc.

By the *cofactor* of a_{ij} we mean the number $(-1)^{i+j}a^{ij}$. The Laplace expansion theorem is

THEOREM 7.11. Given an $n \times n$ matrix A. Select a column (or row), say the ith. Multiply each element of A in that column (or row) by its cofactor. Add the resulting numbers. The result is $\det A$. In symbols,

$$
\begin{aligned}
\det A &= \sum_{j=1}^{n} (-1)^{i+j}a_{ij}a^{ij} & (i = 1, 2, \ldots, n) \\
&= \sum_{i=1}^{n} (-1)^{i+j}a_{ij}a^{ij} & (j = 1, 2, \ldots, n) \quad (7.51)
\end{aligned}
$$

Example
To calculate

$$\det \begin{pmatrix} 1 & 1 & -2 \\ -1 & 2 & -1 \\ 3 & 2 & 1 \end{pmatrix}$$

we choose (quite arbitrarily) the second column. Then the required determinant is

$$-a_{12}a^{12} + a_{22}a^{22} - a_{32}a^{32}$$

$$= -1 \det \begin{pmatrix} -1 & -1 \\ 3 & 1 \end{pmatrix} + 2 \det \begin{pmatrix} 1 & -2 \\ 3 & 1 \end{pmatrix} - 2 \det \begin{pmatrix} 1 & -2 \\ -1 & -1 \end{pmatrix}$$

$$= -1 \cdot 2 + 2 \cdot 7 - 2 \cdot (-3) = 18$$

PROOF OF THEOREM 7.11.   To be specific, we prove the result if we choose to expand along the first row. Hence, we wish to show that

$$\det A = a_{11}a^{11} - a_{12}a^{12} + a_{13}a^{13} + \cdots + (-1)^{n+1}a_{1n}a^{1n} \quad (7.52)$$

The plan of the proof is as follows. We consider the function which assigns to each $n \times n$ matrix the number on the right-hand side of (7.52). We then prove that this function is a determinant function, i.e., satisfies Axioms I–IV for determinant functions. Since there is just one determinant function, namely, $\det A$, we shall have proved Eq. (7.52).

Consider the effect of multiplying a column by α, say the pth column. Then the corresponding columns of each of the determinants a^{ij}, except for a^{1p}, are multiplied by α, and so each of those a^{ij} is multiplied by α. Thus the whole right-hand side of (7.52) is multiplied by α, and Axiom I for determinant functions is satisfied. Axioms II and III are easy to check and are left as exercises. Finally, if two columns of A, say the pth and qth, are interchanged, then each of the minors a^{ij}, except for a^{1p} and a^{1q}, changes sign. The minor belonging to the first row and pth column of the matrix after interchange looks like this:

$$(a^{1p})' = \begin{pmatrix} \mathbf{a_1 a_2 a_3} \ldots \mathbf{a_{p-1} a_{p+1}} \ldots \mathbf{a_{q-1} a_p a_{q+1}} \ldots \mathbf{a_n} \end{pmatrix}$$

where the $\mathbf{a}_j$ are the columns of the original matrix missing its first row. To move the column $\mathbf{a}_p$ back "where it belongs," between $\mathbf{a}_{p-1}$ and $\mathbf{a}_{p+1}$ requires interchanging it with $\mathbf{a}_{q-1}$ then with $\mathbf{a}_{q-2}$, $\ldots$, finally with $\mathbf{a}_{p+1}$. This is a total of $q - p - 1$ interchanges, each of which changes the sign of the minor. After $\mathbf{a}_p$ is "back home," the resulting minor is identical with a^{1q} in the original matrix, i.e., before the pair of columns was interchanged. Hence,

$$(a^{1p})' = (-1)^{q-p-1}a^{1q}$$

Similarly,

$$(a^{1q})' = (-1)^{q-p-1}a^{1p}$$

Thus the two terms in (7.52) which before the interchange of the pth and qth columns were

$$(-1)^{p+1}a_{1p}a^{1p} + (-1)^{q+1}a_{1q}a^{1q}$$

are now

$$(-1)^{p+1}\{a_{1q}(-1)^{q-p-1}a^{1q}\} + \{a_{1p}(-1)^{q-p-1}a^{1p}\}(-1)^{q+1}$$
$$= (-1)^{q}a_{1q}a^{1q} + (-1)^{p}a_{1p}a^{1p}$$

exactly the negative of what they used to be. Thus the interchange of the two columns changes the sign of the right-hand side of (7.52), completing the proof.

THEOREM 7.12.   Let A be a given $n \times n$ matrix. Let its pth column be multiplied by a scalar α and added to its qth column $(p \neq q)$. Then, det A is unchanged by this operation.

PROOF   We have, by Axiom II,

det $(\mathbf{a}_1, \ldots, \mathbf{a}_q + \alpha\mathbf{a}_p, \ldots, \mathbf{a}_n)$
$$= \det(\mathbf{a}_1, \ldots, \mathbf{a}_q, \ldots, \mathbf{a}_n) + \alpha \det(\mathbf{a}_1, \ldots, \mathbf{a}_p, \ldots, \mathbf{a}_n)$$

The second term is zero because the matrix has two identical columns. Theorem 7.12 remains true if "column" is replaced by "row" throughout.

Theorem 7.12 can be used in conjunction with Theorem 7.11 to simplify the evaluation of determinants. Indeed, if when using Theorem 7.12 we are able to convert the matrix A into a new one which has one column of mostly zeros, the work involved in the Laplace expansion down that column will be much reduced.

Example
Find

$$\Delta = \det \begin{pmatrix} 1 & 3 & 1 & 2 \\ 2 & 1 & 3 & 1 \\ 1 & 4 & 0 & 2 \\ 3 & 0 & 1 & 2 \end{pmatrix}$$

Multiply the first column by -3 and add to the second. Multiply the first column by -1 and add to the third. Multiply the first column by -2 and add to the fourth. The result is

$$\Delta = \det \begin{pmatrix} 1 & 0 & 0 & 0 \\ 2 & -5 & 1 & -3 \\ 1 & 1 & -1 & 0 \\ 3 & -9 & -2 & -4 \end{pmatrix}$$

The first row has three zeros. Expanding by Theorem 7.11 across the first row, only one term is nonzero, so we obtain

$$\Delta = \det \begin{pmatrix} -5 & 1 & -3 \\ 1 & -1 & 0 \\ -9 & -2 & -4 \end{pmatrix} = -5(4) - 1(-4) + (-3)(-11) = 17$$

THEOREM 7.13. Let A and B be two $n \times n$ matrices. Then

$$\det (AB) = \det A \det B \qquad (7.53)$$

PROOF This most remarkable property of determinants is quite difficult to prove if one adopts the monstrosity (7.50) as a *definition* of determinant. One of the most elegant aspects of the route we have followed is the very simple proof of (7.53) which we can now give.

Indeed, think of A as a fixed matrix. Having fixed A consider the function G which assigns to every matrix B the number

$$G(B) = \det (AB) \qquad (7.54)$$

It is easy to check that Axioms (I), (II), and (IV), for determinant functions are satisfied by this function (not Axiom III!). Now, Eq. (7.49), as is noted beneath it, was derived using only Axioms I, II, and IV. Hence,

$$G(B) = G(I_n) \sum_{(!)} h\binom{1 \ \cdots \ n}{i_1 \ \cdots \ i_n} b_{1i_1}, b_{2i_2} \ldots b_{ni_n}$$
$$= G(I_n) \det B \qquad (7.55)$$

From (7.54), $G(I_n) = \det A$, and then from (7.55), $G(B) = \det A \det B$, and (7.54) then proves the theorem.

We now get a lovely test for the independence of a given set of vectors.

THEOREM 7.14.   The columns of an $n \times n$ matrix A are linearly independent vectors if and only if $\det A \neq 0$.

PROOF   Suppose the columns of A are independent. The n vectors

$$A\begin{pmatrix}1\\0\\0\\\cdot\\\cdot\\\cdot\\0\end{pmatrix}, \quad A\begin{pmatrix}0\\1\\0\\\cdot\\\cdot\\\cdot\\0\end{pmatrix}, \quad \ldots, \quad A\begin{pmatrix}0\\0\\\cdot\\\cdot\\\cdot\\0\\1\end{pmatrix}$$

are obviously in Im A. But they are the columns of A. Hence, Im A contains n independent vectors, and so the rank of the linear operator which A represents is n. By the corollary to Theorem 7.3, A is nonsingular, and, therefore, has an inverse A^{-1}. Thus

$$AA^{-1} = I_n$$

Hence, by the previous theorem,

$$\det I_n = 1 = \det (AA^{-1})$$
$$= (\det A)(\det A^{-1})$$

and so $\det A \neq 0$.

Conversely, suppose $\det A \neq 0$. If the statement of the theorem were false, the columns of A would be dependent, say

$$\alpha_1 \mathbf{a}_1 + \cdots + \alpha_n \mathbf{a}_n = \mathbf{0}$$

where not all the α_i are zero. We might as well suppose $\alpha_1 \neq 0$. Then, by Theorem 7.12,

$$\det(\mathbf{a}_1 + \frac{\alpha_2}{\alpha_1} \mathbf{a}_2 + \cdots + \frac{\alpha_n}{\alpha_1} \mathbf{a}_n, \mathbf{a}_2, \mathbf{a}_3, \ldots, \mathbf{a}_n) = \det A$$

$$= \det(\mathbf{0}, \mathbf{a}_2, \ldots, \mathbf{a}_n)$$
$$= 0$$

since the determinant of a matrix with a full column of zeros is zero. This proves the theorem, by contradiction of the assumption $\det A \neq 0$.

Exercises

1. Compute the following determinants by Laplace's expansion down the first column, the second column, across the first row, the second row:

   (a) $\det \begin{pmatrix} -1 & 2 & -3 & 1 \\ 2 & 1 & 2 & 2 \\ 3 & 1 & -1 & 2 \\ 4 & 0 & 1 & 2 \end{pmatrix}$

   (b) $\det \begin{pmatrix} a & b & c & d \\ b & c & d & c \\ c & d & c & b \\ d & c & b & a \end{pmatrix}$

2. Find the values of λ for which

$$\det \begin{pmatrix} 1 - \lambda & 2 \\ -1 & 4 - \lambda \end{pmatrix} = 0$$

3. Prove by induction that $\det (A^n) = (\det A)^n$ $(n = 0, 1, 2, \ldots)$.
4. Are the vectors $(1,0,2,1)$, $(3,-1,2,1)$, $(4,1,0,-1)$, and $(0,0,2,3)$ linearly independent?
5. One can *define* a determinant by using the Laplace expansion and mathematical induction. Formulate such a definition.
6. Let A be an $n \times n$ matrix whose first row is $1, x, x^2, \ldots, x^{n-1}$. If the remaining entries of A are independent of x, show that $\det A$ is a polynomial in x of degree $\leq n - 1$. Under what circumstances will this be precisely of degree $n - 1$?
7. Let A be an $n \times n$ matrix. Show that

$$\varphi(\lambda) = \det (A - \lambda I_n)$$

   is a polynomial in λ of degree n. What is the coefficient of λ^n in this polynomial? What is the constant term in this polynomial? Compare with your solution to Exercise 2.

7.8. Solution of Linear Equations

In the Laplace expansion we multiply an element of a row by its cofactor and sum over all elements of the row, obtaining the determinant. We now inquire into the result of multiplying an element of a row by the cofactor of an element in *another* row (same column) and summing as before. As an example, consider the matrix,

$$A = \begin{pmatrix} 1 & 1 & 2 \\ 3 & 1 & 2 \\ 1 & 2 & 0 \end{pmatrix} \tag{7.56}$$

The cofactors of the elements of the matrix A are shown below.

$$\text{Cof } A = \begin{pmatrix} -4 & 2 & 5 \\ 4 & -2 & -1 \\ 0 & 4 & -2 \end{pmatrix} \tag{7.57}$$

That is, $(\text{Cof } A)_{ij} = (-1)^{i+j} a^{ij}$, as the reader should check. We can find $\det A$ across the first row

$$1 \cdot (-4) + 1 \cdot 2 + 2 \cdot 5 = 8$$

or the second row

$$3 \cdot 4 + 1 \cdot (-2) + 2 \cdot (-1) = 8$$

or the third row

$$1 \cdot 0 + 2 \cdot 4 + 0 \cdot (-2) = 8$$

or down any column.

Suppose now, that we multiply the elements of the *first* row of A by the corresponding elements of the *second* row of Cof A and add. We get

$$1 \cdot 4 + 1 \cdot (-2) + 2 \cdot (-1) = 0 \tag{7.58}$$

Using the first row of A and the third row of Cof A,

$$1 \cdot (0) + 1 \cdot (4) + 2 \cdot (-2) = 0$$

Similarly, in each case one can verify that using the "wrong" row or column of Cof A will give zero for an answer.

The reason for this is not hard to find. Consider the matrix A_1 obtained from A by repeating the first row in the second row:

$$A_1 = \begin{pmatrix} 1 & 1 & 2 \\ 1 & 1 & 2 \\ 1 & 2 & 0 \end{pmatrix}$$

Since A_1 has two identical rows, its determinant is zero. Suppose we compute $\det A_1$ by the Laplace expansion across its second row. We would get

$$1 \cdot 4 + 1 \cdot (-2) + 2 \cdot (-1) = 0$$

which is identical with (7.58). This is a small wonder because the cofactors of elements in the second row of A_1 are completely unaware of what we did to the second row of A, and so they have the same values that they had in A. Thus, returning to the original question, if we multiply elements of a row by cofactors of a *different* row and then add, we are, in effect, computing the determinant of a new matrix, which has two identical rows, and so we must get zero for an answer.

The argument given in this special case is actually perfectly general, and proves (compare Theorem 7.11)

THEOREM 7.15. Given an $n \times n$ matrix A. Select a pair of columns (or rows), say the ith and kth ($i \neq k$). Multiply each element of A in the ith column (row) by the cofactor of the corresponding element in the kth column (row). Add these numbers. The result is zero. In symbols

$$\begin{aligned}
0 &= \sum_{j=1}^{n} a_{ij}(-1)^{k+j}a^{kj} \qquad (i \neq k) \\
&= \sum_{j=1}^{n} a_{ji}(-1)^{j+k}a^{jk} \qquad (i \neq k)
\end{aligned} \tag{7.59}$$

Now return to the matrix in (7.57). Turn this matrix on its side so that the first column becomes the first row, etc., getting

$$\begin{pmatrix} -4 & 4 & 0 \\ 2 & -2 & 4 \\ 5 & -1 & -2 \end{pmatrix}$$

Next multiply this matrix by the matrix A in (7.56), say on the left,

$$\begin{pmatrix} 1 & 1 & 2 \\ 3 & 1 & 2 \\ 1 & 2 & 0 \end{pmatrix} \begin{pmatrix} -4 & 4 & 0 \\ 2 & -2 & 4 \\ 5 & -1 & -2 \end{pmatrix} = \begin{pmatrix} 8 & 0 & 0 \\ 0 & 8 & 0 \\ 0 & 0 & 8 \end{pmatrix} \tag{7.60}$$

The result is a matrix with det A on the diagonal and zeros elsewhere. The reason for this is that in carrying out the matrix multiplication we are doing the Laplace expansion. Indeed, the computation of the number 8 in the first row and first column of the answer is the same as the computation of det A across the first row of A:

$$1 \cdot (-4) + 1 \cdot 2 + 2 \cdot 5 = 8$$

The zero in the first row and second column arises as

$$1 \cdot 4 + 1 \cdot (-2) + 2 \cdot (-1) = 0$$

which is (7.58) all over again. Hence, that zero results from computing the Laplace expansion the "wrong" way. To summarize, we may say that, in regard to the matrix A in (7.56), the simple matrix Equation (7.60) actually expresses the full content of Theorems 7.11 and 7.15.

If we take Eq. (7.60) and divide it by 8, we obtain

$$\begin{pmatrix} 1 & 1 & 2 \\ 3 & 1 & 2 \\ 1 & 2 & 0 \end{pmatrix} \begin{pmatrix} -\frac{1}{2} & \frac{1}{2} & 0 \\ \frac{1}{4} & -\frac{1}{4} & \frac{1}{2} \\ \frac{5}{8} & -\frac{1}{8} & -\frac{1}{4} \end{pmatrix} = \begin{pmatrix} 1 & 0 & 0 \\ 0 & 1 & 0 \\ 0 & 0 & 1 \end{pmatrix} \qquad (7.61)$$

The matrix on the right-hand side of (7.61) is I_3, the identity matrix. If we reversed the order of the matrices on the left-hand side of (7.61) we would still get I_3 because (7.60) with the order on the left reversed expresses Theorems 7.11 and 7.15 applied to the columns rather than the rows of A. Hence, if we denote the second matrix in (7.61) temporarily by B, we have

$$AB = BA = I_3$$

In other words, we have found the *inverse* of the matrix A, and it is B. That is,

$$A^{-1} = \begin{pmatrix} -\frac{1}{2} & \frac{1}{2} & 0 \\ \frac{1}{4} & -\frac{1}{4} & \frac{1}{2} \\ \frac{5}{8} & -\frac{1}{8} & -\frac{1}{4} \end{pmatrix}$$

We summarize all of this in the form of a recipe.

GIVEN   an $n \times n$ matrix A, with det $A \neq 0$.
REQUIRED   the matrix A^{-1}.

First, write down the matrix Cof A, which has in its ith row and jth column the cofactor of a_{ij}. Next interchange the rows and columns of Cof A. Finally, divide by det A. You are now looking at A^{-1}.

This recipe tells us how to find the inverse of a matrix whose determinant is not zero. If det $A = 0$, we claim A has no inverse. Indeed, if it did, we would have

$$AA^{-1} = I_n$$

Taking determinants and using Theorem 7.13, $\det A \cdot \det A^{-1} = 1$ and so $0 \cdot (\det A^{-1}) = 1$, which is impossible. Hence, we have

> **THEOREM 7.16.** An $n \times n$ matrix A has an inverse if and only if $\det A \neq 0$.

For a complete discussion of the theory of simultaneous linear algebraic equations we need one more result which tells us how to calculate the rank of a matrix. If A is an $m \times n$ matrix, then it acts on column vectors of E^n as a linear operator to E^m. Its rank is, of course, the dimension of its image. To compute the rank we must first define a $k \times k$ minor.

> **DEFINITION** Given an $m \times n$ matrix. Choose k columns, and delete all the rest. Choose k rows, and delete all the rest. The determinant of the $k \times k$ matrix which remains is called a $k \times k$ minor.

Example
In the 4×5 matrix

$$\begin{pmatrix} 1 & 2 & 3 & 4 & 5 \\ 6 & 7 & 8 & 9 & 8 \\ 7 & 6 & 5 & 4 & 3 \\ 2 & 1 & 2 & 3 & 4 \end{pmatrix}$$

the 2×2 minor determined by the first and fourth rows, the second and third columns is

$$\det \begin{pmatrix} 2 & 3 \\ 1 & 2 \end{pmatrix} = 1.$$

> **THEOREM 7.17.** The rank of a matrix is
> (a) the size of the largest nonzero minor contained in the matrix, i.e., if there is a nonzero $r \times r$ minor, but *all* $(r + 1) \times (r + 1)$ minors are zero, then the rank of the matrix is r.

(b) the maximum number of linearly independent columns in the matrix.

(c) the maximum number of linearly independent rows in the matrix.

We omit the proof of this theorem, and turn to a discussion of the solution of simultaneous linear equations. The most general such system of equations is

$$\sum_{j=1}^{n} a_{ij}x_j = b_i \qquad (i = 1, 2, \ldots, m) \qquad (7.62)$$

which is a system of m simultaneous equations in n unknowns $x_1, \ldots, x_n$. If A is the $m \times n$ matrix whose entries are the numbers a_{ij}, $\mathbf{x}$ is the column vector of unknowns $x_1, x_2, \ldots, x_n$ and $\mathbf{b}$ is the column vector of $b_1, b_2, \ldots, b_m$ then (7.62) may be written as

$$A\mathbf{x} = \mathbf{b} \qquad (7.63)$$

Hence, the determination of all solutions of (7.63) is identical with finding all vectors $\mathbf{x}$ which are carried by the operator A into the given vector $\mathbf{b}$.

We now study the solution of the system (7.63).

CASE I   *There are exactly as many unknowns as equations ($m = n$) and the determinant of A is not zero.*

In this case, there is a unique solution to the given set of equations. Indeed, since $\det A \neq 0$, A^{-1} exists, and so if

$$A\mathbf{x} = \mathbf{b}$$

then

$$A^{-1}(A\mathbf{x}) = A^{-1}\mathbf{b}$$

and

$$\mathbf{x} = A^{-1}\mathbf{b}$$

This tells us that $A^{-1}\mathbf{b}$ is the only possible solution. It is trivial to check that it is a solution. Hence, the unique solution, $\mathbf{x}$, of the equations $A\mathbf{x} = \mathbf{b}$ is $\mathbf{x} = A^{-1}\mathbf{b}$. In particular, if $\mathbf{b} = \mathbf{0}$ (i.e., the equations are homogeneous), then there is only the solution $\mathbf{x} = \mathbf{0}$.

Example

Solve the equations

$$3x_1 + 2x_2 + x_3 = 1$$
$$x_1 - x_2 + x_3 = 2$$
$$x_1 + x_2 + x_3 = 0$$

Here the coefficient matrix is

$$A = \begin{pmatrix} 3 & 2 & 1 \\ 1 & -1 & 1 \\ 1 & 1 & 1 \end{pmatrix}$$

the matrix of cofactors is

$$\text{Cof } A = \begin{pmatrix} -2 & 0 & 2 \\ -1 & 2 & -1 \\ 3 & -2 & -5 \end{pmatrix}$$

and so $\det A = -4$. If we interchange the rows and columns of Cof A and divide by -4,

$$A^{-1} = \begin{pmatrix} \frac{1}{2} & \frac{1}{4} & -\frac{3}{4} \\ 0 & -\frac{1}{2} & \frac{1}{2} \\ -\frac{1}{2} & \frac{1}{4} & \frac{5}{4} \end{pmatrix}$$

and so

$$\mathbf{x} = A^{-1}\mathbf{b} = \begin{pmatrix} \frac{1}{2} & \frac{1}{4} & -\frac{3}{4} \\ 0 & -\frac{1}{2} & \frac{1}{2} \\ -\frac{1}{2} & \frac{1}{4} & \frac{5}{4} \end{pmatrix} \begin{pmatrix} 1 \\ 2 \\ 0 \end{pmatrix}$$

$$= \begin{pmatrix} 1 \\ -1 \\ 0 \end{pmatrix}$$

Therefore the unique solution of our system is $x_1 = 1$, $x_2 = -1$, $x_3 = 0$.

CASE II   *m homogeneous equations* (i.e., $\mathbf{b} = \mathbf{0}$) *in n unknowns.*

In this case we are trying to solve $A\mathbf{x} = \mathbf{0}$. Hence, we wish to describe the kernel of the linear operator $A: E^n \to E^m$. To do this
1. Use Theorem 7.17 to determine the rank r of the matrix A.
2. The nullity of A is then $n - r$, and this is the dimension of Ker A.

3. The complete solution of the equations is known as soon as we have a basis for Ker A. Thus we will be finished when we have found $n - r$ *independent* solutions of $A\mathbf{x} = 0$.

Example

Find the complete solution of the system

$$\begin{aligned}
3x_1 + 2x_2 + x_3 &= 0 \\
7x_1 + 4x_2 + 5x_3 &= 0 \\
12x_1 + 7x_2 + 8x_3 &= 0 \\
5x_1 + 3x_2 + 3x_3 &= 0
\end{aligned}$$

The coefficient matrix is

$$A = \begin{pmatrix} 3 & 2 & 1 \\ 7 & 4 & 5 \\ 12 & 7 & 8 \\ 5 & 3 & 3 \end{pmatrix}$$

This matrix has nonzero 1×1 minors and nonzero 2×2 minors. But every 3×3 minor is zero. Hence, by Theorem 7.17, the rank of A is $r = 2$. The nullity of A is $3 - 2 = 1$. If we can find just one solution, $\mathbf{x}_0$, then all solutions will be of the form $\alpha\mathbf{x}_0$, where α is a real number.

To find one solution take, arbitrarily, $x_3 = 1$, then solve the first two equations for x_1, x_2, namely, the equations

$$\begin{aligned}
3x_1 + 2x_2 &= -1 \\
7x_1 + 4x_2 &= -5
\end{aligned}$$

The solution is $x_1 = -3$, $x_2 = 4$. If we try $x_1 = -3$, $x_2 = 4$, $x_3 = 1$ in the last two equations, we find that they are satisfied also. Thus the vector $(-3,4,1)$ is in Ker A, and all possible solutions of the given system are

$$\mathbf{x} = \alpha(-3,4,1)$$

i.e., $x_1 = -3\alpha$, $x_2 = 4\alpha$, $x_3 = \alpha$, where α is any real number.

CASE III   *m inhomogeneous* (i.e., $\mathbf{b} \neq 0$) *in n unknowns.*

The solution of the general system $A\mathbf{x} = \mathbf{b}$ requires two steps:

1. Find *one* solution of $A\mathbf{x} = \mathbf{b}$, say $\mathbf{x}_0$, if possible (it may not be).

2. Find *all* solutions of $A\mathbf{x} = \mathbf{0}$, say $\alpha_1\mathbf{e}_1 + \cdots + \alpha_\nu\mathbf{e}_\nu$, by following the recipe of Case II above.

If these steps have been carried out, then *all* solutions of the given system $A\mathbf{x} = \mathbf{b}$ are of the form

$$\mathbf{x} = \mathbf{x}_0 + \alpha_1\mathbf{e}_1 + \cdots + \alpha_\nu\mathbf{e}_\nu \tag{7.64}$$

In other words, the general solution is obtained by adding a particular solution to the general solution of the homogeneous equations obtained by replacing $\mathbf{b}$ by $\mathbf{0}$.

To prove that this procedure is correct we note first that the vector $\mathbf{x}$ in (7.64) is a solution of $A\mathbf{x} = \mathbf{b}$ because

$$\begin{aligned}
A\mathbf{x} &= A(\mathbf{x}_0 + \alpha_1\mathbf{e}_1 + \cdots + \alpha_\nu\mathbf{e}_\nu) \\
&= A\mathbf{x}_0 + \alpha_1 A\mathbf{e}_1 + \cdots + \alpha_\nu A\mathbf{e}_\nu \\
&= \mathbf{b} + \alpha_1\mathbf{0} + \cdots + \alpha_\nu\mathbf{0} \\
&= \mathbf{b}
\end{aligned}$$

To prove that *every* solution has the form (7.64), let $\mathbf{x}_1$ be any solution of $A\mathbf{x} = \mathbf{b}$. Then $\mathbf{x}_1 - \mathbf{x}_0$ is in Ker A because

$$\begin{aligned}
A(\mathbf{x}_1 - \mathbf{x}_0) &= A\mathbf{x}_1 - A\mathbf{x}_0 \\
&= \mathbf{b} - \mathbf{b} \\
&= \mathbf{0}
\end{aligned}$$

Hence, $\mathbf{x}_1 - \mathbf{x}_0$ is a linear combination of the basis vectors $\mathbf{e}_1, \ldots, \mathbf{e}_\nu$ for Ker A, i.e.,

$$\mathbf{x}_1 - \mathbf{x}_0 = \alpha_1\mathbf{e}_1 + \cdots + \alpha_\nu\mathbf{e}_\nu$$

from which

$$\mathbf{x}_1 = \mathbf{x}_0 + \alpha_1\mathbf{e}_1 + \cdots + \alpha_\alpha\mathbf{e}_\alpha$$

as required by (7.64).

There remains just one difficult point. How are we to know if there is any vector $\mathbf{x}$ at all such that $A\mathbf{x} = \mathbf{b}$? The vector $\mathbf{b}$ just may not lie in Im A. A simple case of this type is

$$\begin{aligned}
2x_1 + x_2 &= 3 \\
x_1 - x_2 &= 2 \\
3x_1 + 3x_2 &= 1
\end{aligned} \tag{7.65}$$

If we multiply the first equation by 2, the second by -1, and add, we get the left-hand side of the third equation, but not its right-hand side.

Hence, there can be no solution. It would be nice to have a mechanical procedure for testing whether or not a given vector is in the image of a given matrix.

To find such a procedure consider (7.65) once more. If there were a solution, then we could write (7.65) in the form

$$\begin{pmatrix} 3 \\ 2 \\ 1 \end{pmatrix} = x_1 \begin{pmatrix} 2 \\ 1 \\ 3 \end{pmatrix} + x_2 \begin{pmatrix} 1 \\ -1 \\ 3 \end{pmatrix}$$

That is, the vector (3,2,1) would be a linear combination of the columns of the coefficient matrix. Hence, among the *three* vectors

$$\begin{pmatrix} 3 \\ 2 \\ 1 \end{pmatrix}, \quad \begin{pmatrix} 2 \\ 1 \\ 3 \end{pmatrix}, \quad \begin{pmatrix} 1 \\ -1 \\ 3 \end{pmatrix}$$

would be precisely as many linearly independent ones as among the *two* vectors

$$\begin{pmatrix} 2 \\ 1 \\ 3 \end{pmatrix}, \quad \begin{pmatrix} 1 \\ -1 \\ 3 \end{pmatrix}$$

In other words, the maximum number of linearly independent columns of the two matrices

$$\begin{pmatrix} 2 & 1 & 3 \\ 1 & -1 & 2 \\ 3 & 3 & 1 \end{pmatrix}$$

and

$$\begin{pmatrix} 2 & 1 \\ 1 & -1 \\ 3 & 3 \end{pmatrix}$$

would be identical. Referring to Theorem 7.17(b), we see that the ranks of these matrices would be the same. But by Theorem 7.17(a), the rank of the first one is 3 and of the second is 2. Hence, no solution exists.

The general rule is the following: *the equations* $A\mathbf{x} = \mathbf{b}$ *have a solution if the two matrices*

$$(A), \qquad (A \mid \mathbf{b}) \tag{7.66}$$

have the same rank, and no solution if their ranks are different [in (7.66), the second matrix means the result of adjoining an extra column, namely, **b**, onto the matrix A].

Example

Find all solutions of the equations

$$
\begin{aligned}
3x_1 + 2x_2 + x_3 &= 1 \\
7x_1 + 4x_2 + 5x_3 &= 3 \\
12x_1 + 7x_2 + 8x_3 &= 5 \\
5x_1 + 3x_2 + 3x_3 &= 2
\end{aligned}
\qquad (7.67)
$$

Do they have any solution? Consider the two matrices

$$
\begin{pmatrix}
3 & 2 & 1 \\
7 & 4 & 5 \\
12 & 7 & 8 \\
5 & 3 & 3
\end{pmatrix}
\begin{pmatrix}
3 & 2 & 1 & 1 \\
7 & 4 & 5 & 3 \\
12 & 7 & 8 & 5 \\
5 & 3 & 3 & 2
\end{pmatrix}
$$

The rank of the first is 2 (it is the same matrix we met in Case II). The rank of the second is also 2, as one can discover by computing its 3×3 minors, all of which are zero.

Thus, there is a solution. Taking $x_3 = 0$ and solving the first two equations we find $x_1 = 1$, $x_2 = -1$. We then find that these three values satisfy all four of the equations. Hence, a particular solution is

$$
\mathbf{x}_0 = (1, -1, 0)
$$

The general solution of the corresponding homogeneous equations

$$
\begin{pmatrix}
3 & 2 & 1 \\
7 & 4 & 5 \\
12 & 7 & 8 \\
5 & 3 & 3
\end{pmatrix}
\begin{pmatrix}
x_1 \\
x_2 \\
x_3
\end{pmatrix}
=
\begin{pmatrix}
0 \\
0 \\
0 \\
0
\end{pmatrix}
$$

was found, in Case II above, to be

$$
\alpha(-3, 4, 1)
$$

where α is any real number.

The complete solution of the given system is then

$$
\mathbf{x} = (1, -1, 0) + \alpha(-3, 4, 1)
$$

or,

$$x_1 = 1 - 3\alpha$$
$$x_2 = -1 + 4\alpha$$
$$x_3 = \alpha$$

where α is arbitrary.

Exercises

1. Invert each of the following matrices.

(a) $\begin{pmatrix} 1 & 2 \\ 1 & 4 \end{pmatrix}$

(b) $\begin{pmatrix} a & b \\ b & a \end{pmatrix}$

(c) $\begin{pmatrix} 1 & 3 & 2 \\ 2 & 1 & 4 \\ 3 & 4 & 5 \end{pmatrix}$

(d) $\begin{pmatrix} 1 & -1 & 0 \\ 0 & 1 & -1 \\ -1 & 0 & 1 \end{pmatrix}$

2. Let A_1, A_2, A_3, A_4 denote the matrices in Exercise 1. Solve the equations

(a) $A_1\mathbf{x} = \begin{pmatrix} 1 \\ 1 \end{pmatrix}$

(b) $A_2\mathbf{x} = \begin{pmatrix} 1 \\ 0 \end{pmatrix}$

(c) $A_3\mathbf{x} = \begin{pmatrix} 1 \\ 2 \\ 1 \end{pmatrix}$

(d) $A_4\mathbf{x} = \begin{pmatrix} -1 \\ 1 \\ 1 \end{pmatrix}$

3. Compute the rank of each of the following matrices.

(a) $\begin{pmatrix} 1 & 2 \\ 1 & 3 \\ 2 & 3 \end{pmatrix}$

(b) $\begin{pmatrix} -1 & 2 & 1 \\ 1 & -2 & -1 \end{pmatrix}$

(c) $\begin{pmatrix} 3 & 1 & -1 \\ -6 & -2 & 2 \\ -3 & -1 & 1 \end{pmatrix}$

(d) $\begin{pmatrix} 1 & 3 & -1 \\ 1 & 4 & 2 \\ 0 & -1 & -3 \end{pmatrix}$

4. Let B_1, B_2, B_3, B_4 denote the matrices in Exercise 3. Find the most general solution of the equations.

   (a) $B_1\mathbf{x} = \mathbf{0}$
   (b) $B_2\mathbf{x} = \mathbf{0}$
   (c) $B_3\mathbf{x} = \mathbf{0}$
   (d) $B_4\mathbf{x} = \mathbf{0}$

5. With the notation of Exercise 4, find the most general solution of the following equations.

   (a) $B_1\mathbf{x} = \begin{pmatrix} 3 \\ 4 \\ 5 \end{pmatrix}$

   (b) $B_2\mathbf{x} = \begin{pmatrix} 2 \\ -2 \end{pmatrix}$

   (c) $B_3\mathbf{x} = \begin{pmatrix} 4 \\ -8 \\ -4 \end{pmatrix}$

   (d) $B_4\mathbf{x} = \begin{pmatrix} 7 \\ 12 \\ -5 \end{pmatrix}$

7.9. *Computational Methods*

In this section we discuss numerical methods for the solution of systems of linear equations and the computation of determinants. The methods already given, involving the Laplace expansion by minors, are useful only for the theoretical purposes already mentioned and for small computational problems. With larger problems much time can be saved by using more efficient methods, such as the elimination procedures which we now describe.

Consider the system

$$a_{11}x_1 + \cdots + a_{1n}x_n = b_1$$
$$a_{21}x_1 + \cdots + a_{2n}x_n = b_2$$
$$\cdots$$
$$a_{m1}x_1 + \cdots + a_{mn}x_n = b_n$$

To solve it, suppose $a_{11} \neq 0$ (otherwise, renumber the equations). Divide the first equation through by a_{11}, obtaining

$$x_1 + b_{12}x_2 + \cdots + b_{1n}x_n = b'_1$$
$$a_{21}x_1 + \cdots + \cdots + a_{2n}x_n = b'_2$$
$$\cdots \quad \cdots$$
$$a_{m1}x_1 + \cdots + \cdots + a_{mn}x_n = b'_m \qquad (7.68)$$

Multiply the first equation by $-a_{21}$ and add to the second equation; then multiply the first equation by $-a_{31}$ and add to the third, etc. We find

$$x_1 + b_{12}x_2 + \cdots + b_{1n}x_n = b'_1$$
$$b_{22}x_2 + \cdots + b_{2n}x_n = b'_2$$
$$\cdots$$
$$b_{m2}x_2 + \cdots + b_{mn}x_n = b'_m \qquad (7.69)$$

Suppose $b_{22} \neq 0$ (otherwise renumber the equations or the unknowns). Divide the second equation by b_{22}, getting

$$x_1 + b_{12}x_2 + \cdots + b_{1n}x_n = b'_1$$
$$x_2 + \cdots + c_{2n}x_n = b'_2$$
$$\cdots$$
$$b_{m2}x_2 + \cdots + b_{mn}x_n = b'_m$$

Now multiply the second equation by $-b_{12}$ and add to the first; multiply the second equation by $-b_{32}$ and add to the third, etc. The result is of the form

$$x_1 \quad + c_{13}x_3 + \cdots + c_{1n}x_n = b''_1$$
$$x_2 + c_{23}x_3 + \cdots + c_{2n}x_n = b''_1$$
$$c_{33}x_3 + \cdots + c_{3n}x_n = b''_3$$
$$\cdots$$
$$c_{m3}x_3 + \cdots + c_{mn}x_n = b''_m$$

We continue in this way until the process halts. This will happen when, after having carried out r eliminations, we find that all the coefficients of $x_{r+1}, \ldots, x_n$ in the $(r + 1)$st through nth equations are zero, or else we have $r = n$, i.e., we have run out of equations.

In the first case we would have arrived at a system of the form

$$
\begin{aligned}
x_1 \quad + \alpha_{1,r+1}x_{r+1} + \cdots + \alpha_{1n}x_n &= \beta_1 \\
x_2 + \alpha_{2,r+1}x_{r+1} + \cdots + \alpha_{2n}x_n &= \beta_2 \\
&\cdots \\
x_r + \alpha_{r,r+1}x_{r+1} + \cdots + \alpha_{rn}x_n &= \beta_r \\
0 &= \beta_{r+1} \\
0 &= \beta_{r+2} \\
&\cdots \\
0 &= \beta_m
\end{aligned}
$$

If any of the numbers $\beta_{r+1}, \ldots, \beta_m$ is nonzero, then we will have arrived at a contradiction of the assumption that the original system has a solution. In other words, *if any of these numbers is nonzero, the system is incompatible and has no solution.*

If $\beta_{r+1} = \cdots = \beta_m = 0$, we ignore the last $m - r$ equations, and from the first r of them we can immediately express $x_1, \ldots, x_r$ in terms of $x_{r+1}, \ldots, x_n$, namely,

$$
\begin{aligned}
x_1 &= -\alpha_{1,r+1}x_{r+1} - \cdots - \alpha_{1,n}x_n + \beta_1 \\
x_2 &= -\alpha_{2,r+1}x_{r+1} - \cdots - \alpha_{2,n}x_n + \beta_2 \\
&\cdots \\
x_r &= -\alpha_{r,r+1}x_{r+1} - \cdots - \alpha_{r,n}x_n + \beta_r
\end{aligned}
$$

In vector form we would write

$$
\begin{pmatrix} x_1 \\ x_2 \\ \cdot \\ \cdot \\ \cdot \\ x_r \end{pmatrix} = x_{r+1} \begin{pmatrix} -\alpha_{1,r+1} \\ \cdot \\ \cdot \\ \cdot \\ -\alpha_{r,r+1} \end{pmatrix} + \cdots + x_n \begin{pmatrix} -\alpha_{1n} \\ \cdot \\ \cdot \\ \cdot \\ -\alpha_{r,n} \end{pmatrix} + \begin{pmatrix} \beta_1 \\ \cdot \\ \cdot \\ \cdot \\ \beta_r \end{pmatrix} \tag{7.70}
$$

This result is identical with Eq. (7.64). We have in fact, found a basis for the Kernel of the coefficient matrix; namely, the first $n - r$ vectors in (7.70). Equation (7.70) tells us that we can choose any real numbers at all for $x_{n+1}, \ldots, x_n$, and then $x_1, \ldots, x_r$ are determined.

To illustrate the possibilities, consider first the system (7.67)

$$3x_1 + 2x_2 + x_3 = 1$$
$$7x_1 + 4x_2 + 5x_3 = 3$$
$$12x_1 + 7x_2 + 8x_3 = 5$$
$$5x_1 + 3x_2 + 3x_3 = 2 \qquad (7.71)$$

After one elimination we have

$$x_1 + \tfrac{2}{3}x_2 + \tfrac{1}{3}x_3 = \tfrac{1}{3}$$
$$-\tfrac{2}{3}x_2 + \tfrac{8}{3}x_3 = \tfrac{2}{3}$$
$$-x_2 + 4x_3 = 1$$
$$-\tfrac{1}{3}x_2 + \tfrac{4}{3}x_3 = \tfrac{1}{3} \qquad (7.72)$$

After the second round we get

$$x_1 + 3x_3 = 1$$
$$x_2 - 4x_3 = -1$$
$$0 = 0$$
$$0 = 0 \qquad (7.73)$$

The process halts here, the equations are compatible, and

$$x_1 = 1 - 3x_3$$
$$x_2 = -1 + 4x_3$$

or, in vector form,

$$\begin{pmatrix} x_1 \\ x_2 \end{pmatrix} = x_3 \begin{pmatrix} -3 \\ 4 \end{pmatrix} + \begin{pmatrix} 1 \\ -1 \end{pmatrix} \qquad (x_3 \text{ arbitrary})$$

which is identical with the solution previously found.

For a case in which the equations are incompatible take

$$x_1 - 2x_2 = 3$$
$$-2x_1 + 4x_2 = 1$$

In this trivial example after one elimination we obtain

$$x_1 - 2x_2 = 3$$
$$0 = 7$$

and the second "equation" informs us that there is no solution.

Some computational elegance can be gained by carrying out the elimination directly on the matrix of coefficients augmented by the vector of "right-hand sides" of the given system, without ever writing out the equations. Thus, instead of (7.71) we would write

$$\begin{pmatrix} 3 & 2 & 1 & \bigm| & 1 \\ 7 & 4 & 5 & \bigm| & 3 \\ 12 & 7 & 8 & \bigm| & 5 \\ 5 & 3 & 3 & \bigm| & 2 \end{pmatrix}$$

where, to the left of the vertical line we have the coefficient matrix and to the right we have the right-hand sides of the equations. We work directly on the matrix, dividing the first row by 3, subtracting 7 times the first row from the second, and so on, obtaining

$$\begin{pmatrix} 1 & \frac{2}{3} & \frac{1}{3} & \bigm| & \frac{1}{3} \\ 0 & -\frac{2}{3} & \frac{8}{3} & \bigm| & \frac{2}{3} \\ 0 & -1 & 4 & \bigm| & 1 \\ 0 & -\frac{1}{3} & \frac{4}{3} & \bigm| & \frac{1}{3} \end{pmatrix}$$

which is (7.72), in skeleton form. If we divide the second row by $-\frac{2}{3}$, etc., we get

$$\begin{pmatrix} 1 & 0 & 3 & \bigm| & 1 \\ 0 & 1 & -4 & \bigm| & -1 \\ 0 & 0 & 0 & \bigm| & 0 \\ 0 & 0 & 0 & \bigm| & 0 \end{pmatrix}$$

which is (7.73), and we get the solution as before.

This compact elimination procedure in matrix form also suggests a method for the computation of determinants. The operations which we perform on the matrix are (a) multiplying a row by a scalar and (b) adding to one row a scalar multiple of another. The second operation does not change the value of a determinant. The first does change it, but if we keep track of the scalars involved, we shall be able to recover the determinant in the end. To illustrate this we have

$$\det \begin{pmatrix} 2 & 1 & 4 \\ 1 & 3 & 2 \\ 2 & -1 & 3 \end{pmatrix} = 2 \det \begin{pmatrix} 1 & \frac{1}{2} & 2 \\ 1 & 3 & 2 \\ 2 & -1 & 3 \end{pmatrix}$$

$$= 2 \det \begin{pmatrix} 1 & \frac{1}{2} & 2 \\ 0 & \frac{5}{2} & 0 \\ 0 & -2 & -1 \end{pmatrix}$$

$$= 2 \cdot \frac{5}{2} \det \begin{pmatrix} 1 & \frac{1}{2} & 2 \\ 0 & 1 & 0 \\ 0 & -2 & -1 \end{pmatrix}$$

$$= 5 \det \begin{pmatrix} 1 & 0 & 2 \\ 0 & 1 & 0 \\ 0 & 0 & -1 \end{pmatrix}$$

$$= -5 \det \begin{pmatrix} 1 & 0 & 2 \\ 0 & 1 & 0 \\ 0 & 0 & 1 \end{pmatrix}$$

$$= -5$$

In this particular example we actually did more work than would have been required in a straightforward Laplace expansion. In larger problems the balance of economy tips sharply in the direction of the elimination method. The key observation is the fact that at the end of the elimination process, if the determinant is not zero, we arrive at the determinant of a matrix which has 1's on the diagonal, zeros below the diagonal, and various numbers above the diagonal. The determinant of such a matrix is 1, no matter what the numbers above the diagonal are. The proof of this assertion is by induction. It is clear for 1×1 matrices. Suppose it has been proved for $(n - 1) \times (n - 1)$ matrices. If an $n \times n$ matrix of this type is given, expand its determinant by the Laplace development down the first column. Only one term is nonzero, the first, and it is $1 \cdot a^{11}$. But a^{11} is an $(n - 1) \times (n - 1)$ determinant of the type considered, which establishes the proposition.

As a final application of the elimination method, we observe that it is well suited to the numerical inversion of matrices. As an illustration, consider the problem of determining the inverse of the matrix

$$A = \begin{pmatrix} 1 & 2 & 1 \\ 2 & -1 & 3 \\ 2 & 1 & 2 \end{pmatrix}$$

Suppose the inverse is

$$A^{-1} = \begin{pmatrix} b_{11} & b_{12} & b_{13} \\ b_{21} & b_{22} & b_{23} \\ b_{31} & b_{32} & b_{33} \end{pmatrix}$$

and consider the equation $AA^{-1} = I_3$, namely,

$$\begin{pmatrix} 1 & 2 & 1 \\ 2 & -1 & 3 \\ 2 & 1 & 2 \end{pmatrix} \begin{pmatrix} b_{11} & b_{12} & b_{13} \\ b_{21} & b_{22} & b_{23} \\ b_{31} & b_{32} & b_{33} \end{pmatrix} = \begin{pmatrix} 1 & 0 & 0 \\ 0 & 1 & 0 \\ 0 & 0 & 1 \end{pmatrix}$$

The important observation here is that the first column on the right,

$$\begin{pmatrix} 1 \\ 0 \\ 0 \end{pmatrix}$$

is obtained by multiplying the matrix A by the *first column* of A^{-1}, i.e.,

$$\begin{pmatrix} 1 & 2 & 1 \\ 2 & -1 & 3 \\ 2 & 1 & 2 \end{pmatrix} \begin{pmatrix} b_{11} \\ b_{21} \\ b_{31} \end{pmatrix} = \begin{pmatrix} 1 \\ 0 \\ 0 \end{pmatrix} \tag{7.74}$$

Equation (7.74), however, asserts that the first column of the inverse matrix is the solution of a certain system of three equations in three unknowns,

$$A\mathbf{x}_1 = \begin{pmatrix} 1 \\ 0 \\ 0 \end{pmatrix}$$

Similarly, the second column, $\mathbf{x}_2$, is the solution of

$$A\mathbf{x}_2 = \begin{pmatrix} 0 \\ 0 \\ 1 \end{pmatrix}$$

and the third column, $\mathbf{x}_3$, satisfies

$$A\mathbf{x}_3 = \begin{pmatrix} 0 \\ 0 \\ 1 \end{pmatrix}$$

The computation of A^{-1} is, therefore, equivalent to solving three separate systems of simultaneous equations, whose left-hand sides are the same, and whose right-hand sides are different. We can take advantage of the common left-hand sides by solving all three sets at once using a single tableau by elimination. We begin with the array

$$\begin{pmatrix} 1 & 2 & 1 & \big| & 1 & 0 & 0 \\ 2 & -1 & 3 & \big| & 0 & 1 & 0 \\ 2 & 1 & 2 & \big| & 0 & 0 & 1 \end{pmatrix}$$

whose first three columns are the matrix A, and whose last three are the three columns of I_3, the successive "right-hand sides" of the equations we wish to solve. Next we carry out the elimination procedure on this full 3×6 matrix, obtaining in succession

$$\begin{pmatrix} 1 & 2 & 1 & \big| & 1 & 0 & 0 \\ 0 & -5 & 1 & \big| & -2 & 1 & 0 \\ 0 & -3 & 0 & \big| & -2 & 0 & 1 \end{pmatrix}$$

$$\begin{pmatrix} 1 & 2 & 1 & \big| & 1 & 0 & 0 \\ 0 & 1 & -\frac{1}{5} & \big| & \frac{2}{5} & -\frac{1}{5} & 0 \\ 0 & -3 & 0 & \big| & -2 & 0 & 1 \end{pmatrix}$$

$$\begin{pmatrix} 1 & 0 & \frac{7}{5} & \big| & \frac{1}{5} & \frac{2}{5} & 0 \\ 0 & 1 & -\frac{1}{5} & \big| & \frac{2}{5} & -\frac{1}{5} & 0 \\ 0 & 0 & -\frac{3}{5} & \big| & -\frac{4}{5} & -\frac{3}{5} & 1 \end{pmatrix}$$

$$\begin{pmatrix} 1 & 0 & \frac{7}{5} & \big| & \frac{1}{5} & \frac{2}{5} & 0 \\ 0 & 1 & -\frac{1}{5} & \big| & \frac{2}{5} & -\frac{1}{5} & 0 \\ 0 & 0 & 1 & \big| & \frac{4}{3} & 1 & -\frac{5}{3} \end{pmatrix}$$

$$\begin{pmatrix} 1 & 0 & 0 & \big| & -\frac{5}{3} & -1 & \frac{7}{3} \\ 0 & 1 & 0 & \big| & \frac{2}{3} & 0 & -\frac{1}{3} \\ 0 & 0 & 1 & \big| & \frac{4}{3} & 1 & -\frac{5}{3} \end{pmatrix}$$

The process terminates when, as above, the leftmost three columns have been reduced to I_3, and then the rightmost three columns will be A^{-1}. Thus

$$A^{-1} = \begin{pmatrix} -\frac{5}{3} & -1 & \frac{7}{3} \\ \frac{2}{3} & 0 & -\frac{1}{3} \\ \frac{4}{3} & 1 & -\frac{5}{3} \end{pmatrix}$$

In general, given an $n \times n$ matrix A, form the $n \times 2n$ matrix

$$(A \quad | \quad I_n).$$

By elimination, reduce the first n columns to I_n. Then the last n columns will be A^{-1}. The method is quite economical of effort and is a vast improvement, in this regard, over the cofactor method which was used to prove the existence of A^{-1}, when $\det A \neq 0$.

Exercises

1. One measure of the labor involved in carrying out a numerical computation is the number of multiplications of one number by another which must be performed. What is this number (roughly) for

    (a) Finding the determinant of an $n \times n$ matrix by the Laplace expansion.
    (b) Finding the determinant of an $n \times n$ matrix from the formula (7.50).
    (c) Finding the determinant of an $n \times n$ matrix by elimination.
    (d) Computing A^{-1}, by elimination, where A is $n \times n$.
    (e) Multiplying two $n \times n$ matrices.
    (f) Computing A^{-1} by the method of cofactors, where A is $n \times n$; treat the cases where the cofactors are computed as in (a), (b), (c), separately.
    (g) Solving n equations on n unknowns by elimination.

2. Suppose a certain computer can multiply two numbers in 10^{-8} sec. If $n = 100$, *roughly* how much time will the computer spend multiplying in each of (a)–(g) in Exercise 1? Do not try to be exact. Just get a feeling for whether the times are of the order of seconds, hours, or years!

3. Invert by elimination:

    (a) $A = \begin{pmatrix} 3 & 3 & 1 \\ 2 & 2 & 0 \\ 1 & 3 & 1 \end{pmatrix}$

    (b) $A = \begin{pmatrix} 2 & -1 & -1 \\ 0 & -1 & 1 \\ 1 & 2 & 3 \end{pmatrix}$

4. Find the following determinants, by elimination:

    (a) $\det \begin{pmatrix} 1 & 2 & 3 & 4 \\ 4 & 1 & 2 & 3 \\ 3 & 4 & 1 & 2 \\ 2 & 3 & 4 & 1 \end{pmatrix}$

    (b) $\det \begin{pmatrix} 1 & 0 & 1 & 0 & 1 \\ 0 & 1 & 0 & 1 & 0 \\ 0 & 1 & 1 & 0 & 1 \\ 1 & 0 & 1 & 1 & 0 \\ 0 & 1 & 0 & 1 & 1 \end{pmatrix}$

7.10.   Applications

Applications of the techniques and theory of linear algebra are wide-spread throughout the mathematical sciences. These methods are of the highest importance in quantum physics, economic theory, mechanical engineering in the analysis of structures, electrical engineering in circuit analysis, and many other areas. The ubiquitous appearance of problems requiring these methods is of fairly recent origin, and is largely responsible for the introduction of linear algebra in the first year of university mathematics. We can, in the limited space available, only hint at a few of these applications, and we do so in order that the reader may gain some idea of the kinds of contexts in which such problems arise.

As our first application we mention the theory of games, a young branch of mathematics which is concerned with the interplay of conflicting interests, each determined to maximize its own profit. We consider, for concreteness, a game played by two people. Each player has available to him a number of courses of action. A "play" of the game occurs when each player selects one of his possible "moves." After a play, there is a payoff to one of the players, the payoff being determined by the choices of moves just made.

As an example we take the game of "paper–scissors–stone." The players simultaneously exhibit a certain symbol with their right hands. Two fingers represent "scissors," the whole hand represents "paper," and a fist "stone." If both symbols are the same, there is no payoff. Otherwise, payment is determined by the rules "paper covers stone," "scissors cut paper," "stone breaks scissors." There are, therefore, nine possible outcomes of a play, which, together with their payoffs to player 1, are shown in Table VIII.

Table VIII

Player 1	*Player 2*		
	Scissors	Paper	Stone
Scissors	0	1	-1
Paper	-1	0	1
Stone	1	-1	0

This array is called the payoff matrix of the game. The question which we ask concerns the best possible way to play the game. That is, if you are player 1, what is the correct strategy for you to adopt? If you always play "scissors," your opponent will soon discover this, and he will always play "stone," and you will lose. The same is true if you always play "paper" or always "stone." The correct strategy for you to adopt is to mix up your play moves by sometimes playing one and sometimes another. But how should you mix up your moves? Should a play of "scissors" be just as likely as a play of "stone," or should some preference be given to one of the other? In other words, if p_1, p_2, p_3 are the *probabilities* of your playing scissors, paper, or stone, respectively, is it best to use $p_1 = p_2 = p_3 = \frac{1}{3}$ or is some other choice better? In this game it is quite clear that making all choices equally likely is the best strategy.

Consider, then, a different game, with just two possible moves for each player, in which the payoff matrix is as in Table IX. If you always

Table IX

	Opponent		
You	I	II	
I	1	4	Win 1
II	3	2	Win 2

play I, so will your opponent, and you will win 1 on each play. If always II, you will win 2 on each play. If you flip a coin and play I if "heads" and II if "tails," the situation is different. If your opponent adopts the strategy of always playing I, you will win 1 half the time and 3 half the time for an average of

$$\tfrac{1}{2}(1 + 3) = 2$$

If he always plays II, you will average

$$\tfrac{1}{2}(4 + 2) = 3$$

units per play. In either case, then, you would be better off than you were before.

You could do still better, though, by playing one of your moves more frequently than the other, instead of equally often. Indeed, let p_1 denote the probability that you play I and p_2 the probability of II. Of course, $0 \leq p_1 \leq 1$, $0 \leq p_2 \leq 1$, $p_1 + p_2 = 1$. Against move I by your opponent you would score 1 with probability p_1 and 3 with probability p_2 and so you would average

$$1 \cdot p_1 + 3 \cdot p_2 = p_1 + 3p_2$$

Against move II you average

$$4p_1 + 2p_2$$

If one of these averages is smaller than the other, your opponent will always adopt the move corresponding to the lower one. To do as well as you can you should determine p_1, p_2 so that

$$p_1 + 3p_2 = 4p_1 + 2p_2$$

i.e., so that $p_2 = 3p_1$. In other words, you should play II three times as often as I ($p_1 = \frac{1}{4}$, $p_2 = \frac{3}{4}$). If you do this, you will average $p_1 + 3p_2 = 4p_1 + 2p_2 = 2\frac{1}{2}$ no matter which move your opponent chooses. In practice, then, you might flip a coin twice and if both were tails use move I, otherwise, use II. To make the game fair you should pay your opponent $2\frac{1}{2}$ before each play.

Consider now a general case in which n possible moves are available to each player. Suppose the payoff matrix is

$$A = \begin{pmatrix} a_{11} & a_{12} & \cdots & a_{1n} \\ a_{21} & a_{22} & \cdots & a_{2n} \\ \cdot & \cdot & & \cdot \\ \cdot & \cdot & & \cdot \\ \cdot & \cdot & & \cdot \\ a_{n1} & a_{n2} & \cdots & a_{nn} \end{pmatrix}$$

To determine your best strategy, let p_1 be the probability of move $1, \ldots, p_n$ the probability of move n. If your opponent selects move j, then you score a_{1j} with probability p_1, a_{2j} with probability $p_2, \ldots, a_{nj}$ with probability p_n. Hence on the average, you will score

$$a_{1j}p_1 + a_{2j}p_2 + \cdots + a_{nj}p_n \tag{7.75}$$

against your opponent's move j. Aside from certain very important special cases which we blithely ignore in these sketchy remarks one finds the best strategy by requiring that the sum in (7.75) should have the same value for every choice of $j = 1, 2, \ldots, n$, i.e., against every single move of your opponent. We repeat that this recipe is not always the right one but when it leads to an answer it is the right one. Denote the common value of (7.75), for $j = 1, 2, \ldots, n$, by V. Then we have to solve the equations

$$a_{1j}p_1 + a_{2j}p_2 + \cdots + a_{nj}p_n = V \qquad (j = 1, 2, \ldots, n) \qquad (7.76)$$

These are n equations in $n + 1$ unknowns $p_1, \ldots, p_n, V$. The p_i are subject to the additional condition

$$p_1 + p_2 + \cdots + p_n = 1 \qquad (7.77)$$

giving $n + 1$ equations altogether. If we subtract the $(j + 1)$st from the jth equation in (7.76), we get

$$(a_{1,j+1} - a_{1j})p_1 + \cdots + (a_{n,j+1} - a_{nj})p_n = 0 \qquad (j = 1, 2, \ldots, n - 1) \qquad (7.78)$$

which are $n - 1$ homogeneous equations in n unknowns $p_1, \ldots, p_n$. If these have been solved (they may not have a solution other than $0, 0, 0, \ldots, 0!$), and then (7.77) is imposed, the p's may be determined. The number V can then be calculated from (7.76). It is the *value* of the game. If it is zero, the game is fair. Otherwise, player 1 should pay V each time for the privilege of playing.

As an illustration, consider a game in which the players simultaneously exhibit any number of fingers on one hand with payoffs according to Table X.

Table X

	I	II	III	IV	V
I	0	−1	1	1	1
II	1	0	−1	−1	−1
III	−1	1	0	−1	1
IV	−1	1	1	0	−1
V	−1	1	−1	1	0

The Eqs. (7.76) are

$$\begin{aligned}
p_2 - p_3 - p_4 - p_5 &= V \\
-p_1 \quad\quad + p_3 + p_4 + p_5 &= V \\
p_1 - p_2 \quad\quad + p_4 - p_5 &= V \\
p_1 - p_2 - p_3 \quad\quad + p_5 &= V \\
p_1 - p_2 + p_3 - p_4 \quad\quad &= V
\end{aligned}$$

Then (7.78) becomes

$$\begin{aligned}
p_1 + p_2 - 2p_3 - 2p_4 - 2p_5 &= 0 \\
-2p_1 + p_2 + \quad p_3 \quad\quad + 2p_5 &= 0 \\
p_3 + \quad p_4 - 2p_5 &= 0 \\
-2p_3 + \quad p_4 + \quad p_5 &= 0
\end{aligned}$$

Solving these, by elimination or otherwise, we find

$$\begin{pmatrix} p_1 \\ p_2 \\ p_3 \\ p_4 \\ p_5 \end{pmatrix} = \alpha \begin{pmatrix} 3 \\ 3 \\ 1 \\ 1 \\ 1 \end{pmatrix}$$

and invoking (7.77), $\alpha = \frac{1}{9}$ and so

$$p_1 = \tfrac{1}{3}, \qquad p_2 = \tfrac{1}{3}, \qquad p_3 = \tfrac{1}{9}, \qquad p_4 = \tfrac{1}{9}, \qquad p_5 = \tfrac{1}{9}$$

The correct strategy for the game, then, is to spin a roulette wheel before each play. If it stops on 1–12, throw one finger; if 13–24, two fingers; 25–28, three fingers; 29–32, four fingers; 33–36, five fingers. The value of the game is

$$\begin{aligned}
V &= a_{11}p_1 + a_{21}p_2 + a_{31}p_3 + a_{41}p_4 + a_{51}p_5 \\
&= 0 \cdot \tfrac{1}{3} + 1 \cdot \tfrac{1}{3} + (-1) \cdot \tfrac{1}{9} + (-1) \cdot \tfrac{1}{9} + (-1) \cdot \tfrac{1}{9} \\
&= 0
\end{aligned}$$

and so the game is fair.

For a physical application of the methods of linear algebra, consider a system of n identical masses, say of mass m, hanging from a support, and connected by identical springs of spring constant K (Fig. 7.1). Let $y_i(t)$ denote the y coordinate of the ith mass at time t, measured downward from the equilibrium position of that mass. If the system is now displaced from equilibrium, then the force on the ith mass is

$$\begin{cases} k(y_{i+1} - y_i) - k(y_i - y_{i-1}) & \text{if } 2 \leq i \leq n - 1 \\ k(y_2 - y_1) - ky_1 & \text{if } i = 1 \\ -k(y_n - y_{n-1}) & \text{if } i = n \end{cases}$$

Figure 7.1

According to Newton's laws of motion, the force on the ith mass is also equal to its mass times it acceleration, i.e., to $m(d^2y_i/dt^2)$.

Thus, the displacements $y_1(t), y_2(t), \ldots, y_n(t)$ satisfy the differential equations

$$\begin{cases} my_1'' = k(y_2 - y_1) - ky_1 \\ my_2'' = k(y_3 - y_2) - k(y_2 - y_1) \\ \qquad \cdots \\ my_{n-1}'' = k(y_n - y_{n-1}) - k(y_{n-1} - y_{n-2}) \\ my_n'' = -k(y_n - y_{n-1}) \end{cases} \tag{7.79}$$

We do not propose to find the most general solutions of these differential equations, which are n simultaneous linear differential equations in n unknown functions $y_1(t), \ldots, y_n(t)$. Instead we will look for the so-called *characteristic modes of vibration*. These occur when each of the masses executes simple harmonic motion with the *same frequency* as all of the other masses. This means that we try to find a solution of our system of differential equations in the form

$$y_1(t) = a_1 \sin \omega t$$
$$y_2(t) = a_2 \sin \omega t$$
$$\cdots$$
$$y_n(t) = a_n \sin \omega t$$

where the amplitudes a_i are to be determined, as is the common frequency ω. Substituting these into (7.79) and cancelling the factor $\sin \omega t$ we find

$$-a_1 m\omega^2 = k(a_2 - a_1) - ka_1$$
$$-a_2 m\omega^2 = k(a_3 - a_2) - k(a_2 - a_1)$$
$$\cdots$$
$$-a_{n-1} m\omega^2 = k(a_n - a_{n-1}) - k(a_{n-1} - a_{n-2})$$
$$-a_n m\omega^2 = -k(a_n - a_{n-1})$$

If we write $m\omega^2/k = \lambda$, these equations take the form

$$\begin{pmatrix} 2 & -1 & 0 & 0 & 0 \cdots 0 \\ -1 & 2 & -1 & 0 & 0 \cdots 0 \\ 0 & -1 & 2 & -1 & 0 \cdots 0 \\ \cdot & \cdot & \cdot & & \cdot \\ \cdot & \cdot & \cdot & & \cdot \\ \cdot & \cdot & \cdot & & \cdot \\ 0 & 0 & 0 \cdots -1 & 2 & -1 \\ 0 & 0 & 0 \cdots & 0 & -1 & 1 \end{pmatrix} \begin{pmatrix} a_1 \\ a_2 \\ a_3 \\ \cdot \\ \cdot \\ \cdot \\ a_{n-1} \\ a_n \end{pmatrix} = \lambda \begin{pmatrix} a_1 \\ a_2 \\ a_3 \\ \cdot \\ \cdot \\ \cdot \\ a_{n-1} \\ a_n \end{pmatrix} \quad (7.80)$$

or more compactly,

$$A\mathbf{a} = \lambda\mathbf{a} \qquad (7.81)$$

where A is the matrix and $\mathbf{a}$ the vector in (7.79). We can also write (7.81) as

$$(A - \lambda I_n)\mathbf{a} = 0 \qquad (7.82)$$

where I_n is the identity matrix. Now (7.81) is a system of n homogeneous equations in n unknowns. Hence, it has a nontrivial solution if and only if

$$\det (A - \lambda I_n) = 0$$

which is a polynomial equation of degree n in λ, and which determines the n possible values of λ, and so of the frequency ω.

If $n = 2$, for instance, (7.80) reads

$$\begin{pmatrix} 2 & -1 \\ -1 & 1 \end{pmatrix}\begin{pmatrix} a_1 \\ a_2 \end{pmatrix} = \lambda \begin{pmatrix} a_1 \\ a_2 \end{pmatrix}$$

and this has a nontrivial solution if and only if

$$\det\begin{pmatrix} 2 - \lambda & -1 \\ -1 & 1 - \lambda \end{pmatrix} = 0$$
$$= (2 - \lambda)(1 - \lambda) - 1$$
$$= \lambda^2 - 3\lambda + 1$$

Thus $\lambda = \frac{1}{2}(3 \pm \sqrt{5})$ are the two permissible values of λ, and so the two possible frequencies are

$$\omega_1 = \sqrt{\frac{k}{m}} \left(\frac{3 - \sqrt{5}}{2}\right)^{1/2}$$

$$\omega_2 = \sqrt{\frac{k}{m}} \left(\frac{3 + \sqrt{5}}{2}\right)^{1/2}$$

By solving the homogeneous equations, if λ has one of the two permissible values, one finds the amplitudes of the motion. In the fundamental mode, corresponding to the smaller frequency ω_1, both masses move in the same direction. In the second mode, corresponding to ω_2, they move in opposite directions. A problem of the form (7.81) is known as an *eigenvalue problem*, λ is the eigenvalue.

Exercises

1. Formulate the eigenvalue problem for n masses connected by springs in which *both* of the masses at the ends are connected by springs to rigid supports.
2. Find the characteristic frequencies in Problem 1 when $n = 2$.
3. Formulate the problem as in 1 above when the masses are all different and the springs are all different.
4. Find the correct strategies for each of the following two-person games; find the value of each game.

(a) $\begin{pmatrix} 1 & 0 & -1 \\ 0 & 2 & 1 \\ 1 & -1 & 3 \end{pmatrix}$

(b) $\begin{pmatrix} 0 & 2 & 1 \\ 2 & 0 & 2 \\ 1 & 2 & 0 \end{pmatrix}$

(c) $\begin{pmatrix} 0 & 6 & 8 \\ 3 & 4 & 2 \\ 4 & 1 & 3 \end{pmatrix}$

Introduction
Distance, Limits, and Continuity
Partial Derivatives
The Chain Rule
Contact
Extrema

8

An Introduction to
the Differential Calculus
of Several Variables

8.1.   Introduction

We have, until now, studied only the calculus of functions of a single real variable. That is, we have dealt with functions f which assign to real numbers x real numbers $f(x)$. In this chapter we shall investigate functions f which assign to *pairs* of real numbers u, v, real numbers $f(u,v)$, or to *triples* of real numbers u, v, w, real numbers $f(u,v,w)$, etc. We will consider the questions of continuity, differentiation, extrema, and so on, as they apply to functions of several variables, as well as certain concepts which have no direct parallels in the one-variable theory.

As examples of functions of several variables we have the area A of a rectangle of sides h, w, which is

$$A(h,w) = hw \tag{8.1}$$

a function of two variables; the volume of a rectangular parallelepiped of sides a, b, c is

$$V(a,b,c) = abc \tag{8.2}$$

347

a function of three variables. Further examples are

$$f(x_1, x_2, x_3, x_4) = x_1{}^2 + x_2 x_3 + x_2 x_4 \tag{8.3}$$

$$f(x_1, x_2, \ldots, x_n) = \sum_{j=1}^{n} x_j{}^{3/2} \tag{8.4}$$

which define, respectively, functions of four and of n variables.

We adhere to our convention already adopted that the domain of definition of a function is understood to be the largest set for which the given formulas make sense. The domain of A in (8.1) is the set of all ordered pairs (h, w) of real numbers, of V in (8.2) is all ordered triples (a, b, c) of real numbers, and of f in (8.4) is all ordered n-tuples of *non-negative* real numbers.

It is often helpful to think geometrically about the domains of such functions. Thus, a function f of two real variables x and y assigns to an ordered pair (x, y) in its domain a number $f(x, y)$. However, we can think of an ordered pair of real numbers as a point in the plane, namely, the point whose coordinates are (x, y), or we can think of it as a vector. Hence, the domain of f is a set of points in the plane, or a set of vectors. Thus we can think of f as assigning numbers to points of the plane or numbers to vectors.

The function given by

$$f(x, y) = \sqrt{1 - x^2 - y^2} \tag{8.5}$$

is defined for $x^2 + y^2 \leq 1$, that is, its domain is the set of points in and on the circle of radius 1 centered at the origin. The function g of three variables which is defined by

$$g(x, y, z) = \sqrt{1 - x^2 - y^2 - z^2} \tag{8.6}$$

has for its domain the set of all ordered *triples* (x, y, z) of real numbers such that $x^2 + y^2 + z^2 \leq 1$. Geometrically, this is the set of all points in *three*-dimensional space which lie in or on the *sphere* of radius 1 centered at the origin.

To define the *graph* of a function of several variables let us first recall the definition of a graph of a function of one variable. If f is such a function, the graph of f is a certain curve in the plane, namely, the totality of points $(x, f(x))$ as x runs over the domain of f. Thus, the graph of $f(x) = x^2$ is the totality of points (x, x^2) in the plane. If f is a function of *two* variables x and y, the graph of f is the totality of points $(x, y, f(x, y))$

in *three*-dimensional space as (x,y) runs over the domain of f. Thus, to graph such a function we need three mutually perpendicular axes, say x, y, z axes, as shown in Fig. 8.1. Then, if we choose a point (x,y) in the

Figure 8.1

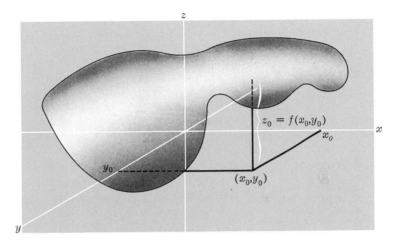

domain of f, we climb above that point a height $f(x,y)$ [below, if $f(x,y) < 0$]. This brings us to a point in E^3 whose coordinates are $(x,y,f(x,y))$ and this is a point on the graph of f. The complete graph of f is therefore a *surface* in E^3 whose height above each point (x,y) in the x–y plane is the value of f at that point. For functions of more than two variables we can retain the geometrical language but cannot draw the pictures. The graph of

$$f(x,y,z) = x^2y^2z$$

is the totality of points (x,y,z,x^2y^2z) in E^4 as (x,y,z) runs over all ordered triples of real numbers. This is a surface in four-dimensional space.

Exercises

1.   Sketch, in the plane, the domains of the following functions.

    (a) $f(x,y) = (4 - x^2 - y^2)^{3/2}$
    (b) $f(u,v) = \sqrt{3 - uv}$

(c) $f(a,b) = \dfrac{1}{a^2 - b^2}$

(d) $f(x,y) = \dfrac{1}{y - x^2}$

(e) $g(\theta,\eta) = \theta\sqrt{\eta}$

(f) $f(x,y) = (1 - 2x^2 + 3y^2)^{1/2}$

(g) $g(u,v) = \log \dfrac{1 - e^v}{u}$

2.   If $f(x,y) = x^2 - 3y^2$, $g(u,v) = (1/u) + v$, find

(a) $f(t - 3, t + 1)$

(b) $g(x + y, f(x,y))$

(c) $g(1/t, -t)$

(d) $f(g(a,b),g(a,b))$

(e) $f(3,3), g(1,-1), f(0,2), f(x,0), g(t,0)$

(f) $\dfrac{d}{dx}(f(x,x))$

(g) $\dfrac{d}{dt}(g(t,t^2))$

(h) $\displaystyle\int_0^x f(\sqrt{t}, 2\sqrt{t})\, dt$

8.2.   *Distance, Limits, and Continuity*

In E^2, the plane, the *length* of a vector $\mathbf{x} = (x_1,x_2)$ is

$$\sqrt{x_1^2 + x_2^2}$$

It is the distance from the origin to the point (x_1,x_2). In E^3, the length of $\mathbf{x} = (x_1,x_2,x_3)$ is

$$\sqrt{x_1^2 + x_2^2 + x_3^2}$$

and, generally, in E^n, the length of $\mathbf{x} = (x_1, \ldots, x_n)$ is

$$(x_1^2 + \cdots + x_n^2)^{1/2}$$

We use the symbol $\|\,\mathbf{x}\,\|$ to denote the length of the vector $\mathbf{x}$. Thus

$$\|(3,4)\| = \sqrt{3^2 + 4^2}$$
$$= 5$$

and

$$\|(x_1, \ldots, x_n)\| = \left(\sum_{i=1}^{n} x_i^2 \right)^{1/2}$$

Obviously, $\|\mathbf{x}\| \geqq 0$ always, and $\|\mathbf{x}\| = 0$ if and only if $\mathbf{x} = \mathbf{0}$. By using this symbol it is easy to express the distance between two points. In the plane, the distance between the points (x_1, x_2) and (y_1, y_2) is

$$\sqrt{(x_1 - y_1)^2 + (x_2 - y_2)^2} \tag{8.7}$$

If $\mathbf{x} = (x_1, x_2)$ and $\mathbf{y} = (y_1, y_2)$, then (8.7) is the same as $\|\mathbf{x} - \mathbf{y}\|$, for

$$\begin{aligned}
\|\mathbf{x} - \mathbf{y}\| &= \|(x_1, x_2) - (y_1, y_2)\| \\
&= \|(x_1 - y_1, x_2 - y_2)\| \\
&= \sqrt{(x_1 - y_1)^2 + (x_2 - y_2)^2}
\end{aligned}$$

The same is true in n dimensions: the distance between a point $\mathbf{x}$ and a point $\mathbf{y}$ is the length of the vector $\mathbf{x} - \mathbf{y}$, i.e., $\|\mathbf{x} - \mathbf{y}\|$.

To say that $\|\mathbf{x}\|$ is small, then, is to say that the point $\mathbf{x}$ is near the origin. To say that $\|\mathbf{x} - \mathbf{y}\|$ is small is to say that the points $\mathbf{x}$ and $\mathbf{y}$ are near each other. For example, the points $\mathbf{x}$ such that $\|\mathbf{x}\| = 1$ lie on the surface of a sphere of radius 1 centered at the origin. The points $\mathbf{x}$ such that $\|\mathbf{x}\| \leqq \epsilon$ are those whose distance from the origin does not exceed ϵ, that is, those which are inside or on a sphere of radius ϵ centered at the origin.

Let $\mathbf{y}$ be a fixed point. The totality of points $\mathbf{x}$ such that $\|\mathbf{x} - \mathbf{y}\| = 1$ are those on the surface of a sphere of radius 1 centered at $\mathbf{y}$. Those for which $\|\mathbf{x} - \mathbf{y}\| \leqq \epsilon$ are those whose distance from $\mathbf{y}$ does not exceed ϵ.

We can now define the limit of a function of several variables. We say that

$$\lim_{\mathbf{x} \to \mathbf{x}_0} f(\mathbf{x}) = L$$

if for every $\epsilon > 0$ there is a $\delta > 0$ such that $|f(\mathbf{x}) - L| < \epsilon$ whenever $0 < \|\mathbf{x} - \mathbf{x}_0\| < \delta$. This definition may be compared with the corresponding definition for functions of one variable. For the limit to exist and have the value L we require that $f(\mathbf{x})$ be near L whenever $\mathbf{x}$ is near (but not equal to) $\mathbf{x}_0$. For example, in two dimensions our definition says that

$$\lim_{(x,y) \to (x_0, y_0)} f(x,y) = L$$

if for every $\epsilon > 0$, there is a $\delta > 0$ such that inside a circle of radius δ centered at (x_0, y_0) we have $|f(x,y) - L| < \epsilon$ except possibly at (x_0, y_0) itself.

Examples

1. If

$$f(x,y) = \frac{x^2 + y^2}{x + y}$$

then

$$\lim_{(x,y) \to (1,0)} f(x,y) = 1$$

2. If

$$f(u,v) = \begin{cases} \dfrac{uv}{u^2 + v^2} & (u,v) \neq (0,0) \\ 0 & (u,v) = (0,0) \end{cases}$$

then we claim that

$$\lim_{(u,v) \to (0,0)} f(u,v)$$

does not exist. Indeed, no matter how small a circle we draw around the origin there will be some points inside the circle where $f(u,v) = \frac{1}{2}$ and others at which $f(u,v) = 0$. To see this, notice that $f(u,u) = \frac{1}{2}$, so that at all points of the line $v = u$, except the origin, f has the value $\frac{1}{2}$. Since there are points of this line in every circle about the origin, the first assertion is established. Next, observe that $f(0,v) = 0$ for all v, so f has the value zero at all points of the v axis. Such points lie in every circle about the origin, and so we have shown that the limit does not exist.

The basic theorems about limits of functions of one variable have immediate generalizations to the present case. Thus, the limit of a sum of two functions is the sum of the limits, if they exist, and similarly for products. The limit of a quotient is the quotient of the limits unless the limit in the denominator is zero. The proofs are almost identical with those in the one-variable case, and are omitted.

A function f of n variables is said to be *continuous* at the point x_0 if

$$\lim_{\mathbf{x} \to \mathbf{x}_0} f(\mathbf{x}) = f(\mathbf{x}_0)$$

The usual theorems about sums, products, etc., of continuous functions being continuous are true and the proofs are omitted.

Exercises

1. Let A be the 2×2 matrix

$$\begin{pmatrix} \cos \theta & \sin \theta \\ -\sin \theta & \cos \theta \end{pmatrix}$$

  If $\mathbf{x}$ is any point in E^2, show that $\|A\mathbf{x}\| = \|\mathbf{x}\|$. Can you explain this geometrically?

2. If $\mathbf{x}$ and $\mathbf{y}$ are in E^2, show that

$$\|\mathbf{x} + \mathbf{y}\| < \|\mathbf{x}\| + \|\mathbf{y}\|$$

3. Sketch, in the plane, the set of all points $\mathbf{x}$ such that

  (a) $\|\mathbf{x} \quad (3,4)\| < 2$
  (b) $\|\mathbf{x}\| < \frac{1}{2}$
  (c) $0 < \|\mathbf{x} + (1,1)\| < 1$
  (d) $0 < \|\mathbf{x} + (2,-1)\| < \delta$

4. Which of the following functions are continuous at the origin?

  (a) $f(x,y) = \begin{cases} \dfrac{x^2 + y^2}{x + y} & x + y \neq 0 \\ 0 & x + y = 0 \end{cases}$

  (b) $f(u,v) = \begin{cases} \dfrac{u^2 - v^2}{u - v} & u \neq v \\ 0 & u = v \end{cases}$

  (c) $f(x) = \begin{cases} \dfrac{x_1 x_2 \ldots x_n}{x_1^2 + \cdots + x_n^2} & \mathbf{x} \neq \mathbf{0} \\ 0 & \mathbf{x} = \mathbf{0} \end{cases}$

5. Prove that if f and g are continuous at $\mathbf{x}_0$, so is $f + g$.
6. Find all points at which the function in Exercise 4(b) above fails to be continuous. Prove.

8.3. *Partial Derivatives*

We now discuss the differentiation of functions of several variables. Partial differentiation, or the computation of partial derivatives, is a very simple affair. To find the partial derivative of a function of several variables with respect to one of those variables we just think of all the other variables as constants and differentiate in the usual way.
    Thus, to find the partial derivative of

$$f(x,y) = x^2 y$$

with respect to x, we think of y as a constant, differentiate with respect to x in the usual way, and obtain $2xy$ for the required derivative. To find the partial derivative of the same function with respect to y, we think of x as a constant, and get x^2 for the derivative. Thus the partial derivative of a function of several variables with respect to one of those variables measures the rate of change of the function which is due to the change of that one variable, holding all others fixed.
    There are many notations for partial derivatives. The partial derivative of $f(x,y)$ with respect to x is sometimes written as

$$\frac{\partial f}{\partial x}$$

sometimes as f_x, and also as f_1. Hence, if

$$f(x,y,z) = x^2 + xy^2 + z$$

then

$$\frac{\partial f(x,y,z)}{\partial x} = 2x + y^2$$
$$\equiv f_x(x,y,z)$$
$$\equiv f_1(x,y,z)$$

and

$$\frac{\partial f(x,y,z)}{\partial y} = 2xy$$
$$\equiv f_y(x,y,z)$$
$$\equiv f_2(x,y,z)$$

while

$$\frac{\partial f(x,y,z)}{\partial z} = 1$$

$$\equiv f_z(x,y,z)$$
$$\equiv f_3(x,y,z)$$

A formal definition of the partial derivative of a function of n variables with respect to the kth variable is

$$\frac{\partial f(x_1,\ldots,x_n)}{\partial x_k} = \lim_{h\to 0} \frac{f(x_1,\ldots,x_{k-1},x_k+h,x_{k+1},\ldots,x_n) - f(x_1,\ldots,x_n)}{h}$$

$$\equiv f_{x_k}(x_1,\ldots,x_n)$$
$$\equiv f_k(x_1,\ldots,x_n)$$

if the limit exists.

Partial derivatives of higher order are defined similarly. Thus, the symbol

$$\frac{\partial^2 f(x,y)}{\partial x\, \partial y}$$

is the second partial derivative of f, first with respect to y, then with respect to x. In other words, this means

$$\frac{\partial^2 f(x,y)}{\partial x\, \partial y} = \frac{\partial}{\partial x}\left(\frac{\partial f(x,y)}{\partial y}\right)$$

Other symbols for the same object are

$$\frac{\partial^2 f(x,y)}{\partial x\, \partial y} \equiv f_{yx}(x,y) \equiv f_{21}(x,y)$$

As an example, if

$$f(x,y) = xy^2 + y \tag{8.8}$$

then the four second partial derivatives of f are

$$\frac{\partial^2 f(x,y)}{\partial x^2} = \frac{\partial}{\partial x}\left(\frac{\partial f(x,y)}{\partial x}\right)$$

$$= \frac{\partial}{\partial x}(y^2)$$

$$= 0$$

$$\frac{\partial^2 f(x,y)}{\partial x \, \partial y} = \frac{\partial}{\partial x}\left(\frac{\partial f(x,y)}{\partial y}\right)$$

$$= \frac{\partial}{\partial x}(2xy + 1)$$

$$= 2y$$

$$\frac{\partial^2 f(x,y)}{\partial y \, \partial x} = \frac{\partial}{\partial y}\left(\frac{\partial f(x,y)}{\partial x}\right)$$

$$= \frac{\partial}{\partial y}(y^2)$$

$$= 2y$$

$$\frac{\partial^2 f(x,y)}{\partial y^2} = \frac{\partial}{\partial y}\left(\frac{\partial f(x,y)}{\partial y}\right)$$

$$= \frac{\partial}{\partial y}(2xy + 1)$$

$$= 2x$$

For this function, we could summarize by writing

$$f_{11} = f_{xx} = 0$$
$$f_{12} = f_{21} = f_{xy} = f_{yx} = 2y$$
$$f_{22} = f_{yy} = 2x$$

A function of two variables has eight third partial derivatives. For the function in (8.8), two of these are

$$\frac{\partial^3 f(x,y)}{\partial x \, \partial y \, \partial x} = \frac{\partial}{\partial x}\left(\frac{\partial^2 f(x,y)}{\partial y \, \partial x}\right)$$

$$= \frac{\partial}{\partial x}(2y)$$

$$= 0$$

and

$$\frac{\partial^3 f(x,y)}{\partial x \, \partial y^2} = \frac{\partial}{\partial x}\left(\frac{\partial^2 f(x,y)}{\partial y^2}\right)$$

$$= \frac{\partial}{\partial x}(2x)$$

$$= 2$$

Thus $f_{121} = f_{xyx} = 0$ and $f_{221} = f_{yyx} = 2$.

For another example, consider

$$f(x_1, x_2, \ldots, x_n) = x_1 + x_2^2 + x_3^3 + \cdots + x_n^n \qquad (8.9)$$

Then

$$\frac{\partial f(\mathbf{x})}{\partial x_i} = ix_i^{i-1} \qquad (i = 1, 2, \ldots, n)$$

and

$$\frac{\partial^2 f(\mathbf{x})}{\partial x_i \, \partial x_j} = \begin{cases} 0 & i \neq j \\ i(i-1)x_i^{i-2} & i = j \end{cases}$$

If f is a function of n variables, we can manufacture an $n \times n$ matrix H from the second partial derivatives of f. To do this, we put $\partial^2 f(\mathbf{x})/\partial x_i \, \partial x_j$ in the ith row and jth column. For instance, if $f(x,y) = x^2 + x^2 y^2$ then H is 2×2 and is given by

$$H(x,y) = \begin{pmatrix} 2 + 2y^2 & 4xy \\ 4xy & 2x^2 \end{pmatrix} \qquad (8.10)$$

For the function of (8.9) the matrix is

$$H(x_1, \ldots, x_n) = \begin{pmatrix} 0 & 0 & 0 & 0 & \cdots & 0 \\ 0 & 2 & 0 & 0 & \cdots & 0 \\ 0 & 0 & 6x_3 & 0 & \cdots & 0 \\ \cdot & & & & & \cdot \\ \cdot & & & & & \cdot \\ \cdot & & & & & \cdot \\ 0 & 0 & \cdots & 0 & & n(n-1)x_n^{n-2} \end{pmatrix} \qquad (8.11)$$

This kind of a matrix will be of importance later on, in our discussion of maxima and minima of functions of several variables.

You have no doubt noticed that in the examples so far given, the order of differentiation has been immaterial. That is, we have always found that, for instance,

$$\frac{\partial f(x,y)}{\partial x \, \partial y} = \frac{\partial f(x,y)}{\partial y \, \partial x}$$

If this were always true then we would be able to calculate say

$$\frac{\partial^6 f(x,y,z,w)}{\partial x \, \partial y \, \partial x \, \partial y \, \partial w \, \partial x}$$

by differentiating three times with respect to x then twice with respect to y then once with respect to w, that is, by calculating

$$\frac{\partial^6 f(x,y,z,w)}{\partial w \, \partial y^2 \, \partial x^3}$$

It is, in fact, the case that, under very mild hypotheses, the order in which we compute partial derivatives is of no consequence. The basic result is

THEOREM 8.1.   Let f be a function of two variables which is defined on a rectangular region of the plane. Suppose f_{xy} and f_{yx} both exist *and are continuous* in this region. Then $f_{xy} = f_{yx}$ throughout the interior of the region.

PROOF   Let (x_0, y_0) be a fixed point inside the region. If θ, η are small enough, the point $(x_0 + \theta, y_0 + \eta)$ will still lie in the region. Define

$$G(y) = f(x_0 + \theta, y) - f(x_0, y) \tag{8.12}$$

Then, by the mean-value theorem of the calculus of one variable,

$$G(y_0 + \eta) - G(y_0) = \eta G'(\xi_1)$$
$$= \eta \, \{ f_y(x_0 + \theta, \xi_1) - f_y(x_0, \xi_1) \}$$

where ξ_1 lies between y_0 and $y_0 + \eta$. Again applying the mean-value theorem, we find

$$f_y(x_0 + \theta, \xi_1) - f_y(x_0, \xi_1) = \theta \frac{\partial}{\partial x} f_y(x, \xi_1) \bigg|_{x = \xi_2}$$
$$= \theta f_{yx}(\xi_2, \xi_1)$$

where ξ_2 lies between x_0 and $x_0 + \theta$. Hence

$$G(y_0 + \eta) - G(y_0) = \eta \theta f_{yx}(\xi_2, \xi_1) \tag{8.13}$$

Next, let

$$H(x) = f(x, y_0 + \eta) - f(x, y_0) \tag{8.14}$$

Then

$$H(x_0 + \theta) - H(x_0) = \theta H'(\xi_3)$$
$$= \theta \{ f_x(\xi_3, y_0 + \eta) - f_x(\xi_3, y_0) \}$$
$$= \theta \eta f_{xy}(\xi_3, \xi_4) \tag{8.15}$$

where ξ_3 lies between x_0 and $x_0 + \theta$, and ξ_4 is between y_0 and $y_0 + \eta$.

Directly from the definitions (8.12) and (8.14) of G and H one sees that

$$G(y_0 + \eta) - G(y_0) = H(x_0 + \theta) - H(x_0)$$

Consequently, the two expressions (8.13) and (8.15) are equal, that is,

$$\eta\theta f_{yx}(\xi_2, \xi_1) = \theta\eta f_{xy}(\xi_3, \xi_4) \tag{8.16}$$

Since we can choose $\eta \neq 0$, $\theta \neq 0$, we can cancel $\theta\eta$ and obtain

$$f_{yx}(\xi_2, \xi_1) = f_{xy}(\xi_3, \xi_4) \tag{8.17}$$

Let $(\theta, \eta) \to (0,0)$. Then $\xi_2 \to x_0$ (because ξ_2 is between x_0 and $x_0 + \theta$), $\xi_1 \to y_0$, $\xi_3 \to x_0$, $\xi_4 \to y_0$. Since f_{yx} and f_{xy} are continuous, by hypothesis, at (x_0, y_0), we can take the limit of both sides of (8.17) as $(\theta, \eta) \to (0,0)$ and obtain

$$f_{yx}(x_0, y_0) = f_{xy}(x_0, y_0)$$

which was to be shown.

By using Theorem 8.1 we see that if f is a function of n variables and if

$$\frac{\partial^2 f}{\partial x_i \, \partial x_j}, \qquad \frac{\partial^2 f}{\partial x_j \, \partial x_i}$$

are both continuous, then they are equal, because the other $n - 2$ variables are treated like constants. By more argument, which we omit, we can show that when taking a higher order derivative, the order of differentiation is irrelevant, provided that, in every order, the derivatives involved are continuous.

Exercises

1. For each of the following $f(x,y,z)$ find $\partial f/\partial x$, $\partial f/\partial y$, $\partial f/\partial z$.

   (a) $x(y + z)$
   (b) $\sqrt{xyz}$

(c) $x \log (y + z)$
(d) e^{x-y+z}

(e) $\dfrac{1}{x^2 + y + z}$

(f) $\sin xy + \sin xz$
(g) $(x + y + z)^4$
(h) $\sqrt{1 - x^2} + \sqrt{1 - y^2}$
(i) $g(x)g(y) + g(z)$
(j) $g(xyz)$
(k) $xg(yz)$
(l) $g(x + y) + z^m$

2.   For each of the following $f(x,y,z)$ find $\partial^2 f/\partial x^2$, $\partial^2 f/\partial y^2$, $\partial^2 f/\partial x\,\partial y$, $\partial^2 f/\partial y\,\partial x$.

(a) $x^2 + y^2 + z^2$
(b) $(x + y + z)^2$
(c) $\sin(x^3 y^2 z)$

(d) $\dfrac{1}{\sqrt{x^2 + y^2 + z^2}}$

(e) $xy + xz + yz$

(f) $x + y + z + \dfrac{1}{x + y + z}$

(g) $f(x) + f(y) + f(z)$
(h) $f(x)f(y)f(z)$
(i) $f(xyz)$
(j) $xf(y + z) + yf(x + z) + zf(x + y)$

3.   (a) For each of the functions f in Exercise 2 compute the matrix H of its
        second partial derivatives at the point $(1,1,1)$.
      (b) Calculate the determinants of each of the matrices in (a).
4.   Suppose $\partial f(x,y,z)/\partial x = 0$ for all x, y, z. What can you say about f?
5.   Show that, for each of the following $f(x,y)$ it is true that

$$\frac{\partial^2 f}{\partial x^2} + \frac{\partial^2 f}{\partial y^2} \equiv 0$$

(a) $e^x \cos y$
(b) $\sin x \cosh y$
(c) $x^2 - y^2$
(d) $e^{(x^2-y^2)} \cos 2xy$

8.4. The Chain Rule

The chain rule for functions of several variables is the generalization of
the rule for differentiation of composite functions

$$\frac{d}{dx} f(g(x)) = f'(g(x))g'(x)$$

in the calculus of a single variable.

Consider a function f of two variables, x and y. Instead of letting x
and y wander over the plane, suppose we restrict them to a certain
curve, say the curve

$$\begin{cases} x = x(t) \\ y = y(t) \end{cases} \quad (0 \leqq t \leqq 1) \tag{8.18}$$

The function values $f(x,y)$, if x and y are so restricted, define a function
of just one variable, namely,

$$F(t) = f(x(t),y(t)) \tag{8.19}$$

We are concerned here with the computation of $F'(t)$.

More generally, consider a function f of n variables $x_1, \ldots, x_n$ and
suppose each x_i is replaced by a certain function of a parameter t

$$x_i = x_i(t) \quad (i = 1, 2, \ldots, n) \tag{8.20}$$

How shall we compute the derivative of

$$F(t) = f(x_1(t),x_2(t), \ldots, x_n(t))? \tag{8.21}$$

That is, how do we differentiate our given function f along the "curve"
(8.20) in E^n?

In the two-dimensional case, to differentiate F in (8.19) we would find

$$\frac{F(t + h) - F(t)}{h} = \frac{f(x(t + h),y(t + h)) - f(x(t),y(t))}{h}$$

We then subtract and add $f(x(t + h),y(t))$ in the numerator, obtaining

$$\frac{F(t + h) - F(t)}{h} = \frac{f(x(t + h),y(t + h)) - f(x(t + h),y(t))}{h}$$

$$+ \frac{f(x(t + h),y(t)) - f(x(t),y(t))}{h} \tag{8.22}$$

By this device we have two numerators in each of which one of the arguments of f is the same in both terms and the other argument changes. Keep t, h fixed and define the function

$$\varphi(s) = f(x(t + h), y(t + s))$$

The first numerator on the right of (8.22) is

$$\varphi(h) - \varphi(0) = h\varphi'(\xi_1)$$
$$= hf_y(x(t + h), y(t + \xi_1))y'(t + \xi_1) \qquad (0 < \xi_1 < h)$$

by the rule for composite functions of one variable. Similarly, the second numerator in (8.22) is

$$hf_x(x(t + \xi_2), y(t))x'(t + \xi_2)$$

where $0 < \xi_2 < h$. Hence, (8.22) becomes

$$\frac{F(t + h) - F(t)}{h} = f_y(x(t + h), y(t + \xi_1))y'(t + \xi_1)$$
$$+ f_x(x(t + \xi_2), y(t))x'(t + \xi_2) \quad (8.23)$$

Suppose f_x, f_y are continuous at $(x(t), y(t))$ and x', y' are continuous at t. As $h \to 0$ we have $\xi_1 \to 0, \xi_2 \to 0$ and we find

$$F'(t) = f_x(x(t), y(t))x'(t) + f_y(x(t), y(t))y'(t) \quad (8.24)$$

This is the chain rule for functions of two variables. For functions of n variables the same device works though the calculations are more involved. The result is

THEOREM 8.2. Let f be a function of n variables $x_1, x_2, \ldots, x_n$, and let $u_1, \ldots, u_n$ be n functions of a single variable t. Suppose $u_1', \ldots, u_n'$ are continuous at $t = t_0$, and that all the first partial derivatives of f are continuous at the point $(u_1(t_0), \ldots, u_n(t_0))$. Then, at t_0,

$$\frac{d}{dt} f(u_1(t), \ldots, u_n(t))$$

$$= f_1(u_1(t), \ldots, u_n(t))u_1'(t) + \cdots + f_n(u_1(t), \ldots, u_n(t))u_n'(t)$$

$$= \sum_{j=1}^{n} f_j(u_1(t), \ldots, u_n(t))u_j'(t)$$

Example 1

Let $f(x,y,z) = xy^2 + xz^2$. We calculate

$$\frac{d}{dt} f(t, t^2, t^3)$$

in two different ways. First, by direct substitution,

$$f(t, t^2, t^3) = t(t^2)^2 + t(t^3)^2$$
$$= t^7 + t^5$$

and so by differentiation,

$$\frac{d}{dt} f(t, t^2, t^3) = 7t^6 + 5t^4$$

For a second method we use Theorem 8.2. We have

$$f_1(x,y,z) = y^2 + z^2$$
$$f_2(x,y,z) = 2xy$$
$$f_3(x,y,z) = 2xz$$

Hence, by the chain rule,

$$\frac{d}{dt} f(t, t^2, t^3) = f_1(t, t^2, t^3) \frac{d}{dt}(t)$$
$$+ f_2(t, t^2, t^3) \frac{d}{dt}(t^2)$$
$$+ f_3(t, t^2, t^3) \frac{d}{dt}(t^3)$$
$$= (t^4 + t^6) \cdot 1 + (2t^3)(2t) + (2t^4)(3t^2)$$
$$= 7t^6 + 5t^4$$

in agreement with our first result.

Exercises

1. If $f(x,y) = e^{xy}$, find

$$\frac{d}{dt} f(t^2 - 1, t + 1)$$

both directly and by the chain rule.

2.   If $f(u,v,w) = u^2vw$, find

$$\frac{d}{ds}f(3s,s^2 + s)$$

both directly and by the chain rule.

3.   At what point of the parabola $y = x^2$ is the function

$$f(x,y) = \frac{1}{x^2 + y^2 + 1}$$

as large as possible? Use the chain rule.

4.   Graph the values of the function $f(x,y,z) = (x^2 + y^2 + z^2)^{-2}$ along the helix

$$x = \cos t$$
$$y = \sin t$$
$$z = t$$

showing maxima and minima, and using the chain rule.

Next, suppose we have a function f of, say, three variables x, y, z. Suppose that, instead of having x, y, z each depend on just one variable t, that they depend on two variables, t and u. In other words, we are considering

$$f(x(t,u),y(t,u),z(t,u))$$

which is a function of two variables. Let us call this function $F(t,u)$. How can we calculate, say, $\partial F/\partial t$? That is, how do we find

$$\frac{\partial}{\partial t}f(x(t,u),y(t,u),z(t,u))?$$

When we compute a partial derivative with respect to t, we hold u fixed. Thus, when we differentiate partially with respect to t, we are thinking of x, y, z as functions only of a single variable t. The problem is thus reduced to the case treated in Theorem 8.2, and we find

$$\frac{\partial}{\partial t}f(x(t,u),y(t,u),z(t,u)) = f_1(x(t,u),y(t,u),z(t,u))\frac{\partial x(t,u)}{\partial t}$$

$$+ f_2(x(t,u),y(t,u),z(t,u))\frac{\partial y(t,u)}{\partial t}$$

$$+ f_3(x(t,u),y(t,u),z(t,u))\frac{\partial z(t,u)}{\partial t}$$

More compactly, we could write

$$F_t = f_x x_t + f_y y_t + f_z z_t$$

Example 2.
Let

$$f(x,y,z) = xye^z$$

Then

$$\frac{\partial}{\partial u} f(u^2 - v^2, uv, u^2 + v^2)$$

$$\begin{aligned}
&= f_1(u^2 - v^2, uv, u^2 + v^2)(2u) \\
&\quad + f_2(u^2 - v^2, uv, u^2 + v^2)v \\
&\quad + f_3(u^2 - v^2, uv, u^2 + v^2)(2u) \\
&= (uve^{u^2+v^2})2u + (u^2 - v^2)e^{u^2+v^2} \cdot v + (u^2 - v^2)uve^{u^2+v^2} \cdot 2u
\end{aligned}$$

Also

$$\frac{\partial}{\partial v} f(u^2 - v^2, uv, u^2 + v^2)$$

$$\begin{aligned}
&= -2vf_1 + uf_2 + 2vf_3 \\
&= -2uv^2 e^{u^2+v^2} + u(u^2 - v^2)e^{u^2+v^2} + 2v(u^2 - v^2)uve^{u^2+v^2}
\end{aligned}$$

Exercises

1. Given $f(x,y,z,w)$, suppose that x, y, z, w are all functions of r, s, t. Write out the chain rule for

$$\frac{\partial f}{\partial r}, \quad \frac{\partial f}{\partial s}, \quad \frac{\partial f}{\partial t}$$

2. Find $\partial f/\partial r, \partial f/\partial s$ if

   (a) $f(x,y) = x \log y; \ x = r^2 - s^2; \ y = r^2 + s^2$

   (b) $f(x,y) = \dfrac{1 + xy}{1 - xy}; \ x = \cos r; \ y = \sin r$

   (c) $f(u,v,w) = uv - e^{uw}; \ u = r\sqrt{s}; \ v = s\sqrt{r}; \ w = r$

   (d) $f(x,y) = \sqrt{1 + x^2 y^2}; \ x = e^{r+s}; \ y = e^{r-s}$

   (e) $f(h,k) = \cos^{-1}(h/k); \ h = r^2 - s^2; \ k = r^2 + s^2$

(f) $f(x,y,z,w) = xy + xz + xw + yz + yw + zw;\ x = r + s + rs;$
   $y = r + s - rs;\ z = r - s + rs;\ w = r - s - rs$

3.   If $g(x,y) = f(y + cx)$ show that

$$\frac{\partial^2 g}{\partial x^2} = c^2 \frac{\partial^2 g}{\partial y^2}$$

8.5.   *Contact*

In this section we wish to prepare the groundwork for a suitable generalization, to functions of several variables, of Taylor's theorem

$$f(x) = f(a) + (x - a)f'(a) + \cdots$$

for functions of one variable. As in Section 4.8 we motivate this theorem by first discussing contact.

If f is a function of two variables, x and y, consider the question of finding a polynomial in x and y which is a good approximation to $f(x,y)$ near, say, the origin $(0,0)$. A polynomial in two variables is an expression of the form

$$P(x,y) = a_0 + a_1 x + a_2 y + a_{11} x^2 + a_{12} xy + a_{22} y^2$$
$$+ a_{111} x^3 + a_{112} x^2 y + \cdots$$

where the a's are various constants.

To make $P(x,y) = f(x,y)$ at the origin, we want

$$a_0 = f(0,0)$$

For

$$\frac{\partial P}{\partial x} = \frac{\partial f}{\partial x} \qquad [\text{at } (0,0)]$$

we need

$$a_1 = \frac{\partial f(0,0)}{\partial x}$$

[Caution: $\dfrac{\partial f(0,0)}{\partial x}$ does not mean $\dfrac{\partial}{\partial x} f(0,0)$, it means the value of $\dfrac{\partial f(x,y)}{\partial x}$ at the point $(0,0)$.]

Continuing, the requirements that $P_y = f_y$, $P_{xx} = f_{xx}$, $P_{xy} = f_{xy}$, $P_{yy} = f_{yy}$ at the origin lead to

$$a_2 = \frac{\partial f(0,0)}{\partial y}$$

$$a_{11} = \frac{1}{2}\frac{\partial^2 f(0,0)}{\partial x^2}$$

$$a_{12} = \frac{\partial^2 f(0,0)}{\partial x\, \partial y}$$

$$a_{22} = \frac{1}{2}\frac{\partial^2 f(0,0)}{\partial y^2}$$

where we have assumed that these derivatives exist and are continuous. Therefore, the polynomial in x and y of degree 2 which, together with its partial derivatives through the second order, agrees with f at (0,0), is

$$P(x,y) = f(0,0) + f_x(0,0)x + f_y(0,0)y$$
$$+ \tfrac{1}{2}f_{xx}(0,0)x^2 + f_{xy}(0,0)xy + \tfrac{1}{2}f_{yy}(0,0)y^2 \quad (8.25)$$

We say that the surface $z = P(x,y)$, where P is defined in (8.25), has second-order contact with the surface $z = f(x,y)$ at the point $(0,0,f(0,0))$ in E^3.

Example 1.
If $f(x,y) = xe^{x+y}$, find the best polynomial approximation to f near (0,0) in the sense of contact of order 2.
    In this case we calculate

$$f(0,0) = 0$$
$$f_x(0,0) = 1$$
$$f_y(0,0) = 0$$
$$f_{xx}(0,0) = 2$$
$$f_{xy}(0,0) = 1$$
$$f_{yy}(0,0) = 0$$

Substituting in (8.25), we find

$$P(x,y) = x + x^2 + xy$$

for the required polynomial.
    By a continuation of this argument one can easily find polynomials of higher degree with higher contact than second order. We defer a

discussion of the exact form of these polynomials because the calculations get very complicated unless the correct notation is first developed. For the application we have in mind, we content ourselves with generalizing (8.25) to the case of a function of n variables.

Hence, let $f(x_1, x_2, \ldots, x_n)$ be given, and let us find a polynomial of second degree in n variables which has second-order contact with f at a given point, say at the point $\mathbf{x}^0 = (x_1^0, x_2^0, \ldots, x_n^0)$. We assume the polynomial to have the form

$$
\begin{aligned}
P(x_1, &\ldots, x_n) \\
&= a_0 + b_1(x_1 - x_1^0) + b_2(x_2 - x_2^0) + \cdots + b_n(x_n - x_n^0) \\
&\quad + c_{11}(x_1 - x_1^0)^2 + c_{22}(x_2 - x_2^0)^2 + \cdots + c_{nn}(x_n - x_n^0)^2 \\
&\quad + 2c_{12}(x_1 - x_1^0)(x_2 - x_2^0) + 2c_{13}(x_1 - x_1^0)(x_3 - x_3^0) \\
&\quad + \cdots + 2c_{1n}(x_1 - x_1^0)(x_n - x_n^0) \\
&\quad + \cdots + 2c_{n-1,n}(x_{n-1} - x_{n-1}^0)(x_n - x_n^0)
\end{aligned} \tag{8.26}
$$

This should be compared with Eq. (4.56). In (8.26) we have simply written out the most general polynomial of degree 2 on n variables. It involves a constant, terms of first degree, and then all possible terms of second degree, i.e., all possible products of one of the x's with another.

We immediately take refuge in summation symbols, and write (8.26) in the form

$$
P(\mathbf{x}) = a_0 + \sum_{j=1}^{n} b_j(x_j - x_j^0) + \sum_{i,j=1}^{n} c_{ij}(x_i - x_i^0)(x_j - x_j^0) \tag{8.27}
$$

which is easier on the eyes. The last sum in (8.27) needs a word of explanation. The sum is over all values of i and j as they run independently from 1 to n, so there are n^2 terms in the sum. One of these terms, for instance, is

$$
c_{27}(x_2 - x_2^0)(x_7 - x_7^0)
$$

but another one is

$$
c_{72}(x_7 - x_7^0)(x_2 - x_2^0)
$$

Since $(x_7 - x_7^0)(x_2 - x_2^0)$ and $(x_2 - x_2^0)(x_7 - x_7^0)$ are the same, the coefficient of $(x_2 - x_2^0)(x_7 - x_7^0)$ in (8.27) is $c_{27} + c_{72}$. It is customary to take $c_{27} = c_{72}$, in which case the coefficient is $2c_{27}$. This accounts for the mysterious 2's in (8.26)

To summarize, we attempt to find the polynomial $P(\mathbf{x})$ in (8.27), where $c_{ij} = c_{ji}$ for all i, j, such that f and P have second-order contact at

$\mathbf{x}^0$. The requirement $P(\mathbf{x}^0) = f(\mathbf{x}^0)$ gives

$$a_0 = f(\mathbf{x}^0)$$

If we ask that

$$\frac{\partial P(\mathbf{x}^0)}{\partial x_k} = \frac{\partial f(\mathbf{x}^0)}{\partial x_k}$$

then by direct differentiation of (8.27) we find

$$b_k = \frac{\partial f(\mathbf{x}^0)}{\partial x_k} \qquad (k = 1, 2, \ldots, n) \qquad (8.28)$$

Finally, if we require f and P to have the same second partial derivatives at $\mathbf{x}^0$, then we get

$$c_{ij} = \frac{1}{2} \frac{\partial^2 f(\mathbf{x}^0)}{\partial x_i \, \partial x_j} \qquad (i, j = 1, 2, \ldots, n) \qquad (8.29)$$

We have now found all the coefficients in (8.27). The polynomial we were looking for is, thus,

$$P(\mathbf{x}) = f(\mathbf{x}^0) + \sum_{j=1}^{n} \frac{\partial f(\mathbf{x}^0)}{\partial x_j} (x_j - x_j^0)$$
$$+ \frac{1}{2} \sum_{i,j=1}^{n} \frac{\partial^2 f(\mathbf{x}^0)}{\partial x_i \, \partial x_j} (x_i - x_i^0)(x_j - x_j^0) \qquad (8.30)$$

and this has second-order contact with f at $\mathbf{x}^0$. Notice that the numbers c_{ij} are precisely the entries of the matrix H which we discussed in Section 8.3.

Example 2.
Find the polynomial of second degree which has contact of order 2 with $f(x,y,z) = e^{x+y+z}$ at $(x,y,z) = (1,1,0)$.

Here $x_1 = x$, $x_2 = y$, $x_3 = z$, $x_1^0 = 1$, $x_2^0 = 1$, $x_3^0 = 0$. From (8.28),

$$b_1 = \frac{\partial f}{\partial x}(1,1,0)$$
$$= e^2$$

and similarly $b_2 = b_3 = e^2$. Next, since all second partial derivatives of this very special function are the same, namely, e^{x+y+z}, their values at $\mathbf{x}^0$

are all e^2, so all $c_{ij} = e^2$. Thus (8.30) takes the form

$$P(\mathbf{x}) = e^2 + \sum_{j=1}^{3} e^2(x_j - x_j{}^0) + \frac{1}{2} \sum_{i,j=1}^{3} e^2(x_i - x_i{}^0)(x_j - x_j{}^0)$$

Written out in longhand this becomes

$$P(x,y,z) = e^2\{1 + (x - 1) + (y - 1) + z$$
$$+ \frac{(x - 1)^2}{2} + \frac{(y - 1)^2}{2} + \frac{z^2}{2}$$
$$+ (x - 1)(y - 1) + (x - 1)z + (y - 1)z\}$$

Exercises

1. Find the polynomial having second-order contact with each of the following at the point indicated.

   (a) $f(u,v) = \sin (uv)$ at $(0,0)$
   (b) $f(x,y) = xe^y - ye^x$ at $(0,0)$
   (c) $f(x,y) = \dfrac{1}{\sqrt{x^2 + y^2}}$ at $(3,4)$
   (d) $f(x,y,z) = \dfrac{1}{xy} + \dfrac{1}{xz} + \dfrac{1}{yz}$ at $(1,1,1)$
   (e) $f(u,v,w) = u \log (1 + v) + v \log (1 + w)$ at $(0,0,0)$
   (f) $f(x_1, x_2, \ldots , x_n) = \displaystyle\sum_{i=1}^{n} \dfrac{1}{x_i{}^2}$ at $(1,1,1, \ldots , 1)$
   (g) $f(x,y,z) = \dfrac{x}{y + z} + \dfrac{y}{z + x} + \dfrac{z}{x + y}$ at $(1,1,1)$

2. (a) If $f(x,y) = g(x)h(y)$ show that the second-order approximation to $f(x,y)$ at (x^0, y^0) is obtained by multiplying the Taylor's series for $g(x)$ about x^0 by that for $h(y)$ about y^0 and throwing away terms of degree higher than the second.
   (b) State a generalization of this result to function of n variables.
   (c) Use the result of part (a) to find second-order approximations to $\sin x \cos y$ at $(0,0)$ and to $e^{x^2-y^2}$ at $(0,1)$.

3. Write out the complete *third-order* best approximation of $f(x,y)$ by a polynomial of degree 3.

8.6. *Extrema*

In this section we discuss the problem of finding maxima and minima of functions of several variables, a task which is vastly more complicated than in the one-variable case. We can get an idea of the situation by considering a function f of two variables, and its graph, which is a surface $z = f(x,y)$ in three-dimensional space. In Fig. 8.2 we show a "nice" surface, in which the function f has a maximum at the point (x^*,y^*) indicated. In Fig. 8.2, imagine yourself taking a walk on the surface

Figure 8.2

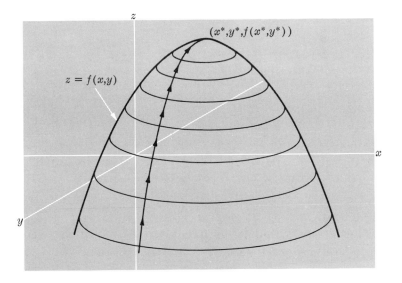

shown while keeping your x coordinate fixed at x^* (follow the arrows in the figure). You would climb a hill to the maximum point, and then descend. Analytically, what we are saying is that the function of *one* variable $h(y) = f(x^*,y)$ has a maximum at $y = y^*$. Hence, $h'(y^*) = 0$, which is to say that

$$\frac{\partial f(x^*,y^*)}{\partial y} = 0$$

Similarly, by taking a walk on the surface while keeping y fixed at y^*, we would find that

$$\frac{\partial f}{\partial x}(x^*,y^*) = 0$$

Thus, at the maximizing point (x^*,y^*), both first partial derivatives of f vanish. In general, if f is a function of n variables, a point $\mathbf{x}^*$, at which *all* of the first partial derivatives of f are zero, is called a *critical point* of the function. The argument given above shows that if we wish to find the points at which f assumes its maximum or minimum values, then we need only look among the critical points of f or on the boundary of the domain of definition of f. That is, if $\mathbf{x}^*$ gives to f a local maximum or minimum, and if $\mathbf{x}^*$ is not on the boundary of the domain of f, then $\mathbf{x}^*$ is a critical point.

Example 1.
If $f(x,y,z) = x^2 + y^2 + z^2$, then

$$f_x = 2x, \qquad f_y = 2y, \qquad f_z = 2z$$

and so the only critical point is the origin. In this case it is obvious that $f(0,0,0) = 0$ is a minimum of f.

Example 2.
Let $f(x,y) = x^2 - 6xy - y^2$. Then

$$f_x = 2x - 6y, \qquad f_y = -6x - 2y$$

Thus f_x and f_y are both zero only at the point $(0,0)$. Now

$$f(x,0) = x^2$$

has a *minimum* at $x = 0$. However,

$$f(0,y) = -y^2$$

has a *maximum* at $y = 0$. To put it more picturesquely, if we start out at the point $(0,0,0)$ on the surface $z = f(x,y)$ and walk, on the surface, keeping x fixed at 0, then we will be walking downhill. If we start at the same point and walk with y fixed at 0, we will be walking uphill.

The surface in question looks like Fig. 8.3. Evidently, the origin is neither a maximizing nor a minimizing point of f. A point on a surface, like $(0,0,0)$ in Fig. 8.2, from which the surface slopes down in some directions and up in other directions, and which is a critical point, is called a *saddle point,* for obvious reasons.

We consider, then, the question of deciding analytically whether a given critical point is a maximum, a minimum, or a saddle point of a function f of several variables. For a clue to the procedure consider once more the case of a function of one variable.

Figure 8.3

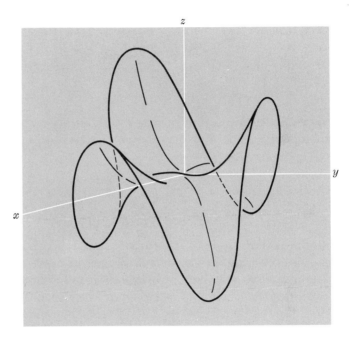

Suppose f is a function of x, and that $f'(x_0) = 0$. If f has enough derivatives then near x_0, f has a Taylor expansion

$$f(x) = f(x_0) + (x - x_0)f'(x_0) + \frac{(x - x_0)^2}{2} f''(x_0) + \text{higher order terms}$$

Since $f'(x_0) = 0$, this is just

$$f(x) = f(x_0) + \frac{(x - x_0)^2}{2} f''(x_0) + \text{higher order terms}$$

From this it is clear that if $f''(x_0) > 0$ then $f(x)$ increases when x moves a bit away from x_0, so we have a minimum, and vice versa, if $f''(x_0) < 0$.

To generalize this idea to n dimensions, let f be a function of $\mathbf{x}$ and suppose that $\mathbf{x}^0$ is a critical point, i.e., that

$$\frac{\partial f}{\partial x_i}(\mathbf{x}^0) = 0 \qquad (i = 1, 2, \ldots, n) \tag{8.31}$$

We suppose that f is well approximated near $\mathbf{x}^0$ by its contact polynomial of second degree, so that

$$f(\mathbf{x}) = f(\mathbf{x}^0) + \sum_{j=1}^{n} \frac{\partial f(\mathbf{x}^0)}{\partial x_j}(x_j - x_j{}^0)$$
$$+ \frac{1}{2} \sum_{i,j=1}^{n} \frac{\partial^2 f(\mathbf{x}^0)}{\partial x_i \, \partial x_j}(x_i - x_i{}^0)(x_j - x_j{}^0)$$
$$+ \text{ higher order terms} \tag{8.32}$$

We defer the discussion of when such an approximation is indeed valid, though it will be if f has enough derivatives. In view of (8.31), (8.32) takes the form

$$f(\mathbf{x}) = f(\mathbf{x}^0) + \frac{1}{2} \sum_{i,j=1}^{n} \frac{\partial^2 f(x^0)}{\partial x_i \, \partial x_j}(x_i - x_i{}^0)(x_j - x_j{}^0)$$
$$+ \text{ higher order terms} \tag{8.33}$$

The behavior of f in the immediate neighborhood of $\mathbf{x}^0$ is governed by the double sum shown. If this sum is *positive* for *every* choice of the vector $\mathbf{x} - \mathbf{x}^0 \neq \mathbf{0}$, i.e., for every choice of a direction in which to walk away from $\mathbf{x}^0$, then $f(\mathbf{x})$ increases in every such direction. The surface is then "bowl-shaped" near $\mathbf{x}^0$, and f has a minimum there.

The next possibility is that the double sum will be *negative* for *every* choice of $\mathbf{x} - \mathbf{x}^0 \neq \mathbf{0}$, in which case f will have a maximum at $\mathbf{x}^0$.

Next, the sum may be positive for some choices of $\mathbf{x} - \mathbf{x}^0$ and negative for others. Then f has a saddle point at $\mathbf{x}^0$.

Finally, if the sum is *nonnegative* for *all* $\mathbf{x} - \mathbf{x}^0 \neq \mathbf{0}$ the second-order approximation (8.33) is not sufficient to decide the status of $\mathbf{x}^0$, and similarly if the sum is *nonpositive* for all $\mathbf{x} - \mathbf{x}^0 \neq \mathbf{0}$.

We are now left with the question of deciding, by inspection of the sum in (8.33), which of these alternatives holds in any particular case. We first simplify the notation. The numbers

$$\frac{\partial^2 f(\mathbf{x}^0)}{\partial x_i \, \partial x_j} \qquad (i, j = 1, \ldots, n)$$

are exactly the entries of the $n \times n$ matrix H which was introduced in Section 8.3. Thus, let us write

$$H_{ij} = \frac{\partial^2 f(\mathbf{x}^0)}{\partial x_i \, \partial x_j} \qquad (i, j = 1, \dots, n)$$

This $n \times n$ matrix is symmetric about the main diagonal,

$$H_{ij} = H_{ji} \qquad (i, j = 1, 2, \dots, n) \qquad (8.34)$$

by Theorem 8.1, if the second partial derivatives of f are continuous at $\mathbf{x}^0$. Further, let us write $\mathbf{u} = \mathbf{x} - \mathbf{x}^0$. The crucial sum in (8.33), whose sign we must investigate, takes the form

$$\sum_{i,j=1}^{n} H_{ij} u_i u_j \qquad (8.35)$$

The question before us is the following. Given an $n \times n$ matrix H of real numbers. Determine whether or not the expression (8.35) has the same sign for *every* choice of the vector $\mathbf{u} \neq \mathbf{0}$.

Such an expression is called a *quadratic form* in the variables $u_1, \dots, u_n$ with coefficient matrix H.

Example 3.
Let H be the matrix

$$\begin{pmatrix} 1 & 2 \\ 2 & 3 \end{pmatrix}$$

A quadratic form with this coefficient matrix is

$$\begin{aligned}
Q &= \sum_{i,j=1}^{2} H_{ij} u_i u_j \\
&= H_{11} u_1^2 + H_{12} u_1 u_2 + H_{21} u_2 u_1 + H_{22} u_2^2 \\
&= u_1^2 + 2 u_1 u_2 + 2 u_2 u_1 + 3 u_2^2 \\
&= u_1^2 + 4 u_1 u_2 + 3 u_2^2
\end{aligned}$$

Let us find out if this particular quadratic form has the same sign for all vectors $\mathbf{u} \neq \mathbf{0}$. We have

$$\begin{aligned}
Q &= u_1^2 + 4 u_1 u_2 + 3 u_2^2 \\
&= (u_1 + 2 u_2)^2 - u_2^2
\end{aligned}$$

This is positive when $u_2 = 0$, $u_1 = 1$, say, and negative when $u_1 = 2$, $u_2 = -1$, and so it does not maintain constant sign.

> **DEFINITION**　Let Q be a quadratic form in n variables $(u_1, \ldots, u_n)$ with coefficient matrix H. If Q has the same sign for every choice of $\mathbf{u} \neq \mathbf{0}$, then the form Q is said to be *definite*. Otherwise, Q is *indefinite*. If Q is definite, it is called *positive definite* if $Q > 0$ for all $\mathbf{u} \neq \mathbf{0}$, and similarly, *negative definite*, *nonnegative definite*, *nonpositive definite*.

Example 4.
Let

$$H = \begin{pmatrix} 1 & 1 \\ 1 & 2 \end{pmatrix}$$

We claim that this matrix defines a positive definite quadratic form. Indeed,

$$\begin{aligned} Q &= \sum_{i,j=1}^{2} H_{ij} u_i u_j \\ &= u_1^2 + u_1 u_2 + u_2 u_1 + 2u_2^2 \\ &= u_1^2 + 2u_1 u_2 + 2u_2^2 \\ &= (u_1 + u_2)^2 + u_2^2 \end{aligned}$$

It is now obvious that $Q > 0$ if $\mathbf{u} \neq \mathbf{0}$.

Example 5.
The matrix

$$H = \begin{pmatrix} 1 & 2 \\ 2 & 4 \end{pmatrix}$$

defines a nonnegative definite form, for

$$\begin{aligned} Q &= u_1^2 + 2u_1 u_2 + 2u_2 u_1 + 4u_2^2 \\ &= u_1^2 + 4u_1 u_2 + 4u_2^2 \\ &= (u_1 + 2u_2)^2 \end{aligned}$$

Evidently $Q \geq 0$ if $\mathbf{u} \neq \mathbf{0}$, but $Q = 0$ when, say, $\mathbf{u} = (2, -1)$, so Q is nonnegative definite but not positive definite.

In the case of a 2×2 matrix H, it is easy to formulate a criterion for testing definiteness by inspection. Indeed, if

$$H = \begin{pmatrix} H_{11} & H_{12} \\ H_{21} & H_{22} \end{pmatrix} \qquad (H_{12} = H_{21})$$

then the form is

$$\begin{aligned} Q &= H_{11}u_1{}^2 + H_{12}u_1u_2 + H_{21}u_2u_1 + H_{22}u_2{}^2 \\ &= H_{11}u_1{}^2 + 2H_{12}u_1u_2 + H_{22}u_2{}^2 \end{aligned}$$

Suppose $H_{11} = 0$. If we fix u_2, then Q is linear in u_1 and so will take positive and negative values unless $H_{12} = 0$ also. In the latter case $Q = 0$ when $u_2 = 0$ and so is not positive definite. Hence, suppose $H_{11} \neq 0$. Then

$$Q = H_{11}\left(u_1 + \frac{H_{12}}{H_{11}}u_2\right)^2 + \frac{1}{H_{11}}\{H_{11}H_{22} - H_{12}{}^2\}u_2{}^2$$

Let $\Delta = H_{11}H_{22} - H_{12}{}^2$. If $\Delta > 0$, then both terms of Q have the same sign, that of H_{11}. If $\Delta = 0$, Q will be zero for some $\mathbf{u} \neq \mathbf{0}$, and similarly if $\Delta < 0$. Hence, Q is positive definite if and only if $H_{11} > 0$ and $\Delta > 0$. Q is negative definite if and only if $H_{11} < 0$, $\Delta > 0$. Notice that Δ is the determinant of the matrix H.

We state, without proof, the generalization of this result to forms in n variables. Let Q be a quadratic form in $\mathbf{u}$ with coefficient matrix

$$H = \begin{pmatrix} H_{11} & H_{12} & \cdots & H_{1n} \\ H_{21} & H_{22} & \cdots & H_{2n} \\ \cdot & \cdot & & \cdot \\ \cdot & \cdot & & \cdot \\ \cdot & \cdot & & \cdot \\ H_{n1} & H_{n2} & \cdots & H_{nn} \end{pmatrix}$$

where $H_{ij} = H_{ji}$ (all i, j). Let $\Delta_1 = H_{11}$,

$$\Delta_2 = \det \begin{pmatrix} H_{11} & H_{12} \\ H_{21} & H_{22} \end{pmatrix}, \qquad \Delta_3 = \det \begin{pmatrix} H_{11} & H_{12} & H_{13} \\ H_{21} & H_{22} & H_{23} \\ H_{31} & H_{32} & H_{33} \end{pmatrix}$$

and, in general, let Δ_k denote the determinant of the $k \times k$ matrix in the upper left-hand corner of H ($\Delta_n = \det H$). Then Q is positive definite if and only if

$$\Delta_1 > 0, \quad \Delta_2 > 0, \quad \Delta_3 > 0, \quad \ldots, \quad \Delta_n > 0 \qquad (8.36)$$

(c) $\begin{pmatrix} 1 & 2 & 3 \\ 2 & 3 & 4 \\ 3 & 4 & 5 \end{pmatrix}$

(d) $\begin{pmatrix} 1 & 2 & 3 \\ 2 & 1 & 2 \\ 3 & 2 & 1 \end{pmatrix}$

(e) $\begin{pmatrix} \lambda_1 & 0 & 0 & \cdots & 0 \\ 0 & \lambda_2 & 0 & \cdots & 0 \\ 0 & 0 & \lambda_3 & \cdots & 0 \\ & \cdot & \cdot & & \cdot \\ & \cdot & \cdot & & \cdot \\ & \cdot & \cdot & & \cdot \\ 0 & 0 & \cdots & 0 & \lambda_n \end{pmatrix}$

Which of the forms (a)–(d) is positive definite? Under what circumstances will the form of (e) be positive definite? Negative definite?

2.   Write out the coefficient matrices of each of the following forms.

(a) $Q = x_1{}^2 - 3x_1x_2 + x_2{}^2$
(b) $Q = 3x_1{}^2 + 4x_2{}^2 + x_3{}^2 - x_1x_2 + x_1x_3 - x_2x_3$
(c) $Q = 2u^2 + uv - 3v^2$
(d) $Q = x_1{}^2 + x_2{}^2 + \cdots + x_n{}^2$
(e) $Q = (x_1 + x_2 + x_3 + x_4)^2$
(f) $Q = (x_1 + x_2)^2 - (x_1 + 3x_2 + x_3)^2$
(g) $Q = (x_1 + x_2 + \cdots + x_n)^2 - x_1{}^2 - x_2{}^2 - \cdots - x_n{}^2$

3.   Test each of the forms in Exercise 2 for definiteness. In each case where the form is indefinite find a point where $Q > 0$ and another where $Q < 0$.

4.   Find the box of volume V, without a top, with minimum surface area.

5.   Find the maximum volume of a rectangular parallelepiped inscribed in the ellipsoid

$$x^2 + 2y^2 + z^2 = 4$$

6.   Find the point on the plane

$$x - y + 2z = 3$$

nearest to the point (1,2,0).

7.   Find the point on the plane (in E^4)

$$2x + y - z + w = 1$$

nearest to the origin (0,0,0).

Appendix: Analytic Geometry

In the plane, let a pair of perpendicular lines be drawn, say one vertically and one horizontally. We will call the vertical line "the y axis," the horizontal line "the x axis," and their point of intersection the "origin." Choose and fix a unit of length. Starting from the origin, mark off units of length in both directions on each of the axes. (See Fig. A.1.)

Next, number the points which have just been marked off, as shown in the figure. We now have a device for describing the location of any point in the plane. Indeed, if we choose the point P (see Fig. A.1), we drop a perpendicular from P to the x axis, noting the point $x = 3$ where the perpendicular meets the axis. Similarly, a perpendicular from P to the y axis meets that axis at $y = 2$. The location of P is completely

Figure A.1

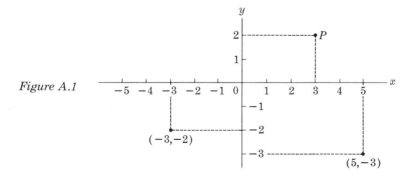

determined by these two numbers, i.e., by the statement that "the coordinates of P are $x = 3$ and $y = 2$."

Conversely, if we are given the coordinates of a point, say $x = 5$, $y = 2$, we go out the x axis to $x = 5$, then up 2 units to the point in question. We abbreviate the assertion that the coordinates of a point are $x = 5$ and $y = 2$ by simply speaking of "the point (5,2)." In general, the point (a,b) is the point whose x coordinate is a and whose y coordinate is b. Thus, with each ordered pair of numbers (a,b) there is associated a unique point in the plane, and vice versa. The numbers a and b are called the *Cartesian coordinates* of the point (a,b). In Fig. A.1 are shown the points $(5,-3)$, $(-3,-2)$, and $(3,2)$.

Let P and Q be two points in a plane. By the distance between P and Q we mean the length of the straight-line segment joining P and Q. If the coordinates of P are (x_1,y_1) and those of Q are (x_2,y_2), then, from the right triangle PQR in Fig. A.2, we see that the distance between P and Q is

$$\sqrt{(x_2 - x_1)^2 + (y_2 - y_1)^2} \qquad (A.1)$$

Figure A.2

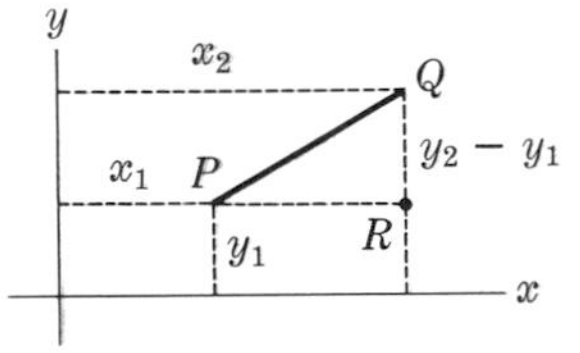

Thus, the distance between $(-3,1)$ and $(4,-2)$ is

$$\sqrt{(4 - (-3))^2 + (-2 - 1)^2} = \sqrt{58}$$

while the distance between $(4,-1)$ and the origin $(0,0)$ is

$$\sqrt{(4 - 0)^2 + (-1 - 0)^2} = \sqrt{17}$$

Cartesian coordinates in the plane are used for making a visual presentation of the relationship between two quantities. Such a presentation is called *a graph*. For example, consider two quantities y and x which are related by the equation $y = x^2$. Thus, if $x = 1$ then $y = 1$; if $x = 2$, $y = 4$; if $x = -5$, $y = 25$, etc. To graph this particular relationship we would plot the points $(1,1)$, $(2,4)$, $(-5,25)$, $(3,9)$, $(\frac{1}{2},\frac{1}{4})$, $(-\frac{4}{3},\frac{16}{9})$, etc. After plotting several of these points and drawing a smooth curve through them, we would have the graph in Fig. A.3. We could call

Figure A.3
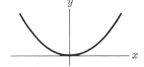

this the graph of the relation $y = x^2$. If we had such a graph we could find the square of any number x by starting at $(x,0)$, going up to the curve, then left to the y axis, reading off the answer. Conversely, to find the square root of some number y, we start at $(0,y)$ on the y axis, go to the right to meet the curve, then down to the x axis, reading off the answer. In a similar way, the graph of the relation $y = 2x$, say, will be a straight line, passing through the origin, as we will see presently.

The points in the plane whose coordinates are of the form $(x,0)$, where $x > 0$, comprise the positive x axis; the points $(x,0)$, with $x < 0$, are the negative x axis; and similarly for the positive and negative y axes. The points (x,y), where $x > 0$ and $y > 0$, are said to lie in the first quadrant. If $x < 0$, $y > 0$, the point (x,y) is in the second quadrant. The third and fourth quadrants contain those (x,y) where $x < 0$, $y < 0$ or $x > 0$, $y < 0$, respectively.

Let an arbitrary straight line be drawn in the plane. We wish to find the equation of the line. That is, we seek a relationship between y and x whose graph is the given straight line. Having drawn the line, we let P be a certain point on it, and suppose the coordinates of P are (x,y). Let b, the y *intercept* of the line, denote the y coordinate of the point where the line meets the y axis, and let θ, the *inclination* of the line, be the angle measured counterclockwise from the positive x axis to the line. From Fig. A.4,

$$\frac{y - b}{x} = \tan \theta$$

and so

$$y = (\tan \theta)x + b \qquad \text{(A.2)}$$

Figure A.4
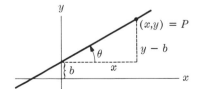

The quantity tan θ, the tangent of the angle of inclination of the line, is called the *slope* of the line and is usually denoted by the letter m. Thus, (A.2) becomes

$$y = mx + b \tag{A.3}$$

where $m = \tan \theta$. Hence, there exist two constants m, b such that for *every* point (x,y) on the given line, Eq. (A.3) holds. Conversely, if we are given two quantities x and y which are related by an equation of the form (A.3), then the graph of the relationship will be a straight line of slope m and y intercept b. This equation is called the *slope-intercept* form of the equation of a straight line.

Example

The equation $y = x + 4$ is of the form (A.3) with $m = 1$, $b = 4$. It therefore represents a straight line of slope 1 and intercept 4. Since $m = \tan \theta = 1$, $\theta = 45°$. The line is the one which passes through the point (0,4) and makes an angle of $45°$ with the positive x axis.

The equation of a straight line may also be determined by any two points on the line. Suppose we know that the points (x_1,y_1) and (x_2,y_2) are on a certain line (see Fig. A.5). Then, if (x,y) is any point on the line, we

Figure A.5

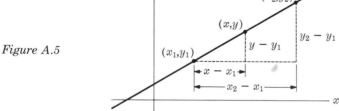

have, by considering the similar triangles,

$$\frac{y - y_1}{x - x_1} = \frac{y_2 - y_1}{x_2 - x_1} \tag{A.4}$$

which is the two-point form of the equation of a straight line.

Example

Find the straight line which passes through (1,1) and (3,4).

From (A.4),

$$\frac{y-1}{x-1} = \frac{4-1}{3-1}$$

or

$$y = \tfrac{3}{2}(x-1) + 1$$

or finally

$$y = \tfrac{3}{2}x - \tfrac{1}{2}$$

is the desired equation. Comparing this result with (A.3), we see that the line has y intercept $-\tfrac{1}{2}$ and slope $\tfrac{3}{2}$.

Let two lines in the plane be given, and suppose they are perpendicular. If θ_1, θ_2 are the respective inclinations of the two lines, then clearly

$$\theta_2 = \theta_1 \pm 90°$$

and so

$$\tan \theta_2 = \tan (\theta_1 \pm 90°)$$
$$= -\cot \theta_1$$
$$= -\frac{1}{\tan \theta_1}$$

If $m_1 = \tan \theta_1$ and $m_2 = \tan \theta_2$ are the slopes of the lines, then we see that

$$m_2 = -\frac{1}{m_1}$$

We have then the result that *if two lines are perpendicular, then the product of their slopes is* -1.

Example
Find the equation of the line which passes through (0,5) and is perpendicular to the line $y = 3x - 2$.

Suppose $y = mx + b$ is the equation of the line we seek. Then, by perpendicularity, $m = -\tfrac{1}{3}$, and since the y intercept is 5, $b = 5$. The answer is

$$y = (-\tfrac{1}{3})x + 5$$

Now let there be given a line and a point P not on the line (see Fig. A.6). By the distance from P to the line we mean the distance between

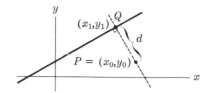

P and the point of the line nearest to P. This shortest distance is evidently measured along the perpendicular to the given line through P. Let $y = mx + b$ be the given line, and let $y = \alpha x + \beta$ be the equation of the dotted perpendicular in the figure. Then $\alpha = -1/m$, and we need to find β. Since the dotted line passes through (x_0, y_0), we have

$$y_0 = -\frac{1}{m}x_0 + \beta$$

and so

$$\beta = y_0 + \frac{1}{m}x_0$$

whence the dotted line in Fig. A.6 has the equation

$$y = -\frac{1}{m}x + y_0 + \frac{1}{m}x_0$$

This perpendicular meets the given line $y = mx + b$ at a point Q. At Q, the y coordinates of both lines are the same, and so

$$mx + b = \left(-\frac{1}{m}\right)x + y_0 + \left(\frac{1}{m}\right)x_0$$

whence

$$x_1 = \left(\frac{y_0 + (1/m)x_0 - b}{m + (1/m)}\right)$$

is the x coordinate of Q. Its y coordinate is

$$y_1 = mx_1 + b$$
$$= \frac{my_0 + x_0 + (1/m)b}{m + (1/m)}$$

The distance from P to the given line is the distance between (x_0, y_0)

and (x_1,y_1), i.e.,

$$d^2 = \left(\frac{y_0 + (1/m)\,x_0 - b}{m + (1/m)} - x_0\right)^2 + \left(\frac{my_0 + x_0 + (1/m)\,b}{m + (1/m)} - y_0\right)^2$$

(A.5)

This formula expresses the distance from a given point (x_0,y_0) to a given line $y = mx + b$. Needless to say, the formula should not be memorized, but the method of derivation should be understood.

Example
Find the distance from $(1,1)$ to the line $y = 3x + 1$.
   Here the perpendicular is $y = (-\frac{1}{3})x + b$. Since $(1,1)$ is on the perpendicular, $1 = (-\frac{1}{3}) + b$ and $b = \frac{4}{3}$. Thus, the perpendicular line $y = (-\frac{1}{3})x + \frac{4}{3}$ meets the line $y = 3x + 1$ at $(\frac{1}{10},\frac{13}{10})$. The distance from $(1,1)$ to $(\frac{1}{10},\frac{13}{10})$ is

$$d = \left[\left(\frac{9}{10}\right)^2 + \left(\frac{3}{10}\right)^2\right]^{1/2} = \frac{3}{\sqrt{10}}$$

Let Q be a fixed point whose coordinates are (x_0,y_0), and let R be a fixed positive number. Consider the set of all points in the plane whose distance from Q is equal to R. Evidently this set is a circle of radius R centered at Q. If (x,y) is any point on the circle, the distance from (x,y) to Q is

$$[(x - x_0)^2 + (y - y_0)^2]^{1/2}$$

and is also equal to R. Hence,

$$(x - x_0)^2 + (y - y_0)^2 = R^2$$

(A.6)

for every point on the circle. Equation (A.6) is therefore the equation of a circle centered at (x_0,y_0) of radius R. In particular, a circle centered at the origin has the equation

$$x^2 + y^2 = R^2$$

(A.7)

where R is its radius.

Example
Find the points at which the line $y = 3x + 2$ meets the circle of radius 2 centered at $(1,1)$.

The equation of the circle is

$$(x - 1)^2 + (y - 1)^2 = 4$$

To find the points of intersection with the line $y = 3x + 2$, we replace y by $3x + 2$ in the last equation, getting

$$(x - 1)^2 + (3x + 1)^2 = 4$$

or

$$10x^2 + 10x - 2 = 0$$

whose solutions are

$$x = -\tfrac{1}{2} \pm \tfrac{3}{10}\sqrt{5}$$

Each y is $3x + 2$, so the y coordinates are

$$y = \tfrac{1}{2} \pm \tfrac{9}{10}\sqrt{5}$$

respectively.

Let P and Q be two points in the plane, and let d be a fixed positive number. Consider the set of all points in the plane the sum of whose distances from P and Q is d. This set is called an *ellipse*. To find the equation of an ellipse, draw the x axis of a Cartesian coordinate system through P and Q, and let the y axis be the perpendicular bisector of PQ. Then the coordinates of P and Q are $(-c,0)$ and $(c,0)$, respectively. If (x,y) is any point on the ellipse, the sum of its distances from P and Q is

$$d = [(x + c)^2 + y^2]^{1/2} + [(x - c)^2 + y^2]^{1/2}$$

After squaring,

$$(x - c)^2 + y^2 = d^2 - 2d[(x + c)^2 + y^2]^{1/2} + (x + c)^2 + y^2$$

or

$$2d[(x + c)^2 + y^2]^{1/2} = d^2 + 4cx$$

Squaring again and simplifying, we get

$$\frac{x^2}{(d/2)^2} + \frac{y^2}{(\sqrt{d^2 - 4c^2}/2)^2} = 1 \tag{A.8}$$

as the equation of the ellipse.

In Fig. A.7 is shown the ellipse (A.8). Notice that the distance from

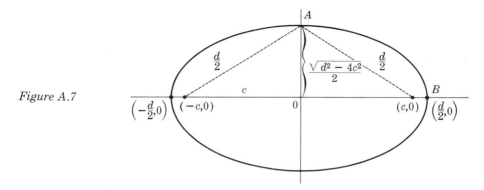

Figure A.7

the center of the ellipse to B is the quantity which is squared in the first denominator of (A.8). Also notice that the distance OA is the quantity squared in the second denominator of (A.8). The segments OB and OA are known, respectively, as the *semimajor axis* and *semiminor axis* of the ellipse, and their lengths are usually denoted by the letters a and b. Thus, (A.8) becomes

$$\frac{x^2}{a^2} + \frac{y^2}{b^2} = 1 \tag{A.8$'$}$$

where a and b are the lengths of the semiaxes of the ellipse. The points $(c,0)$ and $(-c,0)$ are called the *foci* (singular *focus*) of the ellipse.

Let P be a fixed point in the plane, and let L be a fixed line. Consider the set of all points whose distance from P and from L are equal. This set is called a *parabola*. The point P is the *focus* of the parabola, and the line L is its *directrix*. To find the equation of a parabola, let the directrix L be taken as the y axis, and let the focus be chosen as the point $(a,0)$.

Figure A.8

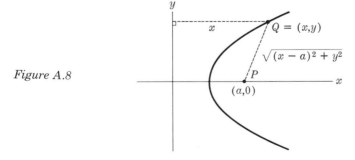

If $Q = (x,y)$ is any point on the parabola, then

$$x = \sqrt{(x - a)^2 + y^2}$$

and squaring we get

$$y^2 = 2ax - a^2 \tag{A.9}$$

as the desired equation. In general, any equation of the form

$$y^2 = \alpha x + \beta y + \gamma$$

or of the form

$$x^2 = \alpha x + \beta y + \gamma$$

always represents a parabola.

Let P and Q be fixed points in the plane, and let $2a$ be a fixed positive number. Consider the set of all points R in the plane such that the difference of the distances from R to P and from R to Q is equal to $\pm 2a$. This set is called a *hyperbola,* and the points P and Q are its foci. To find the equation of this hyperbola, let the foci be taken on the

Figure A.9
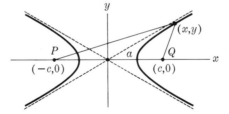

x axis at the points $(c,0)$ and $(-c,0)$, and let (x,y) be any point on the hyperbola. Then

$$[(x + c)^2 + y^2]^{1/2} - [(x - c)^2 + y^2]^{1/2} = \pm 2a$$

After clearing the square roots by successive squaring, we obtain

$$\frac{x^2}{a^2} + \frac{y^2}{a^2 - c^2} = 1 \tag{A.10}$$

for the equation of the hyperbola. If we solve (A.10) for y,

$$y = \pm \frac{\sqrt{c^2 - a^2}}{a} x \sqrt{1 - \frac{a^2}{x^2}}$$

If (x,y) is far away from the origin and on the curve, the factor $\sqrt{1 - (a^2/x^2)}$ is very nearly 1, and so the hyperbola gets very close to the straight lines

$$y = \pm \frac{\sqrt{c^2 - a^2}}{a} x$$

These lines are the *asymptotes* of the curve, and they are the dotted lines in Fig. A.9.

Review Problems in Analytic Geometry

1. Plot the following points in the plane:
   $(1,3)$, $(-2,7)$, $(-3,-6)$, $(2,-4)$, $(1,\sqrt{2})$, $(\frac{3}{2},-\frac{1}{2})$, $(4,0)$, $(-3,\frac{1}{2})$

2. Find the distance between each of the following pairs of points:

   (a) $(1,1)$, $(2,2)$
   (b) $(1,0)$, $(3,-2)$
   (c) $(-1,1)$, $(1,-1)$
   (d) $(a,0)$, $(b,1)$

   (e) $(0,0)$, (x,x)
   (f) $(t, 1 + t^2)$, $(t, 1 - t^2)$
   (g) $(1, 1/(1 + x))$, $(2,-3)$

3. Sketch the graph of each of the following relationships:

   (a) $y = x$
   (b) $y = -\frac{3}{2}$
   (c) $y = 3x$
   (d) $y = 3x - 5$
   (e) $y = -2x + 1$

   (f) $y = 4x - 2$
   (g) $y = x^2$
   (h) $y = 3x^2 + 1$
   (i) $y = x^3$
   (j) $y = 2x^2 + x + 1$

4. In each of the following cases find the coordinates of all points where the given pair of curves intersect each other.

   (a) $y = x$ and $y = 5$
   (b) $y = 2x - 3$ and $y = 3x + 2$
   (c) $y = ax + b$ and $y = cx + d$
   (d) $y = x + 1$ and $y = x + 5$
   (e) $y = 2x + 1$ and $y = x^2$
   (f) $y = 3x - 2$ and $y = ax^2 + b$

5. Given that the straight line $y = ax + b$ meets the curve $y = cx^2 + dx + e$. What can you say about the numbers a, b, c, d, e?

6. Find the equation of the straight line

    (a) through $(0,0)$, of slope 2
    (b) through $(1,2)$, of slope -1
    (c) through (r,s) of slope m
    (d) through $(1,1)$ and $(2,2)$
    (e) through $(1,0)$ and $(6,-1)$
    (f) through (α,β) and (γ,δ)
    (g) through $(1,2)$ and perpendicular to $y = 2x - 1$
    (h) through $(-3,-1)$ and perpendicular to $y = 3x + 2$
    (i) through (α,β) and perpendicular to $y = mx + b$

7. In each of the following cases find the distance from the point to the line:

    (a) $(0,0)$; $y = 3x + 1$ (b) $(1,-2)$; $y = 2x - 3$ (c) $(1,1)$; $y = x$

8. At what points does the circle centered at $(1,0)$, of radius 3, meet the line $y = 2x - 1$?

9. Find the center and radius of the circle $x^2 + 3x + y^2 - 2y = 1$.

10. Sketch each of the following ellipses, showing foci and semiaxes:

    (a) $x^2 + 2y^2 = 1$ (b) $3x^2 + 2y^2 = 4$ (c) $2x^2 + 4y^2 = 3$

11. Sketch the following parabolas.

    (a) $y^2 = 4x$ (b) $y^2 = 6x - 9$ (show directrix and focus)
    (c) $y^2 = 4(x - 1)$ (show directrix and focus)

12. Sketch each of the hyperbolas:

    (a) $xy = 4$
    (b) $2x^2 - 3y^2 = 1$ (show asymptotes)
    (c) $\frac{1}{2}x^2 - \frac{1}{3}y^2 = 2$ (show asymptotes)
    (d) $x^2 - y^2 = 1$ (show asymptotes)

13. Show that the second denominator in (A.10) is a negative number.

Answers to Selected Exercises

Page 4
1. $\sqrt{3}$ sec; $\sqrt{L}$ sec; $\sqrt{6} - 2$ sec; $\sqrt{L + 4} - 2$ sec; $\sqrt{5 + t_0{}^2} - t_0$ sec; $\sqrt{L + t_0{}^2} - t_0$ sec.
2. 1 ft; 17 ft; $3.5^2 - 1.5^2$ ft; $8h + h^2$ ft; $2t_0 h + h^2$ ft.
5. (b) 2 sec (d) $2h + \frac{1}{2}h^2$ ft; $h(t - 1) + h^2$ ft
   (e) $\frac{1}{2}[c - (c^2 - 16c + 48)]^{1/2}$ sec, if c is large enough.

Page 6
1. 3 ft/sec; 8 ft/sec; $T + 2$ ft/sec; $a + b$ ft/sec; $2 + h$ ft/sec; $2 - h$ ft/sec; $2T + h$ ft/sec; $2T - h$ ft/sec.
2. $(t_0, 4 - t_0)$ $(t_0 < 2)$.
3. $(1,2)$.
4. $(t_0, 1 - t_0)$ $(t_0 < \frac{1}{2})$.
5. $(2,3)$.

Page 9
1. (a) $2t$ (b) $2t + 1$ (c) $2t + 1$ (d) $3t^2$ (e) 0 (f) $10t$.
3. (a) 2 (b) 2 (c) 2 (d) $6t$ (e) 0 (f) 10.

Page 15
2. $\pi/4$ ft.

Page **19**

2. (a) $-1 \leqq x \leqq 1$ (b) $x \neq -1$ (c) $x \neq 2, 3$ (d) $x > 0$.
3. (a) $4x - x^2$ (b) $6x^4 + 3$ (c) $2t^2 + 12t + 4$ (d) $2 - 7z - 16z^2$
    (e) -450 (f) $1 - u - v + u^2 + v^2 + 2uv - uv^2 - vu^2$ (g) $\frac{3}{2}$
    (h) $2x + h$ (i) -4.
4. $f(x) = x^2$ if $x \leqq 2, f(x) = 2\sqrt{x + 2}$ if $x > 2$.
5. $A = \dfrac{1}{4\pi} c^2$.
9. $\varphi(3) = 2$; $\varphi(4,5) = 2$; $\varphi(6\frac{3}{4}) = 3$; $\varphi(10) = 4$; $\varphi(\varphi(8)) = \varphi(4) = 2$.

Page **22**

2. (a) $-2 \leqq x \leqq 4$ (b) $1 \leqq x \leqq 3$ (c) $x = -3$ (d) $x = -7, -3$
    (e) $-1 \leqq x \leqq 0$ and $2 \leqq x \leqq 3$ (f) $x \neq 0$
    (g) $-1 < x < 0$ and $0 < x < 1$ (h) $0 < x < 1$ and $1 < x < 2$
    (i) $-6 < x < -4$ and $-4 < x < -2$
    (j) $a - \delta < x < a$ and $a < x < a + \delta$.
3. (a) 28 (b) 1 (c) 2 (d) 0 (e) $4x^3$ (f) 2^{30}.

Page **26**

3. No.
4. Yes.
5. $\delta = \frac{1}{50}$.
7. Use $\delta = \epsilon/10$ if $\epsilon < 5$; if $\epsilon \geqq 5$, use $\delta = \frac{1}{10}$.

Page **30**

2. (a) $\frac{1}{2}$ (b) 1 (c) 0 (d) 0 (e) 1 (f) 3 (g) -1 (h) 0.
4. (a) 1 (b) $\frac{2}{3}$ (c) $-1/x^2$ (d) $2^{7/2} - 1$.

Page **38**

1. (a) $6x$ (b) $6(3x - 2)$ (c) $-2x^{-3}$ (d) 2 if $x < 2, 3$ if $x > 2$
    (e) $2x - 1$ if $x \leqq 1, 4x - 3$ if $x \geqq 1$ (f) 1 if $x > -1, -1$ if $x < -1$
    (g) a (h) $2ax + b$ (i) $-(x + 3)^{-2}$.

Page **41**

2. $y = 0$; $y = (2 - x_0)[(x_0 + 2) - 2x]$.
3. $x = \frac{1}{2}$.
5. $x = \frac{1}{2}a$.
9. (a) $-x^{-2}$ (b) $-(x + 1)^{-2}$ (c) $-7(2x - 1)^{-2}$
    (d) $(ad - bc)/(cx + d)^2$ (e) $3x^2$.

Page **45**

1. $f(x) = 0$ if $x \leqq 1, 1$ if $1 < x \leqq 2, 2$ if $2 < x \leqq 3, \ldots, n - 1$ if $n - 1 < x \leqq n$,
    n if $x > n$.

5. $f(x) = |x - \dfrac{1}{n+1}| + |x - \dfrac{2}{n+1}| + \cdots + |x - \dfrac{n}{n+1}|.$

Page 50
1. $\frac{1}{2}$.

2. (a) $\int_0^1 x^2 \, dx$ (b) $\int_0^1 \dfrac{dx}{1+x}$ (c) $\int_1^2 2^x \, dx$ (d) $\int_1^{n+1} \dfrac{dx}{x}$ (e) $\int_a^{a+1} 1 \, dx$

   (f) $\int_3^4 (1+x)^2 \, dx.$

Page 55
1. (a) $\int_0^1 x \, dx - \int_{-1}^0 (-x) \, dx$ (b) $\int_0^2 (4 - t^2) \, dt - \int_2^3 (t^2 - 4) \, dt$

   (c) $-\int_{-5}^{-2} \left(-\dfrac{1}{x}\right) dx$ (d) $\int_{-1}^0 (1 - 2^x) \, dx - \int_0^1 (2^x - 1) \, dx.$

2. (a) 2   (b) 9   (c) $\frac{3}{2}$ (d) $\frac{3}{2}$.

Page 59
3. (a) x^2 (b) 0   (c) u^4.

Page 62
2. $\xi = \frac{1}{2}$.

Page 67
1. (a) $\frac{1}{3}x^3 + 122$ (b) $\frac{1}{4}x^4 + x + 16\frac{3}{4}$ (c) $\frac{1}{3}(x+1)^3 - 39$
   (d) $\frac{1}{2}x^6 - \frac{7}{5}x^5 + \frac{1}{2}x^2 + x - \sqrt{\pi}.$
2. (a) $\frac{1}{3}$ (b) $\frac{5}{4}$ (c) $\frac{8}{3}$ (d) $\frac{3}{5}$.
3. $f(b) - f(a)$.
4. (a) $\frac{1}{2}$ (b) $\frac{1}{2}$ (c) $\frac{1}{2}$ (d) any point in the interval.
5. (a) $-\frac{7}{6}$ (b) $\frac{14}{3}$ (c) $\frac{15}{4}$ (d) $\frac{1}{2}[(b+1)^2 - (a+1)^2]$ (e) $113 + \frac{1}{15}$

   (f) $a_0 + \dfrac{a_1}{2} + \dfrac{a_2}{3} + \dfrac{a_3}{4}.$

Page 75
   (a) $4x^3 - 1$ (c) $21x^2 - 3 - 4x^5$ (e) $3(x+a)^2$
   (g) $-2(x+3)(x-1)^{-3}$ (i) $-(x^7 + x^6 + 2)^{-2}(7x^6 + 6x^5)$
   (k) $(ad - bc)/(cx + d)^2$ (m) $10x^9 + 21x^6 - (x^2 + 2)^{-2}(2x)$
   (o) $(mx^{2m+1} - x^m)(x^{m+1} - 1)^{-2}.$

Page 78
2. (a) $12(x^{10} + x^{-2})^{11}(10x^9 - 2x^{-3})$ (c) $30\left(\dfrac{3x^2 + 2x + 1}{x^2 + 3}\right)^{29}\left(\dfrac{6 + 16x - 2x^2}{(x^2 + 3)^2}\right)$

   (e) $-11\left(\dfrac{1}{x^5 + 2} - 3\right)^{10}(x^5 + 2)^{-2}(5x^4) + 11\left(\dfrac{x^5}{3 - x} + 1\right)^{10}\left(\dfrac{15x^4 - 4x^5}{(3 - x)^2}\right)$

(g) $n\left(\dfrac{ax+b}{cx+d}\right)^{n-1}\dfrac{ad-bc}{(cx+d)^2}$ (i) $2f^3gg' + 3f^2g^2f'$ (k) $f'(g(x^2))g'(x^2)2x$

(m) $2ff' + 2gg'$

(o) $n\left[\dfrac{f(ax+b)}{g(cx+d)}\right]^{n-1}\left[\dfrac{af'(ax+b)g(cx+d) - cf(ax+b)g'(cx+d)}{g^2(cx+d)}\right]$

Page 80

1. (a) $\dfrac{3}{4}x^{-1/4} + \dfrac{3}{2}x^{-1/2}$ (c) $\dfrac{1}{5}\left(3x^{10} + \dfrac{1}{x}\right)^{-4/5}(30x^9 - x^{-2})$

(e) $f'(x^{1/3})\left(\dfrac{1}{3}x^{-2/3}\right)$ (g) $xf(x^2)^{-1/2}f'(x^2)$ (h) $f(\sqrt{x})f'(\sqrt{x})x^{-1/2}$.

2. (a) $\tfrac{1}{2}x^{-1/2}\cos\sqrt{x}$ (c) $12(\sin x)^{11}\cos x$

(e) $7(3 + 4\sin 2x + \sin 4x)^6(8\cos 2x + 4\cos 4x)$

(g) $\left[\cos\left(x + \dfrac{1}{x}\right)\right](1 - x^{-2})$.

4. (a) $x2^{x^2+1}$.

Page 82

(a) $10142/3$ (c) $3^{7/3} + \tfrac{8}{5}\cdot3^{5/4} - \tfrac{23}{5}$ (e) $19\tfrac{1}{15} + \tfrac{272}{35}\sqrt{2}$.

Page 87

2. (a) $\dfrac{\log_{10} e}{x}$ (c) $\dfrac{1}{2x}(\log x)^{-3/2}$ (e) $2(1 - x^2)^{-1}$ (g) $x^{-1}f'(\log x)$.

Page 91

1. (a) $\dfrac{1}{2}x^{-1/2}e^{\sqrt{x}}$ (c) e^{e^x+x} (e) $2^{(\log x+x)}\log 2\left(1 + \dfrac{1}{x}\right)$ (g) 0 (i) $e^x f'(e^x)$.

6. (a) $\dfrac{1}{4}(e^4 - 1)$ (c) $2 + \dfrac{15}{4\log 4}$.

Page 93

2. $\tfrac{1}{2}(2^x + 2^{-x}); 1 + x^2; \tfrac{1}{2}(2^x - 2^{-x}); 2x + 3x^3$.
4. 1.

6. (a) $\cosh x$ (c) $(\operatorname{sech} x)^{-2}$ (e) $\dfrac{11}{2}(\sinh\sqrt{x})^{10}(\cosh\sqrt{x})x^{-1/2}$

(g) $5\sinh 5x - \dfrac{18}{x^2}\left(\cosh\dfrac{1}{x}\right)^2\sinh\dfrac{1}{x}$.

Page 95

1. $180/\pi$.

Page 100

1. (a) $x^{-1}\cos(\log x)$ (c) $\frac{1}{2}(\sin x)^{-1/2}\cos x\, e^{\sqrt{\sin x}}$ (e) $-(\sin x)^{-2}\cos x$
    (g) $(1-\cos^3 x)^{-2}[9\sin^2 3x\cos 3x(1-\cos^3 x)-3(1+\sin^3 3x)\cos^2 x\sin x]$
    (i) $2\sin x\cos x\, f'(\sin^2 x)$ (k) $\frac{1}{2}[1+\cos(2^{-x})]^{-1/2}\sin(2^{-x})\,2^{-x}\log 2$.

2. (a) 1 (c) 2 (e) $\pi/4$ (g) $e-e^{-1}-e^{-2}$ (i) $\frac{3}{2}-2\sin 1+\frac{1}{4}\sin 2$.

Page 106

1. (b) increases for $x\geqq 0$ (d) increases for $-2^{-1/2}\leqq x\leqq 2^{1/2}$
    (f) increases for $x\leqq -1$ and $x\geqq 0$.

2. Yes; not necessarily.

Page 109

6. $(x^2-1)(x^2+1)^{-1}(1+x^2+x^4)^{-1/2}$

8. $(1-x^2)^{1/2}\, e^{\sin^{-1} x}$.

10. $-\dfrac{\cos^{-1}\sqrt{x}}{\sqrt{x-x^2}}$.

12. $-(2x-x^2)^{-1/2}$.

Page 115

1. $\frac{1}{3}x^3\log x-\dfrac{x^3}{9}+71$ (c) $x\sin x+\cos x-13$ (e) $x(\log x-1)+40$
    (g) $(2x^3-12x^2+48x-4)e^{x/2}$.

2. (a) $(a^{-1}-a^{-2})e^a+a^{-2}$ (c) $\frac{26}{3}\log 2-\frac{59}{18}$ (e) $\frac{1}{2}[e(\sin 1+\cos 1)-1]$.

Page 119

1. (a) $2e-2$ (c) $a^{-1}(e^a-1)-b^{-1}(e^b-1)$ (e) $\sin 1-\sin\dfrac{1}{e}$
    (g) $\frac{1}{4}(\log 2-1)$ (i) $\dfrac{1}{20}(243-25\sqrt{5})$ (k) $\dfrac{1}{5a}[b^{-5}-(a+b)^{-5}]$.

2. (a) $(t+a)[\log(t+a)-1]+33\frac{1}{2}$ (c) $-\frac{1}{3}\cos x^3-12$.

Page 121

2. (a) $\sqrt{2}+\dfrac{9}{2}\sin^{-1}\dfrac{1}{3}$ (c) $\dfrac{1}{b}\tan^{-1}\dfrac{a}{b}$.

Page 127

(a) $\frac{1}{3}\log(3x-4)$ (c) $5\log(x-2)+2\log x-7\log(x-1)+43$

(e) $\dfrac{a-b}{c-b}\log(x+b)-\dfrac{a-c}{c-b}\log(x+c)$

(g) $x+\dfrac{9\sqrt{3}}{10}\log\left(\dfrac{x-5/\sqrt{3}}{x+5/\sqrt{3}}\right)$.

Page **131**

1.   (a) $-\sin x,\ -\cos x$ (c) $\cosh x,\ \sinh x$ (e) $-(x+5)^{-2},\ 2(x+5)^{-3}$.

2.   (a) $(-1)^{k-1/2}a^k \cos ax$ if k is odd, $(-1)^{k/2}a^k \sin ax$ if k is even

    (c) $(-1)^k k!(1+x)^{-k-1}$ (e) $\left(\frac{1}{2}\right)\left(-\frac{1}{2}\right)\left(-\frac{3}{2}\right)\cdots\left(-\frac{2k-3}{2}\right)x^{-(k+1/2)}$.

3. $a = \sqrt{k}$.

Page **136**

1.   (a) $x = e,\ \max$ (c) $x = 0\ \max,\ x = \pm1\ \min$

    (e) $x = \sqrt{3} - 1\ \max,\ x = -1 - \sqrt{3}\ \min$ (g) $x = 0\ \min$.

2. $2\sqrt{K}$.

3. $A^3,\ A^3/4$.

Page **141**

1. $L^2\left\{(4\pi)^{-1}\left(1 + \dfrac{3\sqrt{3}}{\pi}\right)^{-2} + \sqrt{3}\left(6 + \dfrac{2\pi}{\sqrt{3}}\right)^{-2}\right\},\ \dfrac{L^2}{4\pi}$.

3.   Radius $= (V/2\pi)^{1/3}$; Height $= (4V/\pi)^{1/3}$.

5.   Radius $= P/4$; central angle $= 2$ radians.

7. $x = \left(\dfrac{b}{a} - \dfrac{1}{2a^2}\right)^{1/2}$ if $ab \geq \dfrac{1}{2}$; $x = 0$ if $ab < \dfrac{1}{2}$.

Page **149**

1.   (a) 0 (c) $-\frac{1}{6}$ (e) $\sqrt{ab}$ (g) 0.

Page **153**

1. $x_{n+1} = \left(1 - \dfrac{1}{k}\right)x_n + \dfrac{1}{k}x_n^{-k+1}A$ to find $A^{1/k}$.

3.   The left side increases steadily for $x \geq 0$, so is equal to 1 in just one place.

Page **160**

1. $\frac{1}{2}\sqrt{5} + \frac{1}{4}\log(2 + \sqrt{5})$.

3. $\log\left(2 + \dfrac{\sqrt{3}}{4}\right)$.

Page **163**

1.   (a) $\frac{1}{2}\sqrt{5} + \frac{1}{4}\log(2 + \sqrt{5})$ (b) $\sqrt{1 + a^2}$.

3.   (b) $x^2 + y^2 = \left(\tan^{-1}\dfrac{y}{x}\right)^2$ (c) $x^2 - y^2 = 1$ (d) $\dfrac{x^2}{a^2} + \dfrac{y^2}{b^2} = 1$.

Page **167**

1.   (a) $\dfrac{\pi a^2}{5}$ (b) $\dfrac{\pi^2}{2}$ (c) $2\pi[(\log 2)^2 - 2\log 2 + 1]$

$$\pi\left(a_0{}^2 + \frac{a_1{}^2}{3} + \frac{a_2{}^2}{5} + \cdots + \frac{a_n{}^2}{2n+1} + 2\frac{a_0a_1}{2} + 2\frac{a_0a_2}{3} + \cdots + 2\frac{a_{n-1}a_n}{2n}\right)$$

(e) $\pi\dfrac{A^{2\alpha}+1}{2\alpha+1}$.

2. $\frac{1}{3}\pi R^2 H$.

3. $h = \text{height} = H\left(1 - \dfrac{3rt}{\pi R^2 H}\right)^{1/3}$ ft; $\dfrac{dh}{dt} = -\dfrac{r}{\pi R^2}\left(1 - \dfrac{3rt}{\pi R^2 H}\right)^{2/3}$ ft/sec;

$\dfrac{\pi R^2 H}{3r}$ sec to empty.

Page 172

1. (a) $f''(x) = x^{-2} > 0$ (b) $-\log\left(\dfrac{x_1 + x_2}{2}\right) \leqq -\dfrac{1}{2}\log x_1 - \dfrac{1}{2}\log x_2$

   [from (4.42)], so $\dfrac{x_1 + x_2}{2} \geqq (x_1 x_2)^{1/2}$

   (c) $\dfrac{x_1 + x_2}{2} - \sqrt{x_1 x_2} = \dfrac{1}{2}(\sqrt{x_1} - \sqrt{x_2})^2 \geqq 0.$

Page 176

1. $x^2 + (y - \frac{1}{2})^2 = \frac{1}{4}$; $R = \frac{1}{2}$; curvature $= 2$.

3. $(x - 3)^2 + (y + 2)^2 = 8$; $R = 2\sqrt{2}$; curvature $= \frac{1}{4}\sqrt{2}$.

Page 178

1. $x - \dfrac{x^3}{6}$; $x - \dfrac{x^3}{3!} + \dfrac{x^5}{5!} - \dfrac{x^7}{7!} + \cdots$.

2. $e^a\left[1 + (x - a) + \dfrac{(x - a)^2}{2!} + \cdots + \dfrac{(x - a)^n}{n!}\right]$.

3. $x - \dfrac{x^2}{2} + \dfrac{x^3}{3} - \dfrac{x^4}{4} + \cdots + (-1)^{n+1}\dfrac{x^n}{n}$.

Page 182

1. (a) yes   (b) yes   (c) no   (d) no   (e) yes   (f) yes.

2. (a) $\frac{1}{4}$ (c) no   (e) no   (g) $\pi/2$ (i) 2.

Page 188

2. (a) converges   (b) converges   (c) converges   (d) diverges.

3. (a) unless $\sin x = -1$ (b) $x \leqq 0$.

Page 197

1. (a) n (b) 255   (c) $8(2^{409} - 1)$ (d) $\dfrac{a}{1 - r}$ (e) $4^{-1}5^{1-a}$

   (f) $\dfrac{77}{60}$ (g) 2.

Page **200**

1. (a) converges (b) converges (c) converges (d) converges
   (e) converges (f) converges (g) diverges (h) converges.

Page **205**

1. converges 2. converges 3. converges 4. diverges 5. diverges
6. diverges 7. converges 8. diverges 9. converges 10. converges.

Page **207**

1. (a) diverges (b) converges (c) converges (d) diverges (e) diverges
   (f) converges (g) diverges (h) diverges (i) converges (j) diverges
   (k) diverges (l) converges (m) diverges.

Page **210**

1. (a) converges (b) converges (c) diverges (d) converges
   (e) converges (f) converges.

Page **214**

2. (a) diverges (b) converges absolutely (c) converges, not absolutely
   (d) converges, not absolutely (e) converges absolutely
   (f) converges, not absolutely.
3. About $e^{1,000,000}$.

Page **225**

2. (a) 1 (b) $\frac{1}{3}$ (c) 1 (d) 1 (e) ∞ (f) ∞ (g) 0 (h) e^{-2}
   (i) 1 (j) $\frac{1}{4}$ (k) 1.
3. (a) $2 \leq x < 4$ (c) $\sqrt{\frac{47}{6}} < x < \sqrt{\frac{49}{6}}$ (e) no x.

Page **233**

3. (a) 2 (c) 1 (e) $\frac{3}{4}$.

4. (a) $1 - \dfrac{(x - \pi/2)^2}{2!} + \dfrac{(x - \pi/2)^4}{4!} - \cdots$

   (c) $1 + \displaystyle\sum_{k=1}^{\infty} \left(-\frac{1}{2}\right)\left(-\frac{3}{2}\right)\cdots\left(-\frac{2k-1}{2}\right)\frac{x^k}{k!}.$

6. $\displaystyle\sum_{n=0}^{\infty} \frac{1}{(2n + 1)\, n!\, 2^{2n+1}}.$

Page **244**

2. $(n - 1)!$; $(n - p)!$.
9. (a) yes (b) no (c) no.
11. If g has inverses a and b, then $ag = bg = e$. Multiply on the right by a and use the associative law.

Page 250

1. Let $\mathbf{x} = 0\mathbf{f}$. Then $\mathbf{x} + \mathbf{x} = 0\mathbf{f} + 0\mathbf{f} = (0 + 0)\mathbf{f} = 0\mathbf{f} = \mathbf{x}$. Hence $\mathbf{x} + \mathbf{x} = \mathbf{x}$. Add $-\mathbf{x}$ to both sides and get $\mathbf{x} = \mathbf{0}$.
6. Yes.

Page 253

1. $x_n = \frac{1}{2}n(n + 1)$.
6. $y_n = 2^{2^{n-1}}$.
7. 2, 3, 5, 7, 11, 13, 17, 19, 23, 29.

Page 257

3. Given a set of $r > n$ vectors, $\mathbf{x}_1, \mathbf{x}_2, \ldots, \mathbf{x}_r$. By definition of dimension, the first $n + 1$ of these are dependent, say $\alpha_1\mathbf{x}_1 + \cdots + \alpha_{n+1}\mathbf{x}_{n+1} = \mathbf{0}$. Then $\alpha_1\mathbf{x}_1 + \cdots + \alpha_{n+1}\mathbf{x}_{n+1} + 0\mathbf{x}_{n+2} + \cdots + 0\mathbf{x}_r = \mathbf{0}$, and this is a dependence among all r of the given vectors.
4. 1, x are independent, but 0, 1 are not. However, if the derivatives are independent, suppose $\alpha_1\mathbf{f}_1 + \cdots + \alpha_n\mathbf{f}_n = \mathbf{0}$. Differentiating, $\alpha_1\mathbf{f}_1' + \cdots + \alpha_n\mathbf{f}_n' = \mathbf{0}$ and so $\alpha_1 = \cdots = \alpha_n = 0$, hence the $\mathbf{f}$'s are independent also.
5. (a) yes (b) no (c) $ad \neq bc$.
6. (a) yes (b) yes (c) $ad \neq bc$.

Page 263

3. The x_1-x_2 plane.
4. The even polynomials.
5. If $\mathbf{x}$ and $\mathbf{y}$ are in the intersection of U and V, then $\mathbf{x} + \mathbf{y}$ is in U and in V so in $U \cap V$, and $\alpha\mathbf{x}$ is in U and V also. The union need not be a subspace; the x and y axes in E^2 are subspaces but their union is not.
6. (a) no (b) yes (c) no (d) yes (e) no (f) no (g) yes (h) yes.

Page 266

1. (a) 1, x, x^2, x^3 (b) 1, $x - 1$, $(x - 1)^2$, $(x - 1)^3$
   (c) 1, $1 + x$, $1 + x + x^2$, $1 + x + x^2 + x^3$.
4. Basis is $(2,1,-3)$. All solutions are $a = 2\alpha$, $b = \alpha$, $c = -3\alpha$ where α is any real number. Dimension is 1. It is a line through the origin in E^3.

Page 275

1. (a) no (b) yes (c) no (d) yes (e) yes.
2. (a) Ker T = set of all vectors of the form $(0,0,\gamma)$; Im T = set of all vectors of the form $(\alpha,\beta,0)$; $r(T) = 2$; $\nu(T) = 1$
   (c) Ker $T = \mathbf{0}$ alone; Im $T = E^n$; $r(T) = n$; $\nu(T) = 0$
   (e) Ker $T = \mathbf{0}$ alone; Im T = set of all vectors $(\alpha,\beta,0,0)$; $r(T) = 2$; $\nu(T) = 0$.
3. If $T\mathbf{x} = \mathbf{f}$ and $T\mathbf{y} = \mathbf{f}$, then $T(\mathbf{x} - \mathbf{y}) = T\mathbf{x} - T\mathbf{y} = \mathbf{f} - \mathbf{f} = \mathbf{0}$.

Page 283

2. $0(\mathbf{f} + \mathbf{g}) = \mathbf{0} = 0\mathbf{f} + 0\mathbf{g}; \; 0(\alpha\mathbf{f}) = \mathbf{0} = \alpha(0\mathbf{f}).$

3. $(A + (-1)A)\mathbf{f} = A\mathbf{f} + (-1)A\mathbf{f}$
$$= A\mathbf{f} - A\mathbf{f}$$
$$= \mathbf{0}$$
    so $A + (-1)A$ is the zero map and $(-1)A$ is the negative of A.

6. (a) $A^2(\alpha_1, \alpha_2, \alpha_3) = (\alpha_1, 2\alpha_1 + \alpha_2, 3\alpha_1 + 2\alpha_2 + \alpha_3)$
    (b) $AB(\alpha_1, \alpha_2, \alpha_3) = (\alpha_3, \alpha_1 + \alpha_3, \alpha_1 + \alpha_2 + \alpha_3)$
    (c) $BA(\alpha_1, \alpha_2, \alpha_3) = (\alpha_1 + \alpha_2 + \alpha_3, \alpha_1, \alpha_1 + \alpha_2)$
    (e) $A^{-1}(\alpha_1, \alpha_2, \alpha_3) = (\alpha_1, \alpha_2 - \alpha_1, \alpha_3 - \alpha_2).$

7. (b) It rotates the vector clockwise through an angle θ (c) $A_\theta^{-1} = A_{-\theta}.$

8. If $\alpha_1 A\mathbf{u}_1 + \cdots + \alpha_r A\mathbf{u}_r = \mathbf{0}$ then $A(\alpha_1\mathbf{u}_1 + \cdots + \alpha_r\mathbf{u}_r) = \mathbf{0}$ and so
    $\alpha_1\mathbf{u}_1 + \cdots + \alpha_r\mathbf{u}_r$ is in Ker A. But Ker A is $\mathbf{0}$ alone. Hence,
    $\alpha_1\mathbf{u}_1 + \cdots + \alpha_r\mathbf{u}_r = \mathbf{0}$. Since the $\mathbf{u}_i$ are independent, $\alpha_1 = \cdots = \alpha_r = 0.$

Page 289

1. (a) $(0,0)$ (c) $(1,-1).$

2. It maps a space U into a space of the same dimension.

4. (a) $\begin{pmatrix} 3 \\ 8 \end{pmatrix}$ (c) $\begin{pmatrix} 0 \\ 0 \end{pmatrix}$ (e) $-1.$

6. No.

7. (a) $\begin{pmatrix} 3 & -1 \\ 1 & 0 \end{pmatrix}.$

Page 295

1. $3A = \begin{pmatrix} 3 & -3 \\ 6 & 9 \end{pmatrix}; \; A^2 = \begin{pmatrix} -1 & -4 \\ 8 & 7 \end{pmatrix}; \; A^3 = \begin{pmatrix} -9 & -11 \\ 22 & 13 \end{pmatrix};$

$A^3 - 2A + I_3 = \begin{pmatrix} -10 & -9 \\ 18 & 8 \end{pmatrix}.$

3. $mn.$

Page 300

1. $(4, \frac{10}{3}, -\frac{4}{3}).$

2. $-8, 64, 64.$

3. (c) 10   (d) 10   (e) 10.

5. $a_{11}a_{22}a_{33} - a_{11}a_{23}a_{32} - a_{12}a_{21}a_{33} + a_{12}a_{23}a_{31} + a_{13}a_{21}a_{32} - a_{13}a_{22}a_{31}.$

Page 311

2. $0; \; -1.$

Page 317

1. (a) $-21.$

2. $1, 5.$

4. Yes.

Page 328

1. (a) $\begin{pmatrix} 2 & -1 \\ -\frac{1}{2} & \frac{1}{2} \end{pmatrix}$ (c) $\frac{1}{5}\begin{pmatrix} -11 & -7 & 10 \\ 2 & -1 & 0 \\ 5 & 5 & -5 \end{pmatrix}$.

2. (a) $x = \begin{pmatrix} 1 \\ 0 \end{pmatrix}$ (c) $x = \begin{pmatrix} -3 \\ 0 \\ 2 \end{pmatrix}$.

3. (a) 2 (c) 1.

4. (a) $\begin{pmatrix} 0 \\ 0 \end{pmatrix}$ (c) $x = \alpha\begin{pmatrix} 1 \\ 0 \\ 3 \end{pmatrix} + \beta\begin{pmatrix} 0 \\ 1 \\ 1 \end{pmatrix}$.

Page 337

1. (a) $n!$ (b) $n \cdot n!$ (c) n^3 (d) n^3 (e) n^3 (f) $n^2n!$; $n^3n!$; n^5 (g) n^3.
2. 100! is about $(100/e)^{100}$ or around 10^{160}. Thus in (a), (b) in Exercise 1 one needs about $10^{160} \times 10^{-8}$ sec or about 10^{140} years. In (c), (d), (e), (g) we need about $10^6 \times 10^{-8}$ sec, or $\frac{1}{100}$ sec.

Page 349

2. (a) $-2t^2 - 12t + 6$ (c) 0 (e) $-18, 0, -12, x^2, 1/t$ (g) $2t - 1/t^2$.

Page 359

1. (a) $y + z$; x; x (c) $\log(y + z)$; $\dfrac{x}{y+z}$; $\dfrac{x}{y+z}$

    (e) $(x^2 + y + z)^{-2}2x$; $(x^2 + y + z)^{-2}$; $(x^2 + y + z)^{-2}$
    (g) $4(x + y + z)^3$; $4(x + y + z)^3$; $4(x + y + z)^3$
    (i) $g'(x)g(y)$; $g(x)g'(y)$; $g'(z)$ (k) $g(yz)$; $xzg'(yz)$; $xyg'(yz)$.
2. (a) 2; 2; 0; 0 (g) $f''(x)$; $f''(y)$; 0; 0 (h) $f''(x)f(y)f(z)$; $f(x)f''(y)f(z)$; $f'(x)f'(y)f(z)$; $f'(x)f'(y)f(z)$
    (i) $y^2z^2f''(xyz)$; $x^2z^2f''(xyz)$; $xyz^2f''(xyz)$; $xyz^2f''(xyz)$.
3. (a): (a) $\begin{pmatrix} 2 & 0 \\ 0 & 2 \end{pmatrix}$ (g) $\begin{pmatrix} f''(1) & 0 \\ 0 & f''(1) \end{pmatrix}$

    (h) $\begin{pmatrix} f''(1)f(1)^2 & f(1)f'(1)^2 \\ f(1)f'(1)^2 & f''(1)f(1)^2 \end{pmatrix}$ (i) $\begin{pmatrix} f''(1) & f''(1) \\ f''(1) & f''(1) \end{pmatrix}$.

    (b): (a) 4 (g) $f''(1)^2$ (h) $f(1)^2[f''(1)^2f(1)^2 - f'(1)^4]$ (i) 0.

Page 363

1. $(3t^2 + 2t - 1)e^{(t^2-1)(t+1)}$.
3. $(0,0)$.

Page 365

1. $\begin{pmatrix} f_r \\ f_s \\ f_t \end{pmatrix} = \begin{pmatrix} x_r & y_r & z_r & w_r \\ x_s & y_s & z_s & w_s \\ x_t & y_t & z_t & w_t \end{pmatrix} \begin{pmatrix} f_x \\ f_y \\ f_z \\ f_w \end{pmatrix}.$

2. (a) $f_r = (\log y)(2r) + \left(\dfrac{x}{y}\right)(2r) = 2r\left[\log(r^2 + s^2) + \dfrac{r^2 - s^2}{r^2 + s^2}\right]$

   $f_s = (\log y)(-2s) + \left(\dfrac{x}{y}\right)(2s) = 2s\left[-\log(r^2 + s^2) + \dfrac{r^2 - s^2}{r^2 + s^2}\right].$

   (c) $f_r = (v - we^{uw})\sqrt{s} + (u)\dfrac{s}{2\sqrt{r}} + (-e^{uw}u).$

Page 370

1. (a) uv (c) $\dfrac{1}{5} - \dfrac{3}{5}(x - 3) - \dfrac{4}{5}(y - 4) + \dfrac{1}{2}\left[\dfrac{2}{3125}(x - 3)^2\right.$

   $\left. + \dfrac{72}{25}(x - 3)(x - 4) + \dfrac{23}{15625}(x - 4)^2\right]$

   (e) $uv + vw.$

Page 379

1. (a) $x_1^2 + 4x_1x_2 + 6x_2^2$ (c) $x_1^2 + 3x_2^2 + 5x_3^2 + 4x_1x_2 + 6x_1x_3 + 8x_2x_3$
   (e) $\lambda_1 x_1^2 + \cdots + \lambda_n x_n^2$. Forms (a), (b) are positive definite; (e) will be positive definite if all $\lambda_j > 0$.

2. (a) $\begin{pmatrix} 1 & -\frac{3}{2} \\ -\frac{3}{2} & 1 \end{pmatrix}$ (c) $\begin{pmatrix} 2 & \frac{1}{2} \\ \frac{1}{2} & -3 \end{pmatrix}$

   (e) $\begin{pmatrix} 1 & 1 & 1 & 1 \\ 1 & 1 & 1 & 1 \\ 1 & 1 & 1 & 1 \\ 1 & 1 & 1 & 1 \end{pmatrix}$ (g) $\begin{pmatrix} 0 & 1 & 1 \cdots 1 \\ 1 & 0 & 1 \cdots 1 \\ 1 & 1 & 0 \cdots 1 \\ \cdot & \cdot & \cdot & \cdot \\ \cdot & \cdot & \cdot & \cdot \\ \cdot & \cdot & \cdot & \cdot \\ 1 & 1 & 1 \cdots 0 \end{pmatrix}.$

Index

Abelian group, 244
Absolute convergence, 211
Absolute value, 22
  derivative of, 37
Abstraction, 237
Acceleration, 4
Alternating series, 208
Arc length, 156
Area, 13
Asymptote, 142
Average speed, 5

Basis, 264
Bounded sequence, 190

Cauchy convergence criterion, 189
Chain rule,
  for functions of one variable, 76
  for functions of several variables, 361
Characteristic modes of vibration, 343
Circle of curvature, 176
Cofactor, 312
Column vector, 296
Commutative group, 244
Comparison test, 197
Composite functions, 76
  differentiation of, 76
Conditional convergence, 212
Contact, 172
  in several dimensions, 366
Continuity, 43
  and the derivative, 44

Continuity (*cont.*)
  of a function of several variables, 352
  and integrability, 51
Convergence of a sequence, 186
  absolute, 211
  conditional, 212
  radius of, 217
  of a series, 194
Convexity, 167
Critical point, 372
Curvature, 174
  circle of, 176
  radius of, 174
Curve sketching, 142

Decreasing function, 104
Decreasing sequence, 190
Derivative, 33
  of absolute value function, 373
  definition of, 34
  partial, 354
  as a slope, 40
Determinant, 298
  Laplace expansion of, 312
  properties of, 311
Determinant function, 299, 306
  value of, 310
Differential equations, 343
Differentiation, 8
  of algebraic functions, 71
  of composite functions, 76
  and continuity, 44

Differentiation (*cont.*)
  of inverse trigonometric functions, 108
  partial, 354
  of products, 72
  of quotients, 73
  repeated, 130
  rules for, 71 *et. seq.*
Dimension, 256
Divergent sequence, 187
Domain, 17

Eigenvalue, 345
Euclidean *n*-space E^n, 249
Euclidean plane, 246
Even function, 93
Even permutation, 301
Exponential function, 88
  differentiation of, 89
Extremum problems, 137
  in several dimensions, 371

Factorial, 131
  size of, 223
Factorization of polynomials, 122
Function, 15, 16
  continuous, 17
  decreasing, 104
  domain of, 17
  exponential, 88
  hyperbolic, 92
  image of, 102
  increasing, 104
  inverse, 101
  inverse trigonometric, 107
  logarithmic, 83
  monotone, 104
  nondecreasing, 104
  nonincreasing, 104
  odd and even, 93
  one-to-one (1-1), 103
  range of, 17
  of several variables, 347
  trigonometric, 94
Fundamental theorem of calculus, 58

Games, theory of, 338
Geometric series, 196
Graph, 19
  in several dimensions, 348
Group, 238
  commutative, 244
  definition of, 244

Harmonic series, 203
Homogeneous equations, 259, 296

Homomorphisms, 266
  of groups, 267
  nullity of, 272
  rank of, 272
  of vector spaces, 267
Hyperbolic functions, 92

Identity matrix, 293
Image of a function, 102
Image of a homomorphism, 270
Improper integral, 179
Increasing function, 104
Increasing sequence, 190
Indefinite integral, 111
Independent vectors. *See* Linear independence
Induction, 250
Infinite series, 193
Inflection, point of, 171
Inhomogeneous equations, 324
Instantaneous speed, 7
Integral, 46 *et. seq.*
  definition of, 49
  as function of upper limit, 56
  improper, 179
  indefinite, 111
  properties of, 51
  test, 201
Integral calculus, 4, 9
Integration,
  of exponential functions, 90
  by parts, 109
  of powers, 81
  of rational functions, 122
  by substitution, 116
  of trigonometric functions, 100
Inverse functions, 101
Inverse matrix, 320
Inverse trigonometric functions, 106
  differentiation of, 107
Iteration, 150

Kernel, 270

Laplace expansion, 312
L'Hospital's rule, 142
Limit, 15, 21
  definition of, 21, 23
  of function of several variables, 351
  L'Hospital's rule for, 142
  superior, 218
Linear combination, 254
Linear dependence, 254
  test for, 316
Linear equations, 260
  solution of, 317

Linear independence, 254
Linear mapping, 267
Linear operator, 267
Linear transformation, 267
Local maximum (minimum), 132
Local maximum in several variables, 371
Logarithmic functions, 83

Mathematical induction, 250
Matrix, 277, 284 *et seq.*
  addition, 291
  algebra, 290
  determinant of, 298
  identity, 293
  inverse, 320
    calculation of, 335
  multiplication, 291
  pay off, 339
  rank of, 321
  zero, 294
Maxima and minima, 132
  of functions of several variables, 371
  problems in, 137
Mean-value theorem,
  of differential calculus, 62
  of integral calculus, 68
Minor, 311
Monotone function, 104
Monotone sequence, 190

Neutral element, 241, 243
Newton's laws of motion, 343
Newton's method, 150
Newton's method for square roots, 152
Nondecreasing function, 104
Nonincreasing function, 104
Nonincreasing sequence, 190
Norm of a partition, 47
Nullity of a homomorphism, 272
Numerical integration, 153
  in linear algebra, 329
Numerical methods, 150
Numerical solution of equations, 150

Odd function, 93
Odd permutation, 301
One-to-one function, 103
Order-of-magnitude test, 206

Parametric form, 160
Partial derivative, 354
Partial-fraction expansion, 126
Partial sums, 195
Partition, 47
  norm of, 47
  refinement of, 48

Payoff matrix, 339
Permutation, 240
  even, 301
  odd, 301
Point of inflection, 171
Positive definite, 376
Power series, 215

Quadratic form, 375
  definite, 376
Quotient rule for differentiation, 72

Radius,
  of convergence, 217
  of curvature, 174
Range, 17
Rank,
  of a homomorphism, 272
  of a matrix, 321
Rate, 6
Rational functions, 122
Rearrangements of series, 214
Repeated differentiation, 130
Riemann sum, 49
Rolle's theorem, 60
Rotations of the square, 239

Saddle point, 373
Scalar, 248
Scalar multiplication, 248
Sequence, 185
  bounded, 190
  convergence of, 186
  divergence of, 187
  Fibonacci, 189
  of functions, 215
  monotone, 190
Series,
  alternating, 208
  of functions, 208
  geometric, 196
  harmonic, 203
  infinite, 193
  power, 215
Simultaneous linear equations, 260
Singular operator, 281
Slope, 39
Solid of revolution, 163
Speed, 3, 4
  average, 5
  instantaneous, 7
Subspace, 258
  generated, 258
Substitution,
  integration by, 116

Substitution (*cont.*)
   trigonometric, 120
Surface, 349

Tangent line, 40
Taylor's series, 229
Taylor's theorem, 226
Transposition, 303
Trapezoidal rule, 154
Triangle inequality, 27
Trigonometric functions, 94
   differentiation of, 99

Value of a game, 341
Vector space, 245
   abstract, 248
   column, 296
   dimension of, 256
   homomorphisms of, 267
   length of, 350
Volume of solid of revolution, 163

Well-ordering principle, 250